SAINT BLOODBATH

FREDERICK DOUGLASS REYNOLDS

Delton Ramsey, LLC

Published by Delton Ramsey, LLC.

ISBN 13: 978-0-578-27732-5 (Paperback Edition)

ISBN 13: 979-8-9880007-1-6 (Hardcover)

ISBN 13: 979-9880007-0-9 (Ebook)

Cover by Michael P. Corvin

corvin.bookcoverdesign@gmail.com

❀ Created with Vellum

INTRODUCTION

This book is an account of six murders that occurred in Southern California in 2008 and 2009 and the story of how the investigations unfolded. Although these cases have gone through the appeals process and are now matters of public record, some names and identifying details have been changed to protect the privacy of certain individuals. The author has interviewed the investigators involved in the cases covered herein and had first-hand knowledge of most of the victims of these brutal crimes.

"*Saint Bloodbath* is a great read with visceral language...Frederick Douglass Reynolds has crafted another Masterpiece!"

  - The American Writing Awards

"*Saint Bloodbath* tells a bloody, violent story of drugs, murder, and gangs that truly is not for the faint-hearted. It is incredibly descriptive, leaving nothing to the imagination, but sadly, real-life murders are like that. It reads like a fictional story, but it most assuredly is not, and it is an eye-opener."

  - Reader's Favorite Reviews

"*Saint Bloodbath* is a heart-pounding read that will keep you turning pages long past your bedtime."

  - Estrada Book Reviews

"In this real-life story it is left to five detectives to enter the hellish darkness that even Dante couldn't imagine, clean up the mess and shine the light of justice when no one else cares. *Saint Bloodbath* is nothing less than a modern true crime tour-de-force."

  - Ralph Pezzullo, bestselling author, and host of the podcast Heroes Behind Headlines

"Frederick Reynolds has done the impossible. He has written a true crime book that captures both art and reality. Reynolds takes no prisoners in *Saint Bloodbath*. The lucky reader will ride shotgun with a real murder cop, both aghast and fascinated by his story of a massacre that will shatter any illusions that crime is cool or that dope-selling gangsters are pop heroes worthy of respect."

  - Kent Harrington, Author of the "The Good Physician," *voted by the Library Journal of America as one of the 100 best thrillers of the last ten years.*

"Frederick Reynolds's words allow you to pierce the veil and see how detectives handle the slog that is a homicide investigation. While reading this book, you might forget that this is not fiction but was an actual murder investigation. Here's to hoping for and anticipating the next book by Mr. Reynolds."

  - Paul Pantani, Commander, Riverside County DA's Office

"A masterfully written look at a world most people do not know, but which the reader experiences up close, as if an actual witness to the events and people Reynolds brings alive. This is not just a well-written account but also a deep examination that raises real questions, not only about the characters involved, but unpretentiously about ourselves. As a retired prosecutor with almost forty years of experience in criminal law and the people in that system, I unreservedly recommend this honest and true account."

- Bryant E. Bushling, LA County DA's Office (Retired)

"If you are interested in the genre of true crime, this book is a must read. Once I started the book I couldn't put it down. I do not recall the last time I read a book in three days. I look forward to Frederick Reynolds's next book, because there *must* be one."

-Stephen Vaughan, Lieutenant, LA County Sheriff's (Retired)

"Readers of non-fiction will not want to miss out on this one! The retelling of lives lost, the lives impacted by the ripple effect, and the efforts of the police to bring justice will keep you riveted to the end."

- Seraphia Sparks, Bookworm Bunny Reviews

"The best true crime novel since Joseph Wambaugh's *The Onion Field*."

- Henry "Bud" Johnson, Redondo Beach Police Officer (Retired)

"One of the best true crime stories that I have read. It stimulates all the senses and emotions. You can feel, smell, and 'see' the crime scenes and people. In this endeavor, Reynolds has seamlessly meshed the melting pot that is LA County into a brilliant piece of storytelling."

- Cecil Rhambo, LAX Chief of Police

"Mr. Reynolds's descriptions of suspects and witnesses—their pain, deceit, and fear—are raw. I was captivated, not only by the book's real-life drama, but also by its ability to reveal unusually insightful truths about the often hidden and misunderstood world of homicide detectives."

- Ralph Ornelas, Commander, LA County Sheriff's (Retired)

"I had the honor and privilege of working with the author at the beginning of his distinguished law enforcement career. His outstanding investigative

skill set, and his innate and extraordinary writing skills manifested themselves early on in his career. In reading *Saint Bloodbath*, it is clear that he is at the zenith of his literary skills. He is the new Joseph Wambaugh."
 - Hour L. Taylor, Chief of Police, Compton Police Department (Retired)

"*Saint Bloodbath* is an outstanding non-fiction crime novel that takes place in LA County, California. Reynolds writes so that the reader understands the mindset of gang members, the hard work and political pressure put on the detectives responsible for solving these crimes, and the effects that it takes on their personal lives."
 - Kay Reeves, Compton Police Detective (Retired)

"*Saint Bloodbath* invites the reader into the dark and violent world in which Homicide Investigators must live and operate. Reynolds uses his writing prowess and attention to detail to share this journey with you. Unlike a 60-minute TV docudrama that wraps everything up in one show, this book shows how it *really* is out on the streets."
 - Kenneth Roller, Los Angeles County Sheriff's Sergeant (Retired)

"Well, he's done it again! With his second work, *Saint Bloodbath*, Frederick Douglass Reynolds is proving himself to be one of the best up-and-coming authors in the USA."
 -LeNeice L. Gavin, MSW, LMSW

For Desmond and Emma Reynolds

Once you kill another human being, there is no going back. It's a bit like being reborn, I suppose. But no ordinary birth—it is a metamorphosis. What emerges from the ashes is not a Phoenix, but an uglier creature: deformed, incapable of flight, a predator using its claws to cut and rend.

—Alex Michaelides, *The Maidens*

FOREWORD

by Danny R. Smith, Author
L.A. Sheriff's Homicide, Ret.

ON A BRISK FEBRUARY NIGHT IN 1993, two Compton police officers were gunned down at Rosecrans and Wilmington Avenue in the city of Compton, not far from the Nickerson Gardens, the largest and perhaps most dangerous housing project west of the Mississippi.

I was a deputy sheriff, assigned as a night car detective at Firestone Station, located just a couple miles north of that horrific scene. The officer down call was broadcast throughout our station. My partner and I fastened our gun belts as we ran to our Chevy Caprice that sat backed up just feet from the Detective Bureau door, and we stormed out of the rear parking lot among a throng of sheriff's radio cars racing to Compton.

There is nothing so chilling as the sound of "officer down" shouted over a police radio and broadcast through station loudspeakers. Less than a year had passed since we at Firestone had buried one of our own, Nelson Yamamoto, a beautiful human being of just twenty-six years, gunned down in the line of duty. Reflections of that dreadful night undoubtedly weighed on all of us as we headed south to help our brothers in blue.

I've stood at the scenes of too many murdered cops. It's something you never get over. That night in Compton, Frederick "Fred" Reynolds stood among two team members fallen before him, men who were not only his partners but also his friends—his brothers: Officers Kevin Burrell and James MacDonald. I didn't know either of them, nor did I know Officer Reynolds then or any of the other Compton officers who were there that night. But they were my brothers, and my heart was broken for them. For all of us. For society.

That was the first time I know for certain that my path had crossed with that of a great cop—Fred Reynolds. Our worlds had many parallels, yet they couldn't have been farther apart, either. I had grown up on a dirt road in rural Newhall during the sixties and seventies while Fred negotiated his way through the mean streets of Detroit, flirting with a life of crime. I barely graduated from high school; Fred narrowly avoided prison. I went on to work various jobs until the day came that I chose law enforcement as a career; Fred joined the United States Marine Corps and served his country honorably.

But Fred's tough days were far from over. After being discharged from the service, he floundered for a bit and even experienced homelessness in Los Angeles for a time before eventually being hired as a security officer in Compton. It was 1985, and by then, I had left a security officer gig of my own, had graduated from the sheriff's academy, and was assigned to Men's Central Jail in downtown Los Angeles. By the end of '86, Fred had graduated from the same sheriff's academy I had attended. He was a police officer in the City of Compton, and I worked a few miles north at Firestone Station. There is no doubt our paths crossed more than a few times during those years, on the streets, in the courthouses, or perhaps at other crime scenes.

In 2000, the City of Compton dissolved its police department and contracted with the Los Angeles County Sheriff's Department to provide law enforcement services. Most of the officers were absorbed into the Sheriff's Department, including Fred Reynolds, who had been a homicide detective in Compton and promoted to the rank of sergeant. Now a sergeant in the Sheriff's Department, Fred was assigned to Lomita Station, where he would decompress after fifteen years on the bloody streets of Compton.

I was in my third year at Sheriff's Homicide. We were informed that the active and unsolved Compton murder cases would be distributed among each of us, adding to the existing burden of cases we already carried. I inherited the triple murder case of Lisa Butler, Anthony Colbert, and Willie Calhoun, a gang-related murder that remains unsolved. Fred had been the Compton homicide detective who was assigned the case, his sixth murder callout in a two-day period, he would later tell me. Now it was mine. Our paths had crossed once again, our universes still parallel yet seemingly far apart.

I retired from the Sheriff's Department at the end of 2004, leaving the Homicide Bureau several years before Fred arrived. His experience and knowledge of gangs didn't allow for him to waste away as a patrol sergeant in Lomita, so he had been tasked with supervising a gang detail. Eventually, he was chosen to join the ranks of the Homicide Bureau with the Sheriff's Department. Fred Reynolds was now a fellow bulldog—a member of an exclusive club of hard-charging detectives who had earned their spots at The Show, the big leagues—yet we still didn't *know* one another.

Despite all of these intersections, it wasn't until many years after I retired that the name Fred Reynolds would land on my desk again, a desk now free of murder books and subpoenas but littered with manuscripts of detective novels in various stages of completion, sticky notes with scribblings about plots and characters scattered about, and books every writer should have on hand: *The Chicago Manual of Style,* Strunk & White's *Elements of Style,* and an autobiographical "how-to-write book" by Stephen King titled, *On Writing,* to name my big three.

A former Compton PD officer who had finished his career with Redondo Beach PD, Bud Johnson, reached out to tell me he enjoyed my detective novels. When I asked how he found my writing, he said Fred Reynolds told him about me.

Grateful for his recommending my books to others, I reached out to Fred on Facebook, and we became "friends" in the social media world. Of course, we had many mutual friends—real ones, I would discover—each of us having been blessed to work with some of the greatest cops on earth. A few of them are mentioned in the pages of this brilliantly scribed story of a sadistic killer and the unrelenting cops who "caught" him.

Soon, Fred began posting excerpts from his (at that time) forthcoming memoir, *Black, White, and Gray All Over.* I hadn't known before then that he, too, was a writer, and I read every excerpt he posted with a critical eye. There was no doubt that Fred was not just another cop who wanted to tell his story; he was an exceptionally gifted master of prose, and I couldn't wait to read his debut manuscript. I was not disappointed. Fred's personal narrative chronicled in his memoirs is nearly unbelievable, but it's as true as it is provocative. (Read that one next, if you haven't already.)

We've become good friends through the writing—the commonalities of our backgrounds make a solid foundation of brotherhood. We talk about books and old cases and mutual friends, and we've joined forces on occasions to promote our books to a common fanbase. On one such occasion, I was privileged to meet one of his best friends, Mark McGuire. Fred brought him to a book signing that we had collaborated on. It was an evening filled with friends old and new, our mutual friend Bud Johnson among them. After reading this book—*Saint Bloodbath*—I regret not having had more time that evening to visit with Mark. You might feel the same as you come to know this selfless homicide cop through the following pages.

Fred's autobiography set the bar high for his future compositions. He has raised it with this masterfully penned true crime story about a sadistic killer, his victims, and the investigators who worked tirelessly to attain justice. The many moving parts of *Saint Bloodbath*—related murder cases and their players spread throughout the county—are carefully woven into this tragic tale about the night five people were slaughtered at a homeless encampment in Long Beach. Though at times it will seem surreal, like a Netflix horror thriller, it is not. This is real life and death on the perilous streets of Los Angeles County, up close, personal, and unrelenting.

So, lace up your wingtips and take a journey with Fred beyond the yellow tape. And when you come to the blank page, perhaps you will do so reflectively, with reverence for the departed and a new appreciation for those who speak on their behalf.

PART ONE

CHAPTER ONE

KEVIN SULLIVAN'S HANDS were slippery with his own blood.

They clutched at his throat as he gasped for air, listening to the screams all around him while he lay on the concrete driveway of a house in a gang-infested area of Carson, California. Voices mixed in with the screams, some of them calling his name and telling him to hold on, others saying that help was on the way, most of them begging God to spare his life. Silence and darkness quickly descended, and Sullivan accepted the inevitable as gravity took control of his hands and they fell away, allowing the blood to flow without obstruction.

It was 2:10 a.m. on May 6, 2006. At least forty people, most of them Black, were leaving a house party. Someone yelled, "Fuck you, *putos!* Get out of my hood! This is Dominguez Thirteen, West Side!" right before gunshots rang out. Everyone scattered at the first shot. People who reside in areas like this know the sound, their instincts to survive on autopilot.

Had Sullivan not been accustomed to the sound and moved slower, had he gone left instead of right, had he frozen in place, had he done anything other than try to save his life, he probably would have survived. But he died *because* he wanted to live, the fickleness of our existence revealing itself in the form of a random bullet that struck him exactly where needed to end his life.

Leonard Lloyd, aka Hoodlum, went to a nearby house afterward, where he bragged to Lorenzo Villicana about what he had done. Both men were members of Dominguez 13, a Mexican gang in Carson and the adjacent city of Long Beach. Lloyd had taken umbrage at a party given by Black people in the neighborhood. His answer was to fire a handgun indiscriminately at them.

The ensuing investigation was resolved when a witness identified him as being in the area at the time of the shooting. Villicana then broke the cardinal rule in his world: He testified for the prosecution.

"LET US GET SOME CHILI-CHEESE FRIES AND TWO CUPS OF WATER."

The cashier, a plump, dirty-blonde Mexican woman wearing a shade of purple lipstick and heavy makeup should have just asked the man if he wanted the usual when he walked up. She had a crush on him, but she didn't want it to be too obvious, especially right now. Not with the woman standing next to him, glaring at her.

"That'll be two seventy-five," she said.

It was the week before Halloween, 2008. Lorenzo Villicana, aka LV, and Vanessa Malaepule had not long ago snaked their way through Santa Fe Avenue traffic on rusty bicycles with dirt-caked tires before arriving at Fantastic Burgers. Since LV had assisted in sending Leonard Lloyd to prison for forty years, they had been hiding out in one of two homeless encampments on the side of the 405 Freeway, not far from the restaurant.

"I got it, Vee," LV said. "You got it last time."

"You're too slow, *cabrón*," Vanessa said as she reached inside her bra and removed several crumpled-up one-dollar bills. She held three of them in front of her rather than extending them. The cashier frowned and leaned forward to get the money, her large breasts causing the restaurant logo on her shirt to disappear against the counter.

LV had been involved in gangs for well over half his life. He knew the possible consequences of testifying against Lloyd, but he did it anyway. It hadn't been the first time he testified, either. But the first time, it was against a member of a different gang in another city. This time, he had testified against one of his own, and as a result his life had been turned upside down.

Although LV skirted the etiquette of the streets, he could not completely leave his old world behind. He was forty-four years old now, and he still wore typical homeboy attire: knee-length shorts, white tube-socks, and Nike tennis shoes with wife beaters, oversized T-shirts, and athletic jerseys.

Vanessa was an attractive Pacific Islander with beautiful long black hair. She dressed like LV and even talked like him. She had a charming smile when she chose to display it, which didn't happen often as she and LV scowled in tandem most of the time. They had fallen in love over a pookie, a street term for a meth pipe based on the crackhead character played by Chris Rock in the movie *New Jack City*.

After getting the change and a receipt, they parked their bikes against the wall near the order window and sat down at a table in front of the restaurant, watching traffic speeding past. There was a gas station on the corner, and a beer and wine store boasting of serving the coldest beer in Long Beach across the street. A Mexican-owned flower shop, a dry cleaners, a barbershop, and a small Baptist church where drums, cymbals, and singing could be heard blocks away during the nightly services filled the remainder of the block.

The businesses were set up in a strip mall configuration and presented a rhythmic pattern to the urbanity of the area, a redundancy of despair for those forced to live there: strip mall, graffiti-marred apartment complex, strip mall, graffiti-marred apartment complex, continuing all the way south on Santa Fe to Cabrillo High School and the Long Beach Police Department's West Division Station a few miles away.

Several crows walked around an overflowing trash can not far from where LV and Vanessa were seated. A bank of freestanding newspaper racks was close to them. The *Long Beach Press-Telegram*, *La Opinión*, and another paper advertising massage parlors were the selections. The latter had a picture of a nearly nude woman on the front page with ruby-red lips, enticing potential customers to choose pleasure over the news. LV wasn't aware that his eyes had already made his decision for him.

"Oh, you like that bitch, huh *vato*?"

"What? No, Vee! You know I only got eyes for you."

Vanessa peered into them. No matter what state of mind he was in, they were always the same. He didn't have the cliché "dreamy" eyes so often written about in dime-store romance novels, except for when he was hitting the pookie, or when he was about to finish when they were doing

5

the nasty. Then, they rolled back in his head until all you could see was the sclera.

"What's up *mi amor*? Why you staring?"

"Nothing, *ese*. I'm just sitting here wondering why I love your whore ass so much."

He glanced down at his crotch and then looked at her.

"You know why."

Maybe this cabrón's eyes are dreamy after all, she thought. *I just can't see them when it counts.*

"I better not catch you fucking with any of these hood rats around here, *pendejo*. I'll kill them all and cut that thing off and feed it to the crows. And that includes that fat-ass cashier who keeps making googly eyes at you."

They both laughed, but LV knew how serious Vanessa was. She was jealous and would fight anyone for him. He had known from the first time he laid eyes on her that she was his soulmate, his ride-or-die chick, his endgame.

Vanessa was on the streets because she wanted to be. She had six children, who were being taken care of by family members at a house not far away in Carson. She could go there whenever she needed to; she could even live there if she would only stop using. But she loved LV as much as she loved getting high, so she stayed with him, even if it meant sleeping on the ground in a tent by the freeway.

"Number seventeen!"

LV picked up the receipt and looked at it.

"That's us."

He got up and took the food from the cashier, wondering how she wiped her ass with fingernails that long. He set it on the table and went back to get the two cups of water, napkins, and two plastic forks before sitting down to share the thick french fries slathered with chili and cheap government cheese with Vanessa.

"Do you think they still after you, babe?"

LV studied her plump light brown face, her dark eyes betraying the difficulties of their lives. She tried to act hard, as usual, but her face showed her concern. And she had good reason to feel this way. They both knew he was now a well-known snitch, a *rata*. But he thought he would be all right if he stayed away from his former gang. He had done what he did to survive, and above everything else, he was a survivor. If he had to testify against someone—a *tinto* no less—to get out of a pending criminal case he had for selling meth, then it was a no-brainer. The other time he testified, well, that was for money he needed for his family.

Hoodlum wasn't well liked by D-13 members, though, so LV didn't believe any of them would go out of their way to avenge him since he was Black. They had only allowed him in the gang because he had grown up in the neighborhood.

"We'll be okay, Vee. The homies don't give a shit about that nigga," LV replied as he kicked at several crows that ventured too close to their table. "I hate these fucking crows. My *abuela* told me they were bad luck. I don't want them anywhere near me."

"Your *abuela* is full of shit. They just fucking birds. Ain't nothing magical attached to them."

LV shrugged and shoveled a forkful of food in his mouth, smiling as he chewed.

Vanessa smiled back. *Tough guy, huh? Scared of fucking birds*, she thought as she returned his gaze, inhaling him like a long, gratifying hit off a pookie. With his shaved head and absence of facial hair, which highlighted his sleek nose and prominent cheekbones, she thought he was gorgeous. He had an exoticness about him, a mixture between an Italian and an Indian on the warpath. He was also full of shit right now. She could tell that he was worried. And not about no fucking crows, either. He was deflecting. Whatever his true worries, they didn't matter to her. She had his back regardless.

THEY FINISHED EATING IN LESS THAN TEN MINUTES.

They got on their bikes and rode toward a two-story building on the corner of Wardlow Street and Santa Fe Avenue. It was the home of the Kohler Company, a business that produced generators. The two homeless encampments were north of the building: one on the south side of the 405 Freeway on-ramp and one on the north side. An access road east of the building led to four tunnels that went under the on-ramp. As they rode past several concrete poles put there to block vehicle traffic onto the road, a crow dive-bombed LV.

"Whoa! You see that shit, Vee?"

"Man up, *coño!*" Vanessa replied. "Those crows don't give a shit about you. Stop being paranoid and hurry up."

She picked up speed and pulled away. LV stood up in his seat and started pedaling faster as they rode into the quiet, middle-class neighborhood less than a half mile from where the two homeless encampments were. The next morning was trash pick-up day. They would be back in the wee hours, fighting off raccoons and opossums digging through the trash cans sitting in front of the houses. What the people who lived in the houses thought to be trash, the unhoused deemed to be necessities. But until then, LV and Vanessa were going to Vanessa's favorite spot: the Halloween Fest: Dark Harbor show at the Queen Mary. Long believed to be a haven for ghosts, it was a great place for the event, the ubiquitous sea fog providing the perfect ambiance.

The bike path on the L.A. riverbed is a straight shot to downtown Long Beach and the Queen Mary. A steep, concrete, graffiti-marred riverbank extends from the path down to the riverbed, which ends at the Pacific Ocean and the Port of Long Beach. Bike rides are filled with the wonders of nature; Birds of prey fly overhead, ducks waddle below, and storks high-step in the water, all under the watchful eyes of seagulls, fearless in testing the limits of their comfort zones.

Bird watchers and animal conservationists with expensive cameras set up on tripods barely noticed Vanessa, LV, or any of the other cyclists riding past. They were more concerned with catching sight of a rare species than anything else, including the plight of the unhoused living in a suburbia of shantytowns all around them.

Another crow flew past LV's head. Was it the same one he had kicked at earlier? Or the one that dive-bombed him when he and Vanessa were leaving Fantastic Burgers? Or was it another one—one of the ones he threw rocks at whenever they came too close to their tent? Sammy, one of their neighbors in the homeless camp, had advised him on several occasions to leave them alone, that they had long memories and didn't forget disrespect. LV didn't care about the warnings. All he cared about at that moment was something else that his *abuela* had told him.

Death comes with the crows, mijo.

CHAPTER TWO

"HEY, I BROUGHT YOU SOMETHING."

Hamid Shraifat held up a brown paper bag as he stuck his head into a tent in the homeless encampment just north of the Kohler building. A gaunt, ruddy-complected, forty-one-year-old man, he was mild-mannered and respectful. His given name was Arabic for *praiseworthy* and *honest,* but he preferred being called Sammy, likely as protection against the post-9/11 hysteria sweeping America at the time. In truth, he could pass as a Black man.

"C'mon in. Make yourself at home."

Sammy accepted the invitation, removing a bottle of Cisco, one of the cheapest wines on the market, from the bag. He showed it to the old white man lying on a rug, surrounded by the trappings of their world: a milk crate used for everything from a dinner table to a nightstand to storage for items obtained from trash cans in front of expensive homes, and a plastic bucket to urinate and defecate in.

"Ah! You got the good stuff! I applaud you, my friend. Your impeccable taste knows no bounds," the white man said, sounding as if, in another life, he might have been accustomed to Chateau Lafite Rothschild.

He was of German descent and instantly made a casual observer think of Santiago from Ernest Hemingway's *The Old Man and the Sea.* His name was Frederick Doyle Neumeier, and although only fifty-three years old, he

9

looked more like he was seventy-five. He suffered from alcoholism, diabetes, and high blood pressure and walked with a cane. The diabetes had weakened his kidney function, and the condition of his prostate caused him to use his bucket at least twice during the night.

"Why do you do that, Sammy?" Frederick asked as he watched Sammy pour some of the contents out before taking a long drink. "It seems like such a waste."

"This goes back thousands of years," Sammy said as he wiped his mouth with the back of one of his dirty hands. "It originated in the land of my ancestors. It's to honor the dead, and you honor me by respecting the tradition."

Frederick never "honored the dead" when he drank alone. He thought it a silly custom, but he always tried to respect other cultures. After all, his own ancestors once believed in a guy with a hammer who could summon lightning upon demand.

Like many people experiencing homelessness, Frederick didn't talk much about his family life or the life he had left behind, always leaving room for speculation. He could very well have been a surgeon, a lawyer, a CEO, or perhaps a teacher at one time. If this was true, he had traded calf-skin loafers for the filthy steel-toe construction boots with frayed laces he now wore every day.

Sammy lived in the same encampment as LV and Vanessa, the one on the opposite side of the freeway on-ramp. To get to Frederick's encampment, he had to either dodge traffic or crouch-walk through one of the four tunnels, which were small but long and covered with nonsensical graffiti on the walls and detritus on the ground. Built for water runoff during flooding, those living in the two camps used them or the thick vegetation west of both encampments as toilets or to dump the overnight contents of their plastic buckets, the stench of urine and feces so overwhelming it could sometimes be smelled all the way to Wardlow Street.

Sammy visited Frederick often. It was far easier for him than it was for his hobbled friend. The two of them would honor the dead, talk about finances, and what they would do if they could get off the streets and had access to money. But here, in two encampments tucked away by the side of a freeway, they were masters of their worlds, Frederick the chancellor of his encampment and Sammy the shah of his.

LV and Vanessa were on their way back from the Queen Mary.

Their minds were clear whenever they got back from the boardwalk, a glimpse of life on the other side of the hell they inhabited. Everyone who noticed them as they rode through the boardwalk area probably thought LV was just another over-the-hill gang member with his angry gun moll ready to rip someone's head off. The scowls they wore were misunderstood, however. They were self-defense mechanisms directed at everyone else in a world filled with enemies, disapproving family members, and those who couldn't understand the depths of gangster love.

They turned onto the access road leading from Wardlow Street just as Sammy was leaving Frederick's tent. After exchanging pleasantries, Vanessa and LV dismounted, Vanessa in possession of a souvenir cup from the Halloween Fest.

They crouched low and rolled their bicycles through the third and fourth tunnels, careful to avoid urine and feces. Sammy was a little tipsy now and not as mindful as he crouch-walked through the second tunnel, his thighs tightening up during the long journey. He wore the same dingy white Nike tennis shoes every day, so he could afford to be loose with where he stepped. Human shit or dog shit, it was all the same to him.

The first tunnel was often occupied by a homeless Native American woman whom everyone called Lobster Girl because of deformities that gave her fingers the appearance of claws. She spent most of her time there when she wasn't out panhandling or foraging for food, oblivious to the stench because of her constant exposure to it.

LV and Vanessa laid their bicycles on a dirt path near their tent. A lean white man with a pockmarked face walked up to them. His name was Elmore. LV had never liked him, thinking that he was nothing more than a kiss-ass who loved to get high on other people's dime.

"Yo! What up, dawg?" Elmore asked, in an unflattering attempt to sound like a Black gang member.

"Not a thang, *ese*. What up with you?"

It irked Elmore when LV called him that. *I ain't no fucking Spanish-American*, he always thought. *I'm one hundred percent 'Murican.*

He grinned and shrugged before going into a tent where his girlfriend,

11

Juanita, was sitting on a milk crate, smoking a Kool cigarette. He unwittingly rubbed one of his shoulders as he kneeled next to her.

"Let's get outta here. I'm starving."

Sammy walked up as they were leaving.

"We going to get something to eat, Sammy. You hungry?"

"No thanks, Juanita. I'll grab something later."

Sammy only had two dollars. Although he had no problem begging or asking complete strangers for money, he hated asking people that he knew. He decided to take a quick nap before going out with his hand-made sign proclaiming that he was homeless and hungry.

LV and Vanessa were in their tent now, resting from the long bike ride.

"I don't like that dude, Vee. Him or his hood rat bitch. And he always trying to talk like a fucking *tinto* with that 'yo,' and that 'dawg' bullshit. I know what he is. He's a fucking hillbilly. A hillbilly and a hood rat, that's all the fuck they are."

"You stooo-pid, *cabrón!*" laughed Vanessa. "But I don't like him either. It's something about him. Why he always wearing long-sleeved shirts, anyhow? He don't bang H, so he ain't hiding track marks."

LV stroked the lower half of his face like he always did when thinking hard about something. He then shrugged, lit a pookie, and sucked on it before passing it to Vanessa. After holding the smoke in for a few seconds, he blew it out and watched it dissipate along with any more thoughts of Elmore.

ELMORE AND JUANITA WERE AN ODD COUPLE, TO SAY THE LEAST.

He was ten years older than she was and had grown up in the South near the Mason-Dixon line before making his way to California by way of the military. The recipient of a dishonorable discharge for drug use, he wore long-sleeved shirts to ensure that the rebel flag tattoo on his shoulder was always covered up. He tried hard to conceal his southern twang by trying to sound like people his ancestors despised, but it often slipped out when he was scared or angry.

And Juanita was indeed a hood rat. Although initially a term used for sexually promiscuous females who got high and drank with gang members, the term had expanded to include any female who was not doing particularly well in life.

Juanita had spent most of her twenty-seven years on earth in Compton, an impoverished city next to Carson and dominated by Hispanics and Black people. There was no shortage of hatred there for white people, but a chance encounter with Elmore while purchasing meth from the same dealer had made her color blind. Their common interest in the drug removed racial barriers and now they forever chased the sexual bliss they shared when they first got high together. It was so strong they both left their respective spouses and children for each other.

Elmore lagged and let Juanita go ahead. He was hoping they might get lucky—that someone would proposition her for sex. Then they could get food *and* meth. Elmore sat down on the curb when a car driven by an older Hispanic man pulled next to her. She leaned on the passenger side door and stuck her head in the window. When she opened the door and got in, Elmore smiled and thought, *That dog'll hunt.* He got up just as an eruption of cymbals, drums, and off-key singing of praise for the lord came from one of the storefront churches. He hitched up his britches, smiled, and walked to a nearby secluded street with broken streetlights where he knew Juanita would have the man drive to.

Elmore would watch from afar, waiting for her signal if the man had a significant amount of money worth robbing him for. Then, he would sneak up and brandish the buck knife he always carried and take it. If the man had only brought enough for a hand job or blow job—as a rule, ten or twenty dollars—then he would let her do her thing.

Fuck that no count wetback LV, Elmore thought. *His shit ain't all that anyhow.*

KATHERINE VERDUN WAS BEAUTIFUL BEFORE SHE FELL VICTIM TO DRUGS.

At just twenty-four years old, she had long, curly black hair and an oval face. She liked alcohol and smoking meth, but she preferred heroin and always carried a hidden syringe. Still relatively attractive, she was a personable woman who would have made a fine high-end realtor, given her bright smile and disarming charm. She lived in Frederick's encampment but was a social butterfly and could be found at either encampment at any time in any tent.

"Mind if I come in, Fred?"

"You know you don't have to ask, Kat. Come on in."

She entered the tent, not too long after getting out of a parked car on one of those secluded streets with broken streetlights. The man in the car was what women in her position called a "midday" trick, cheap bastards who didn't care who they paid for sex or what they looked like. They were really no different from the midnight tricks.

Frederick liked Kat. They talked a lot. She was normally secretive, but he had gotten her to reveal her full name during one of their conversations.

"Verdun? That is a city in France where a huge battle in World War One took place," he'd said. "Are you sure you aren't royalty?"

She'd laughed and punched him in the arm, not realizing their ancestors were probably shooting at each other between 1914 and 1918.

Kat smoothed out her hair, straightened her brown Calvin Klein eyeglasses on her face, and made herself comfortable on the ground near a milk crate that doubled as a table.

"How are you doing today, my dear?" Frederick asked.

"Oh, you know. Just living the *dream*. You got any booze?"

"No. Sammy and I finished off a bottle not twenty minutes ago. I'll go back out in a little bit and get some more."

Kat glanced at the cane by the tent entrance. She felt bad for him. In a way, she saw him as a sort of father figure.

"Don't worry," she said, thinking how much he resembled the driver of the car she had recently gotten out of. "I'll go. You got any money?"

Frederick thought about the twelve dollars he had in his pocket. He was fond of her, but not enough to trust her with money, given her love affair with heroin.

"No, I'm flat-busted," he said.

Kat knew he was lying. Everyone in their world lied about their finances. "Okay," she said as she smiled, revealing smudges of red lipstick on her teeth. "I'm gonna go out for a bit. If I come across something, I'll bring a bottle back."

She was lying, too, knowing full well that if she found any other men seeking sexual satisfaction, she would quickly service them and then go straight to the dope man's house. Maybe he would let her shoot up there if she promised to repay him with a blow job afterward. If not, she would take her little balloon of H, find a dark doorway in one of the businesses that littered Santa Fe, and shoot up there.

Every now and then, she would come across a regular, like George, the guy she had met about two months before. Everyone called him "George Bush" because of his striking resemblance to the former president (W, not the old man). He would sometimes pick her up in his van where they would have sex. Kat preferred Black and Hispanic men—or women—but it wasn't personal with George. It was business.

As she walked down Wardlow just before dusk, the traffic was heavy with drivers exiting the 405 Freeway on the way home after work. Cars sped past, but no one stopped for her. She was wearing an oversized black Raiders jersey with *Jamarcus Russell #2* on the back, and a pair of jeans. Not exactly seductive, but the midnight and midday tricks didn't care what she wore. The after-work crowd was a little more discerning, for the most part.

"Hey, beautiful. You working?"

Kat was so deep in thought she hadn't even heard the car pull next to her. She looked at the driver. He was another older white man, probably in his late fifties. He was the perfect trick. She didn't like the young ones, no matter what race they were. She had been robbed by them too many times. But the older men? All they wanted to do was get off quick and go back home to their loving families. Unless they were serial killers or liked to hurt women, but she knew how to handle them too.

"Hey, stud. It's your lucky day," she said as she ran her hand through her hair, straightened her glasses, and subconsciously patted the knife in her back-pocket before getting in the car.

JUANITA HAD JUST EARNED TEN DOLLARS FROM A TRICK IN THE FRONT seat of his car.

He was a *paisa*, an unsophisticated person from a region in the north-west of Colombia. Most of them are farmers or hire themselves out as gardeners. Juanita was done with him in less than three minutes. She and

Elmore then put the money with what they already had and decided to spend it all on meth.

After making a quick stop at a nearby dealer's house, they were back in Sammy's tent thirty minutes later. Sammy never bothered to mention that they hadn't brought any food back. It wasn't necessary. He'd known where they were going as soon as they left.

Elmore put some of the meth he and Juanita purchased into a pipe. He held a Bic lighter under the bowl and inhaled. The flame cast an eerie orange glow across his face, and his eyes crossed as he watched it ignite the substance that stole the souls of its users. The sound of the drug burning was like a combination of water boiling and dry leaves being trampled on a crisp autumn morning.

"There were a lot of fucking ravens out today, huh baby?"

Elmore nodded in agreement as he held the smoke in his lungs for what seemed like an impossibly long time before passing the pipe and lighter to her.

"Those are crows, Juanita," Sammy said, opening up a bottle of wine and sharing it with his ancestors. "I keep telling y'all that. They both look the same, but they are different as night and day. People associate them both with death and bad luck, that much is true, but ravens like to be alone. Crows are like these gang bangers around here. They'll rat-pack you."

Elmore exhaled slowly. He watched the swirling smoke disappear in the small tent, his lover's face now bathed in the same orange glow after loading the rest of their meth into the pipe and lighting it. She inhaled deeply as Elmore stared, anxiously rubbing his hands on the knees of his Wrangler jeans.

"And damn if they aren't called a 'murder' when they're together," Sammy continued after taking a drink. "Scientists don't call them that, though. They still call them a flock. Whatever. I like murder. It's more poetic."

Juanita exhaled and held out the pipe and lighter in front of her. She heard Sammy talking, but she couldn't quite make out what he was saying. She was past the point of caring. The pookie had taken over everything.

"And they have long memories, too. They don't forget faces. That's why I don't feed them. Once you start, they come around every day and if you don't have anything for them, they will chase you. The motherfuckers even mourn their young when they die or get stolen by raccoons. The scariest thing about them is that they can smell death. They'll gather around a corpse and eat it if they get a chance. They always start with the eyes."

"Yeah? Well, what happens then, old man?" Elmore asked Sammy while reaching into the smoke Juanita had exhaled.

"Then they feast."

Elmore disregarded the ominous tone in Sammy's voice as he grabbed the pipe. Juanita pulled her knees close to her chest, and put her head down, basking in the high. Elmore put fire to the bottom of the bowl and sucked hard, the ecstasy of the drug causing an involuntary fluttering of his closed eyelids as he consumed what was left. He didn't give a shit about what Sammy was saying now, either. He was more concerned with the fact that he had finished the bowl.

Silent now, Sammy just watched him and Juanita. He knew they wouldn't be around much longer. What they had smoked was only enough to make them want more. The pleasantries were gone, now, as they abruptly got up a few minutes later and left without saying another word. This time, they would do whatever it took to get money for another hit. Elmore wouldn't wait for a signal.

Sammy thought about the crows and how he and his neighbors spent most days fighting with them over food. At night, the crows slept on the roof of the Kohler building where they kept their nests. It was a perfect place for them. The ambient light from streetlights combined with white noise from intermittent cars on Wardlow Street and the freeway created a peaceful atmosphere. They needed the light so they could see birds of prey or raccoons approaching. And although they liked white noise, they did not like loud, sudden sounds.

CHAPTER THREE

IT WAS ALMOST DUSK.

Maleko E. Laki, aka Lucky, a muscular, tattooed Samoan man who wore wire-rimmed glasses, was hanging out with three other men at his house in Long Beach near Carson. They were smoking blunts and rapping along to a song made by one of a thousand criminals trying to parlay their experiences on the streets into a payday. Lucky, who was also a drug dealer with ambition, suddenly interrupted the collective rap dreams.

"Any of you niggas seen or heard from LV? I got a hundred dollars for whoever tell me where he at."

LV owed him money and had been ducking him for over a year now. Everyone knew that LV was a snitch, but Lucky didn't care about that. In his mind, that was internal stuff with the D-13 gang. It didn't concern him. He only wanted his money.

One of the other men, a local crackhead, quickly stepped up. He had not long ago seen LV and a hood rat on bicycles going through some tunnels under the 405 Freeway. He would have given this information to Lucky for a single hit off a crack pipe. For one hundred dollars, he would take him directly there.

"I know where he's at. I'll show you," he said.

The four of them then got into a black Hyundai sedan, and the crackhead directed the driver to the access road east of the Kohler building.

"Park right here. There's a homeless camp through those lil ass tunnels on the other side of the freeway. That's where I seent him go," he said, his arm like an extension of a boom mic as he pointed.

Lucky wanted someone with him for backup, but he was strong, well over six feet tall, and close to three hundred pounds. It didn't seem likely he would need them, but he aspired to be the boss of the area. If he were to establish dominance in the drug trade here, it would have to be through intimidation. Bringing other guys with him would help, but not if one of them was a crackhead.

"Stay here," Lucky said as he and the other two men went through the tunnels to the encampment. LV and Vanessa were just coming out of one of the three tents that were there.

"Where my money at, muthafucka?" Lucky asked LV, a spark of recognition at the sight of Vanessa.

"Fuck you, Lucky!" LV said.

He was a gangster again now. He had broken other gang rules, but he refused to break the one where you never back down from a threat. Lucky charged him with his head down, but LV was a fighter, having been jumped into the D-13 gang when he was only fourteen years old.

Vanessa cursed Lucky out as he picked up his glasses less than a minute later and dusted himself off, a trickle of blood coming from his nose. Lucky ignored her. He knew the Malaepule family. That was a hornet's nest that he wanted no part of, so he addressed LV instead.

"If you don't have my fucking money before Halloween, we coming back to shoot up this whole fucking camp!"

One of the men with Lucky stared at LV.

"You know who the fuck I am, don't you?" he asked.

"Naw, dawg," LV said. "I don't know you."

The man laughed and then looked at Vanessa.

"You got a big fucking mouth, bitch."

Vanessa spat on the ground and said, "Fuck you!"

Not wanting to get into a confrontation with her, Lucky decided that he and the two men should leave.

Sammy had just emerged from the heavy vegetation behind the encampment after relieving himself. Before walking out of the encampment, the other man with Lucky grabbed him by the shirt collar and demanded his money. The last time Sammy resisted during a robbery hadn't turned out well for him, so he reached into his pocket and gave the man his last two dollars.

Lucky may not have gotten what LV owed him, but in his mind, it was okay. There were other people out there who owed him as well. Not long ago he had started expanding his business, tapping into the wide-open market in the Antelope Valley area.

For years a barren wasteland where white, meth-addled users with missing teeth wandered around, it was now home to more and more Black and Hispanic people from the South L.A. area and Compton. Lucky already had someone up there selling for him. Maybe he would collect from him in the meantime, or send him to see LV. Maybe that bitch, Vanessa, would be there and get hers, too. It was no longer about the money. Now, Lucky had to save face. It was the only way to survive in his world.

October 29, 2008

Eighteen-year-old Tony Duane Bledsoe, aka Cat Eyes, had just been released from the Lancaster Sheriff's Station jail. Arrested for robbery, the case was dropped when the victim declined to press charges. Bledsoe had only been in custody for a few days, but it was a piece of cake for him as he just told jokes and kept the other inmates laughing. He was happy to be free in time for Halloween. He enjoyed painting his face like a clown and putting on a hoodie.

At slightly under one hundred miles from Long Beach, Lancaster is frequently called hell on earth. It is the kind of place where animal skulls with rattlesnakes crawling out of the eye sockets litter the landscape while turkey vultures perch on nearby Joshua trees. There is a hodgepodge of street gang activity there, with a mixture of gang members from an area formerly known as South Central L.A. Local politicians changed the name because of the stigma attached to a place so dangerous that the rapper Ice Cube made a song giving instructions on how to survive there.

Several members of the predominantly Black Rolling 60s Crip gang had planted a flag in Lancaster. Bledsoe was a member, even though he was white. Black gangs will allow other races to become members, under the right circumstances, just as Mexican gangs will. Had Leonard Lloyd grown up around Crips, or Bloods, then he most likely would have been one of them instead of a member of D-13.

Bledsoe was the result of a flawed welfare system that had failed many more kids than just him. After he was abandoned by his birth parents, he became a ward of L.A. County and was in and out of foster care facilities until a couple living in Lancaster took him in. One day, he came home, and they were gone. No word, no notice, no forwarding address, no reason why. They were just...gone.

He never told his friends why he suspected that they left. He had his suspicions, but he kept them to himself. He survived by couch-hopping at the houses of various friends. Snake, a fellow Rolling 60s member and one of Bledsoe's best friends, was someone he could always count on. He earned his nickname because he rarely talked, and was lean and sinewy.

Snake had moved to Lancaster after trying to get out of gang life with the help of the *Homeboy Industries* program, founded in East L.A. by Father Gregg Boyle. The guiding principle of the organization was, "Nothing stops a bullet like a job," and it was created to assist at-risk youth, gang members, and inmates by offering free services such as mental health and legal counseling, tattoo removal, education, and employment assistance. But far too many gang members used the program just to comply with their parole conditions, and they often went back to their gangs after a few months. Others went back because of a lack of commitment, which is what Snake had done.

Bledsoe had another friend named José Salamanca, who also looked out for him. Snake and Salamanca knew each other, but they didn't hang out together. Bledsoe's girlfriend was a cute young woman named Rhonda. There was a lot of jealousy when they first hooked up because she was Black, but Snake had squashed any potential beef right away.

Unwanted by his birth parents, thrown away by his foster care providers, and considered a lost cause by everyone around him, Bledsoe survived by whatever means necessary. When he wasn't robbing people, he made his money by selling meth or marijuana on consignment from more established dealers. The drug sales were the most lucrative and steady source of income for him, but he smoked more of the product than he sold, so he was constantly behind on his payments. At the time he owed money to a dangerous individual who lived in the Long Beach area. He wasn't worried about him, though. Favors were just as precious a commodity as dope and money. Bledsoe was sure he could work his debt off. If a car was required, he could always get Snake or Salamanca to drive.

Bledsoe pulled his hoodie over his head and shoved his hands deep into his pockets, incidentally fingering the plastic bag containing his property. *Fuck that fat apple head cracker,* he thought as he remembered the deputy who processed his release. He looked down at his Timberland boots and trudged forward, the strong winds buffeting him and spinning tumbleweed across the street as he began his search for someplace to sleep.

CHAPTER FOUR

HALLOWEEN HAD BEEN a great night for Sammy.

It was close to midnight when he got back to his tent with a bag of candy, and three bottles of Cisco that he had pilfered from the beer and wine store across the street from Fantastic Burgers. It had been easy; the store owner was under siege by Disney characters screaming "trick or treat." He stashed two of the bottles under the milk crate, and excitedly emptied out the candy on his blanket. He then drank the other bottle, ate some candy, and fell asleep.

Sammy spent most of the next day doing what he normally did, and when he finally got back to his tent, it was after 10 p.m. He turned on the battery-operated flashlight that doubled as his lamp, and opened another bottle of wine. While pouring some out, he heard Juanita and Elmore and invited them into his tent. They sat down, ate candy, and drank with him, but their conversation was different. It was more subdued, the threats by Lucky and his goons hanging over the encampment like a tattered white flag.

"You don't thank those dudes coming back, do you, Sammy?"

"I don't know, Juanita, and I don't care. I don't have anything to do with whatever LV has got going on. That's between him and those guys."

"Fuck them, and LV too," Elmore said. "Uppity muthafucka."

"I had me a dream last night, Sammy," Juanita said, her hand shaking as she put a Kool to her mouth and took a drag.

"What did you dream about, honey?"

"I dreamt I was living in a real nice house, with a big backyard and a view of the mountains. There was a lotta trees behind my backyard before you get to the mountains. I heard crows. A lot of them. Real soft at first, but then the noise got so loud it hurt my ears. And when I looked out the window, I seen a big ole owl. It was just sitting on a post in the back yard looking at me. And then, all'a sudden, it flew off into the trees with hundreds of crows chasing it. I know it was just a dream, but it scared me. And I don't e'en know why."

"You don't have anything to worry about, Juanita. Dreams are funny things. You just have to read them right. It's all about the right interpretation. Owls and crows hate each other, but Owls represent wisdom, and crows represent death. Seems to me like that owl was leading death away from your house. You ain't got nothing to be afraid of."

"Whatever," Elmore said, clearly not a fan of the conversation. "Fuck those Black motherfuckers. I cain't stand 'em. Dreams, good luck, bad luck—it's all bullshit if you axe me." He finished the bottle and grabbed a few fun-sized Snickers.

"You got anythang else to drank, Sammy?"

"I'm afraid not, Elmore."

"Well then, I guess that's our cue. G'night."

Sammy looked at Elmore with disdain. He didn't like him nearly as much as he liked Juanita, who also wished him a good night as she and Elmore left.

They went to their tent and laid down under several blankets and quilts, snuggling close to each other for the additional heat emanating from their bodies. They always slept fully dressed—shoes included—like most homeless people did, except for those with cultural customs, like Vanessa. She didn't wear shoes in her family's home, so neither she nor LV wore them in their home by the freeway.

Sammy lay down after they left. He hadn't been able to sleep lately, for some reason. He was hopeful that tonight would be different. He wanted to wake up fresh and early, take a drink from the last bottle under the milk crate, and then share with the crows behind Fantastic Burgers or Angel Food as they all searched through the trash for breakfast.

A VEHICLE PARKED EAST OF THE KOHLER BUILDING A LITTLE BEFORE midnight.

The three occupants, two of whom were wearing black hoodies, sat there quietly for a few minutes. Although Halloween was over, the front-seat passenger still had his face painted white. He was armed with a 9mm semi-automatic pistol with a fully loaded seventeen-round magazine. He had removed every cartridge and wiped each one down with a rag, wearing gloves to avoid leaving DNA.

There was no need to pull the slide back and inject a round into the chamber for effect like in the movies. He had charged his weapon before he got in the car. Real gangsters rolled with one in the pipe just like the cops did. He took a long drag from a blunt, passed it to the driver, and peered into the back seat. He was in charge, the conductor of what was about to happen.

"No witnesses," he said. "All dome shots. Nothing to the body. When I let off, you let off."

The rear passenger was armed with a .32 caliber revolver. There was no need for him to wipe down the cartridges in his gun. Unlike semi-automatic pistols, nothing ejects from a revolver. They don't have as many shots as a semi-auto; the majority only have six, but between him and his partner in crime, they would have plenty.

The front passenger took one more hit of the blunt before putting it out in the ashtray. He looked at the driver and said, "Wait here until we get back. And don't smoke the rest, either."

The two gunmen got out of the car and walked northbound toward the four tunnels. They were looking for LV. The shot caller wanted him taken care of, specifically, but the man armed with the 9mm was hoping Vanessa was with him. Everybody knew that that bitch had a big fucking mouth.

LV AND VANESSA WERE SITTING WITH KAT IN THEIR NEW TENT.

They passed the pookie around as they listened to music, Vanessa hitting it in between polishing her nails and munching on chili-cheese fries from a container near LV. Kat was holding her glasses in her hand. For

25

whatever reason, whenever she smoked meth or banged H, she had a habit of taking them off and holding them. Perhaps it was her way of not actually "seeing" herself destroying her life. Or perhaps it was merely a comfort thing.

None of the three had any intention of shutting it down yet. The meth wouldn't let them. They would probably stay in the tent after getting high; Vanessa watching the whites of LV's eyes at the climax of their special time. If Kat couldn't convince them to engage in a threesome, she would put her glasses back on and go back out to make money on a secluded street.

Vanessa was vexed, however, and the meth only increased her paranoia. Her mind drifted back to the day Lucky tried to collect money from LV. She could remember what they talked about afterward like it happened an hour ago:

Did you know those other two guys, babe? I know the one you got in a fight with. They call him Lucky, right? Fucking puto. I think he threatened my sister's friend and her kids with a gun before.

Yeah, Vee, he'd said. *He an off-brand nigga from some bullshit barrio called the Reefer Mob or some shit like that. What the fuck kind of name is that for a gang, anyhow?*

But what about the other two, LV? Do you know them? That one fucker said that you knew him.

No, Vee. I don't know either of them.

But why would that vato say that you knew him?

I don't know. You know how these young muthafuckas are. He was probably trying to show off in front of Lucky. But if it makes you feel any better, we'll move to Fred's camp. In case they do come back. Which they ain't. Lucky don't want to see me again.

Having heard what she wanted to hear, Vanessa had wrapped her thick thighs around LV, put her head on his chest, and danced with the sandman. As she snored, loud enough to be sexy but not annoying, LV was glad she had let it go. He had lied to her, but it was for her own good.

Yeah, I knew him. Not well, but how could anyone forget those eyes? he'd thought. *I only met him once, but I knew his reputation. He was known as a killer.*

As LV had drifted off, all he saw were those eyes glaring at him until it was his turn to dance, his own snores like a tuba to Vanessa's clarinet.

FREDERICK HAD NEVER LIKED CANDY, BUT HE LOVED HALLOWEEN.

People were overly generous, especially when they saw an old man with a cane and a cardboard sign. He had panhandled so much money that he was able to purchase a bottle of the expensive stuff, the kind they keep behind the counter on a shelf so high a stepladder is needed to get to it. There would be no tributes to long-lost ancestors tonight. He knew that for what he'd paid for that bottle, he could have bought enough Cisco or Boone's Farm wine for the next week. But for some reason, he felt like drinking something other than rotgut for a change; something inside telling him to treat himself.

Alcohol had been the ruination of his professional life, and deep down inside, he knew that it would most likely be the end of his existence as well. He thought about something he'd heard a long time ago as he drank the warm, smooth liquid from the bottle that had an X and an O on it:

It has been said that the greatest gift in life is to be prepared to die.

Frederick knew that he would never be prepared to die. A gift like that is as rare as a white peacock. He knew that the way his life was going, he would pass out drunk one night and never wake up, or his heart would give out on him as he stood on a corner holding that damned cardboard sign and leaning on his cane.

He listened to the music coming from LV and Vanessa's tent as they talked and laughed with Kat about some guy named George, their silhouettes animated in the glow of LV's battery-operated lamp. Frederick finished off his bottle, reminded why the good stuff cost so much more. He lay on his stomach, chuckled, and thought about dancing with kings and queens before passing out.

IT WAS A MILD SIXTY-DEGREES.

Fog from the nearby ocean had started to roll in, creating a ghastly, grayish-colored miasma. Under a crescent moon with only 11 percent illumination, the sound of the wind blowing through tree leaves and bushes meshed ominously with growling dogs and screeches of cats fighting them off.

Lobster Girl had just taken a long drink of a 40-ounce bottle of Olde English beer when she heard a car stop. She was in her tunnel, the one closest to Frederick's encampment. Two men emerged from the enveloping fog. Because of years of surviving on the streets with only her wits and guile, Lobster Girl had developed a sixth sense for when something wasn't right. As the hairs on the back of her neck stood up, she pressed her back tightly against the wall, trying to conceal herself as best she could. The men were walking with purpose toward the tunnels, which were pitch-black at night. She could see out while anyone looking in would only see voids, four event horizons beckoning. If the men didn't enter her tunnel, they would never even know that she was there. With mounting dread, she watched them pull out guns and bend down to enter the middle two tunnels. She could hear them shuffle through until they exited the other side and disappeared into the fog.

The men walked down the dirt path and into Sammy's encampment. They knew exactly where to go, but when they got there, LV and Vanessa's tent was gone. *Somebody in one of these other two tents knows where LV went,* the gunmen thought, and without rhyme or reason, the one with the painted face chose Sammy's tent. He squatted in front of the entrance, where Sammy was tossing and turning.

"Yo," the man said in a harsh voice that was barely above a whisper.

"Elmore?" Sammy asked.

"No. Show your face, G."

Sammy crawled to the entrance. The gunman grabbed him by his shirt collar, stood him up, and put the 9mm in his face.

"Hey, homie. Where LV at?"

"Why? What's up?"

"What the fuck you mean, 'What's up?' Where the fuck is LV?"

"He moved to the other side of the freeway. Over there," Sammy said as he pointed south. "Please, don't hurt me!"

The man spun Sammy around by the shoulder and said, "Show us, muthafucka. Walk."

Rather than go through the tunnels, Sammy led them to the on-ramp. His hope of perhaps seeing a California Highway Patrol unit was quickly dashed. Not a single car drove onto the freeway. What would ordinarily be seen as luck, Sammy now saw it as a bad omen. With two guns at his back, he took the men to the other encampment.

CHAPTER FIVE

THE HILLBILLY AND the hood rat heard everything.

They lay as still as corpses, too afraid to move. Minutes later, they heard gunshots and screams coming from the other campsite. After several more seconds they fled into the fog and toward the most difficult way out of the encampment, their flailing arms creating a troglodytic topiary out of the heavy vegetation, not yet realizing that if the gunmen had chosen their tent instead of Sammy's, they would no longer be alive.

Lobster Girl pressed harder against the tunnel wall. She couldn't tell exactly where the shots were coming from. Being in the tunnel made them sound like they were coming from everywhere. She couldn't take a chance on running and getting seen by the two men, so she remained still, silently wishing she could become one with the graffiti on the urine-stained wall. But the men didn't come back through the tunnels. They walked from the direction of LV and Frederick's encampment toward Wardlow and disappeared into the fog once more.

The man armed with the revolver got in the back seat of the waiting car. As the other gunman went to open the front passenger door, he looked down.

"Dammit! I got blood on my Timbs."

It did nothing to temper his excitement. He was in a zone, like he had stopped at the end of a roller coaster ride and was waiting to be unhooked. He got into the car and looked in the back seat.

"Did you see that, fool? That's how you do it! That's that old school killa shit. It ain't nothin' but a G-thang, homie!"

The other gunman was more subdued and just mumbled something about not believing what he had done as he leaned back in his seat. The driver was just as excited as the front passenger and reached over and pulled the front passenger's sun visor down.

"Damn! That shit sounded like Vietnam! Look at yo' face!"

The vanity light around the mirror exploded in the darkness. The front passenger stared at his reflection. Beautiful eyes set in a crimson Rorschach test stared back. He adjusted the mirror slightly and looked in the back seat again. He laughed before flipping the visor back up. Then, he picked up the blunt from the ashtray and lit it as the car eased from the curb.

Barely visible between the low light from the crescent moon and the fog, a murder of crows flew over the tunnels and Lobster Girl. She shrugged her shoulders, finished her 40-ounce, and threw it on the ground with the rest of the trash as a lonesome foghorn blew.

ELMORE CREPT INTO FREDERICK'S ENCAMPMENT AT AROUND 6 A.M.

His curiosity and need to get high had overcome his fear. He had to see what happened, and maybe, if he was lucky, there might be some meth still around. Juanita was terrified and had refused to go with him. What Elmore saw when he got to the encampment horrified him. Still, single-minded in his task, he quickly rifled through LV's pockets. Everyone else was too bloody; he was not going to touch them. His task now complete, he crept out of the encampment area, completely unaware of the pookie with at least two more hits in the bowl lying on the ground under Kat's leg. When he got back to Juanita, she smoked Kool after Kool as he relayed what he had seen. And when he was finished, she screamed and threw up.

Two hours later, George Bush and his friend, Agapito, wanted to get high. They decided to go to LV's camp to buy some meth from him. George didn't want to take a chance on seeing Kat again so soon. He had seen her on Halloween at a friend's house where they got high. All she would do was beg for money and he didn't have any for her, so he chose to stay in the van.

Agapito was glad that LV had moved from the other side of the on-ramp. He wouldn't have to go through those disgusting tunnels, even though he and Lobster Girl sometimes engaged in brief romantic encounters in them, her holding his manhood in her hands like a seal holds a fish, him holding his breath and leaning back against the piss-stained wall she had not long ago tried to melt into. As he walked past the concrete poles onto the access road, he expected to see her in her usual spot, but she wasn't there.

When he got to the encampment, he noticed several crows walking near two tents. They were fearless as he well knew, but it was unusual for them to be so close this early. There were usually people still sleeping inside the tents, and no one ever left food unattended. Agapito heard a low buzzing sound as he got closer. The undeterred birds just hopped further away instead of flying off. He stopped in his tracks when he saw Sammy lying face down near one of the tents. The buzzing sound was coming from a swarm of flies around his body.

Several crows frightened Agapito when they flew out of the tent. He opened the entrance and looked inside. The stench was overwhelming. Kat, LV, and Vanessa were covered with flies. The crows weren't there for them, however. They had been eating from a container of food. Agapito held his hand over his mouth to keep from throwing up, as he turned to run. When he saw Frederick lying face down in blood in the other tent, he began dry heaving.

George Bush was listening to loud music and smoking a blunt when he saw his friend sprinting toward the van.

"They're fucking dead, George!"

"Who? Who's dead?"

"All of them! We gotta call the cops!"

Agapito snatched open the passenger door and got in as George sped to the freeway on-ramp. He stopped at one of the emergency phones secured in yellow metal boxes. With his head on a swivel, Agapito got out of the van and frantically punched the keypad.

"Nine-one-one, CHP Office, can I help you?"

"There's five bodies on the side of the freeway over by Santa Fe and Wardlow!"

Click.

The CHP dispatcher didn't get a chance to ask any obligatory follow-up questions. She called back, but there was no answer. More than likely, it was a prank. It could have also been an ambush by someone waiting to shoot at cops when they showed up, so she sent two units and a supervisor. The first officers to arrive parked their cars in the dirt on the south side of the 405 Freeway on-ramp before walking down the embankment and finding the horrific scene.

The freeways in California are the jurisdiction of the Highway Patrol. They could handle crimes other than those involving vehicles, but they chose not to. The sheriff's departments and municipal law enforcement agencies were better equipped and had the expertise for such complicated cases, so the CHP always deferred to them. But these murders were on the *side* of the freeway, making jurisdiction a moot issue. The supervisor advised the dispatcher to contact Long Beach PD. This was most definitely their case.

PART TWO

CHAPTER SIX

"MCGUIRE SPEAKING."

"It's Holly from dispatch. You and your partner got five homicides on the 405 at Wardlow."

It was 9:30 a.m., and Long Beach PD Homicide Detective Mark McGuire was almost finished with his second cup of decaffeinated coffee.

"Excuse me?"

"You and your partner got five homicides on the—"

"No, I heard you the first time, but seriously? Five? Are they *on* the freeway? Or on the *side* of the freeway?"

"On the side of it. Near Wardlow. Our west patrol station guys are there securing the area."

"Is CHP there?"

"Yeah. According to patrol, it looks like a bunch of them walked all over the place."

"Okay, ETA half hour," McGuire replied, seething at the incompetence of what were supposed to be seasoned law enforcement officers. No matter how much training they got, their lurid curiosity always took over.

Most cops preferred to use the metaphor of law enforcement officers being sheepdogs protecting the community, composed of sheep, from criminals, who were wolves. But McGuire chose to see criminals as dragons and cops as noble knights protecting the realm. Only the dragons he fought didn't fly, breathe fire, or protect their gold. They drove cars and spat fire from exotic firearms; they didn't protect gold, they stole it. And in place of slaying them with lances or swords, metaphors for nightsticks or firearms, McGuire preferred to use his mind.

Clean-shaven and well-groomed, he was the exact opposite of the hulking ex-baseball slugger with the same name. He was Black, honest, and the epitome of a small man who cast a considerable shadow. Being the senior detective, he was responsible for notifying his partner, Hugo Cortes, regarding their callouts. They made quite an impression whenever they showed up.

Cortes was a first-generation Mexican American who came to the United States when he was just seven years old. Tall and built like a world-class soccer player, he was a physical fitness fanatic who brought his lunch to work every day in an Igloo Playmate Cooler. He was dark complected with a mustache and salt and pepper hair and had a slight Spanish accent when he got angry. He often called people *amigo* or *amiga*, and frequently introduced himself as "Cortes with an *s*, not a *z*."

McGuire speed-dialed him, put the phone on his shoulder and pressed his chin against it to hold it in place as he rinsed out his cup.

"What's up, *amigo*?"

"You up, bitch?"

"Just got back from a run."

"Well put on your Rockports. It's time to dance."

"Where's the party?"

"On the side of the 405 at Wardlow. And you might want to put some extra food in your cooler this time. We got five."

"Five what? Bodies? *Chingalé!*"

"I'm leaving home in a few. I'll be there in less than thirty minutes."

"Okay, motherfucker. I'll see you there."

McGuire didn't live far from the scene, but it would not have mattered in any event. He always beat his partners to their callouts. He lived in the city, whereas most of the other Homicide Bureau detectives, including Cortes, lived in adjacent counties. But McGuire and his wife, Kim, a beautiful light-skinned Black woman with blue eyes who was also a terrific soccer player, were still in the same house they had been in even before he became a cop, when he was a drummer for the legendary Barry White and his Love Unlimited Orchestra.

Having already eaten breakfast, he put his Smith & Wesson 9mm pistol in a black leather holster on his belt before clipping his badge close to it. A plainclothes cop always wore them next to each other. In the event they had to draw their weapon, both would be visible and perhaps prevent a tragedy caused by some overzealous police officer who never should have graduated from the academy.

Fastidious in his dress, likely a result of being the son of a retired US Navy chief of thirty years, McGuire preferred ties from Nordstrom Rack—tying them in Windsor knots like his father had taught him—and Rockports, which he called his "dancing shoes." He always wore them unless he was going to court. Investigating crime scenes was a tedious process with investigators on their feet for up to twelve hours at times. They had to wear something comfortable for the dance, which continued long afterward, sometimes decades, until the dragon was slain.

Having ensured that he had all his gear for work, McGuire hugged and kissed Kim at the door as if he were going off to war. They didn't embrace each other every time he left the house, but they never failed to do it when he left for work.

"I'll see you later, Baby. Much later."

"Okay. Stop by the house to eat if you get a chance. And please, be careful."

"A'ight den."

Kim was the perfect spouse for a homicide investigator. She was accustomed to her husband being gone for extended periods of time, having dealt with it when he was a musician. Besides, she was perfectly fine home alone with the .38 caliber detective special she kept in her nightstand drawer, and with Cain, their 125-pound short-haired German shepherd, sleeping by the front door at night.

MCGUIRE STARTED THE CITY-ISSUED BLUE FORD CROWN VICTORIA parked in his driveway.

As he drove off, he thought about how great a wife Kim was. A lot of spouses couldn't deal with the rigors of being married to a homicide detective, but Kim was a rock for him, and for their two daughters. He adored his "Baby," a pet name he had given her in the early eighties when they first met. She was his soulmate, his ride-or-die chick, his endgame.

Helicopters were overhead when he pulled up to the scene fifteen minutes later. At least a dozen cars were parked on the 405 on-ramp, along with the department's sixty-foot Mobile Command Post, known as the CP. The entire area had been cordoned off with yellow tape and CHP officers were conducting traffic control.

McGuire walked to the CP where the mayor, the city manager, the chief of police, and every other police administrator in the department were drinking coffee and eating donuts from Angel Food. Others from the mayor's office were there as well, sycophants with sinecure positions, lackeys who cared more about their careers than the people who had lost their lives.

McGuire had worked in this area for years when he was a beat cop and a gang detective. He knew that there was another encampment on the other side of the on-ramp, so there was a favorable chance that there could be evidence there as well. There could also be additional victims there. Hell, the killer might even be hiding there, although McGuire didn't think that to be likely.

During daylight hours and well into the night, the on-ramp had a high volume of speeding cars on it. If someone had crossed it to get from one encampment to the other, it would have occurred during late night, or early morning hours. And although it wouldn't make much sense for the killer to park on the on-ramp and walk down the embankment, it certainly couldn't be ruled out.

"Chief, can I talk to you?"

"Yeah, Mac. What's up?"

McGuire nodded toward the others.

"Can we talk alone?"

"Sure," the chief said before they moved several feet away.

"Two things. First, has anyone checked the other encampment for victims or potential suspects?"

"What other encampment? Where?"

"There's another encampment on the other side of the freeway, which brings me to my second thing. Since the CP is smack dab in the middle of two potential crime scenes, I'm gonna need all these people out of here."

"What? The mayor and the city manager are here."

"I don't care who they are. Now *you* can either ask them, or *I* will."

Realizing that the request would most likely be better coming from him, the chief contacted the mayor and his command staff. Within a few minutes, all the vehicles were gone.

The first thing McGuire noticed were the tire tracks in the dirt where the CP had been. If the killer had parked on the side of the on-ramp and walked down the embankment, that evidence was now compromised. There were also dozens of boot prints present. McGuire knew right away they belonged to emergency personnel.

Cortes arrived not long afterward. His idea of business attire was cotton Dockers with comfortable button-down dress shirts, the top button unfastened. He wore his ties loosely around his neck and rolled his sleeves up to the middle part of his thick, sinewy forearms. He never wore suits, instead choosing to wear sports coats, which he frequently left on a hanger in the back seat of his car.

McGuire, on the other hand, always wore suits, and he rarely left his jacket in the car. Were it not for the blue name plate in his jacket pocket displaying a small badge between his name and *Long Beach Homicide*, one could assume that he was an attorney. Conversely, Cortes exuded cop vibes. And not just any cop vibes; he gave off the kind that made you think of a brooding cop holding a telephone book while standing over a suspect in a small room with a light-bulb swinging from the ceiling.

"What's up, *amigo*. Has anyone checked the other encampment?"

"What's up, Hugo. The chief didn't know, but I haven't asked the handling unit yet."

"That guy never knows anything. He was a shit street cop, and he's a shit administrator."

"Y'all the handling unit?" McGuire asked when he and Cortes got to the new CP and contacted two uniformed cops, one with a battle-hardened face and two stripes on his sleeves, the other one with a highly creased uniform, shiny brass, spit-shined shoes, and a deer-in-the headlights look.

"What's up, Mac, Hugo," the two-striper said. "Yeah, it's us."

Cortes smiled as he took the crime scene log and signed in with the date and time. After McGuire did the same, the two-striper looked at his trainee and said, "Well? What the fuck are you waiting for? We ain't got all day."

When the trainee was done briefing them, McGuire asked, "Has anyone checked the other homeless encampment yet?"

"Yes, sir. It's completely empty, no bodies, no blood, and no other evidence that we could find."

"Outstanding. I love a beat cop who knows his or her area," McGuire said. "Still, we would like to take a quick look ourselves."

The two-striper looked at his trainee and said, "Go with them. I'll handle the log until you get back."

There were only two tents in the encampment. Both of them were empty.

"Look at this one, Mac. A lot of blankets and quilts."

"A couple? Or at least two occupants. And it looks like someone ransacked the tent, or whoever was in there got the hell out quick. I know these places aren't normally the neatest and cleanest, but everything isn't usually turned over and the quilts and blankets thrown all over the place, either."

"Not as many blankets and quilts in the other tent," Cortes said. "And everything is neat."

After checking around for a few minutes more, McGuire looked at the trainee and said, "Now you can take us to the bodies."

When he started to walk toward the embankment leading back to the on-ramp, McGuire said, "No. We're going through the tunnels."

"Tunnels? What tunnels, sir?"

McGuire and Cortes walked toward a concrete pathway that ran north and south, the trainee following behind. McGuire pointed south and said, "Those tunnels. They go *underneath* the on-ramp."

Each man took a tunnel, shining their flashlights while they walked through looking for evidence, careful to avoid broken glass and human waste. When they got to the other side, Cortes told the trainee to check the fourth tunnel.

"A bunch of CHP officers walked through the scene," McGuire said to Cortes while the trainee was searching. "We should collect the boots and shoes from every one of those idiots who was at that CP, including the mayor and the city manager."

"I'm game. I'll hold the mayor down while you snatch off his penny-loafers. Then we'll switch up and I'll take the city manager's shoes. But seriously, though. Why the hell did the CHP have to trample the scene? They weren't going to investigate *caca*, or even write a report."

"I didn't find anything, sir," the trainee said when he emerged from the tunnel.

"Okay, young man," McGuire said. "Get on your radio. We need some cops down here to expand the crime scene. The killer parked on Wardlow."

"How do you know that, sir?"

"Because that's where I would've parked. It's easier. Crooks like easy shit. To be a good cop, you gotta learn to think like them. Now, take us to the bodies."

A blue girl's bicycle and a red, rusty boy's bicycle were lying on a dirt pathway close to three tents. Several plastic bags of trash, one containing a 64-ounce cup from the Queen Mary Halloween Fest bearing the words *Where Nightmares Come Alive,* littered the area near the bikes. Sammy was lying next to one of the tents, his hands splayed out on the ground. A Sparkletts water bottle near him was covered in dried blood, and a walking cane was next to the bottle. Three pairs of shoes were lined neatly near the entrance to the tent.

"Mac, look over here."

McGuire turned to where Cortes was pointing. Frederick was face down inside another tent less than five feet away. He had been shot multiple times. A paisley print runner was on the ground separating the two tents. Being careful not to disturb the presence of several 9mm shell casings on the rug, they looked inside the tent next to Sammy.

It harbored the culmination of the nightmare that had occurred in the encampment.

CHAPTER SEVEN

Long Beach is not without its share of notoriety.

Randy Kraft, one of the worst serial killers in American history, made his home there in the 1970s. Incompetent police work had enabled him to go on to kill dozens of young men after a thirteen-year-old boy, dazed, bloodied, and shoeless, ran into a bar in Belmont Shores in March of 1970. He had been drugged and raped at Kraft's apartment not far away but managed to escape. Rather than getting a warrant, the police broke into the apartment and arrested Kraft. He was later released because of the unlawful entry. He would go on to become the Freeway Killer, sometimes called the Scorecard Killer. He raped and murdered gay young men for the next ten years, mutilating, castrating, and decapitating them in and around Long Beach.

On May 14, 1983, a CHP officer pulled over what he thought was a drunk driver on the 405 Freeway. It was Kraft. He was arrested after failing a field sobriety test, and when the officer checked the car, he saw a dead US Marine in his dress blue uniform with his genitals exposed in the front passenger seat. He had been strangled to death, and Kraft was driving around, fondling the man's penis. Kraft now sits on death row at San Quentin prison, convicted of eleven murders and suspected of sixty-seven others.

McGuire and Cortes had a combined thirty-two years on the job. They had seen gruesome murders on numerous occasions, several even rising to the level of Kraft's work. Still, before looking into two tents at a homeless encampment in a secluded area next to the 405 Freeway, they thought they had seen the worst one human being could do to another.

The odor coming from inside the tent that Sammy lay next to was repugnant, a malodorous smell that caused them to pinch their noses. Randy Kraft was a monster, no question. But as horrific as his murders were, he killed his victims, one, maybe two at a time. This was wholesale slaughter.

Cortes was not a religious zealot, but he was raised a Catholic. McGuire was Baptist and the choir director at one of the largest churches in the city. He said a silent prayer for the victims, and Cortes made the sign of the cross as they looked at the scene.

No cop wants to get caught lacking in the faith category after taking a bullet or while in a fight for their life. Almost all of them believe in some type of higher power and most wear religious jewelry, like a crucifix, a cross, or the Star of David. A lot of other cops have tattoos of Michael the Archangel or Matthew 5:9, the verse wherein peacemakers are called the children of God, somewhere on their bodies. Or they carry prayer cards with Michael, the patron saint of police officers, in their pockets or behind their bullet proof vests.

Cortes and McGuire needed every bit of their belief systems as they took it all in. To process a crime scene properly, an investigator must have "soft eyes" and look at everything macroscopically. Despite the gruesomeness of the scene, they noted the accessories of a dangerously debauched lifestyle: a CD containing explicit lyrics, an unused condom, and a fixed blade knife on the ground close to the victims.

"Look there, Mac," Cortes said as he pointed at Kat. "What is that? There, under her leg."

McGuire looked closer and said, "It looks like a pookie."

Kat was lying on her back and partially on the lower portion of Vanessa's legs. Her Raiders jersey and jeans were now covered in blood. She lay just inside the tent entrance, her legs slightly bent but spread apart and fixed in rigor. It was obvious that she had vacated her bladder and bowels as demonstrated by the odor and presence of a wet spot.

Her left hand was folded across her stomach, holding her glasses in a death grip. There was high-velocity, or "blow-back," blood on her wrist, hand, and lower arm. A prominent gun-shaped burn marred her throat. The killer had placed the gun underneath her chin and fired upward, resulting in a corresponding perforation wound to the top of her head near her hairline. She had another gunshot wound to her left temple. Either wound would have been instantly fatal.

Vanessa lay on her back next to LV. Her freshly painted nails were surreal amidst the carnage, the only thing of beauty left. She wore a pair of gray, blue, and white shorts with horizontal stripes and a black T-shirt. The shirt rested slightly above her mid-section, exposing numerous stretch marks, the evidence of her having given birth multiple times. Her feet were touching one of LV's legs. Neither of them were wearing shoes.

Dried blood surrounded Vanessa's head, and most of her hair was now matted and stuck to the side of her face. She had been shot multiple times, which included a penetrating wound to the back of her head and one to her left temple.

LV was wearing a pair of clean athletic socks, black and white plaid shorts, and a wife beater. The pockets of the shorts were inside out, as if he had been searched by someone. He was lying on his left side and facing Vanessa. Like the others, he had been shot multiple times, mostly in the face and head.

An empty food container lay on the ground near LV's feet. His body was next to a milk crate covered with a Samoan tapa cloth. A CD player and a bottle of nail polish rested on top of the milk crate. A cup from Fantastic Burgers and additional nail polish bottles were on the floor near the cup. Dried blood covered everything.

Much like guns are charged for effect in cinema, blood is depicted as bright red, and watery. In real life, however, it is thick and coagulates, sometimes giving the appearance of maroon-colored pudding. Serum separates from it, creating a condiment for the coming feast of the insect activity that puts the final exclamation mark on life. A gurgle, a rattle before cessation, even a loud fart as the essence of life evaporates serve as a dinner bell for blow flies and ants.

As with Sammy and Frederick, insects feasted on Kat, LV, and Vanessa, completing their benefaction to the planet's brutal biology. All living things are as connected in death as they are in life, providing nourishment for whatever life form is most in need. Now, both inside and outside of the tents, an army of ants and a squadron of blowflies were making their contributions.

None of the victims would have suffered any physical pain. Loss of life from gunshot wounds to the head is instantaneous. The suffering would have come from knowing their demise was upon them after seeing the person next to them murdered. They would have heard every gunshot except the one that ended their life.

There were thirteen 9mm shell casings scattered on the runner and in the tent. There were also several projectiles present, which suggested that some of the wounds were close-range or contact shots wherein the bullets passed completely through the victims. All five had bulging, purple and blackish-colored eyelids. Gunshot wounds to the head cause severe trauma to the orbital and occipital areas, resulting in the eyes darkening and swelling which makes the victim look not unlike a raccoon. Head wounds also cause darkening and swelling of the lips.

"I know that guy, Hugo," McGuire said while pointing at Sammy. "I had a case with him once. Somebody robbed and shot him years ago. He was with a Samoan guy. I can't remember either of their names right now, but I know they were both very uncooperative."

Cortes pointed at LV and said, "Look at how clean this guy's clothes and socks are. He doesn't look homeless."

"Neither does she. Check out her nails."

Cortes tucked his tie in his shirt so that it didn't sweep the ground as he crouched down to get a better view.

"Yeah, you're right."

"Actually, only three of these people look homeless—the chick in the Raiders jersey, and the two old men," McGuire said, referring to Sammy and Frederick, Sammy in his shit-caked Nikes, Frederick in his beloved boots, both in clothing that hadn't been washed since the first time they donned it.

"And check out the rigor, Hugo. They've all been dead for a while now."

"People are in and out of these encampments all the time, Mac. This means that dozens of them probably saw the bodies and none of them called the cops or paramedics. How can you be so apathetic?"

"There ain't enough lifeboats."

"Lifeboats? What does that have to do with anything?"

"It's the world, Hugo. We're losing our humanity, bit by bit. The world has become one big Titanic, and that iceberg is us looking in the mirror."

NONE OF THE BODIES HAD ANY IDENTIFICATION.

There would be no fanfare, no memorials or dedications, no periods of mourning unless they were identified. Until then, they were only John and Jane Does, destined to be cremated, the ashes held for three years before being interred in a common gravesite at the L.A. County Cemetery.

McGuire had his dispatch center notify the coroner's office. With so many bodies, they decided to respond with their mass casualty unit, a large trailer containing a huge tent, a portable X-ray machine, and metal tables where the pathologist would perform the general autopsies. The specific autopsies would be conducted later at 1104 Mission Road in L.A.

All five victims had been tentatively identified, but until results from the Automated Fingerprint Identification System came in, they would keep their John and Jane Doe numbers. Now, only yards from where they lived in tents, panhandled, stole, foraged for food, and tricked for money, they were lying in a tent of another sort while multiple bullet trajectory rods stuck out from their heads.

Kat had several tattoos, including one on her chest of two cat eyes with whiskers. A syringe containing heroin was in her bra between the eyes. Women often hid contraband in places they knew the police wouldn't search; Vanessa had a bag of meth secreted under her left armpit.

Another tattoo, a swastika with a rose on her back, gave away another possible side of Kat. These types of tattoos are favored by members of the Aryan Brotherhood, a vicious white supremacist prison gang. At some point, this had to be checked out when looking at potential motives. Kat hanging out with what the AB considered "sand niggers" and "wetbacks" would be a bone of contention for them and cause a death sentence for her. It could also be a motive for someone Black or Hispanic to kill her as well.

McGuire and Cortes scanned the scene as the CSI's photographed and marked potential evidence with yellow number placards. Processing crime scenes was painstaking work in an immaculate setting. In a homeless encampment, it was a nightmare. Trash was everywhere, and everything had to be inspected, turned over, and shaken out, in the event there was a bullet, shell casing, or other type of evidence hidden somewhere. It would be easy to overlook something, maybe even something that could crack the whole case. And since the tents were considered homes by law, warrants had to be considered.

"Fuck, Hugo," McGuire said. "Look at all this crap. The only thing worse would be searching in a hoarder's house. I had a few domestic violence cases like that when I worked patrol. There was shit everywhere. Just like here."

"You don't have to tell me. I got a friend whose *abuela* lives like that. There is only one other place that I would hate to search more."

"Where's that?" McGuire asked as a musical praise for the lord from one of the nearby storefront churches punctuated his question.

"At a *bruja negra's* house."

"What the fuck does that mean?"

"Black witch."

"Here *you* go. How do you say white witch?"

"*Bruja blanca.*"

"How come you're not scared to search those houses?"

"Because the white witches are the good ones."

"That's some bullshit! Why does everything bad have to be Black?"

"I don't make the rules, *amigo*. That's just the way it is."

"One more question, bitch. How do you say, 'kiss my Black ass' in Spanish?"

THE ON-SITE PATHOLOGIST PERFORMED THE GENERAL AUTOPSIES WITHIN a few hours.

The bodies were gone, but news vans were still all over the place with reporters milling about. With the broadcasting of the murders came the never-ending phone calls from concerned people wondering if an estranged family member may have been one of the victims. A couple from out of state called. They had adopted a child who was a ward of the court due to neglect. The couple called because they knew their son's birth mother hung out in that area. Her name was Katherine Verdun.

At close to 11:30 p.m., McGuire got a call from a gentleman who was concerned about his estranged wife.

"Hello. My name Bobby Beck. My wife name Juanita. We been separated for 'bout three or four years now. We got four kids together, but I cain't let her 'round them while she strung out like she is. She live in a camp by the freeway with some redneck. The last time I heard from her was in June."

"What's her description, sir?"

"She still pretty, but she on that fucking meth, so she ain't got no front teeth now. And she real thin."

"None of the victims match that description, I'm glad to say."

"I gotta bad feeling. Will somebody call me if one of them is her?"

"Absolutely."

McGuire hung up, thinking about the devastation that hard drugs bring down upon communities. The ripple effect is unfathomable as it often takes years, sometimes decades, to see the full results. The woman the man described would rather smoke meth and sleep in a tent than be at home raising her children. And communities expected law enforcement to solve that problem? If there was a better metaphor than having a finger in a dike to stop a dam from leaking, McGuire couldn't think of it.

He got another phone call less than twenty minutes later.

"Detective McGuire speaking."

"Is this the detective doing the investigation at the homeless camp?"

"Yes, I'm one of them. How can I help you?"

"One of the people kilt is LV from D-Thirteen. He got his cap peelt 'cause he snitched on one of his own homies. He sold meth for a living."

Whenever McGuire heard the term, "cap peeled," it always took him back to the first time he ever heard someone use it. It was during an interview with a potential witness to one of the other one hundred murders he had investigated up to then. He later found out that the term was coined by gang members and refers to a procedure performed during autopsies, where the pathologist removes the brain for examination. It is done by cutting the upper portion of the head and then pulling the scalp back as if peeling an orange before the skull cap is cut open with a buzz-saw, allowing access to the brain.

"How do you know this?" McGuire asked.

"Er' body in the neighborhood know. The word all over the streets."

48

"What's your name, sir?"

"I'd rather not say."

"A'ight, den. Can you at least describe him?"

McGuire took out his notebook and looked at it as he listened.

"Could be him," he said after comparing the caller's description with notes he had taken while at the scene. "I need a way to get in contact with his family."

"I don't know where he live, but his girl always with him. Her name Vanessa. I know where *she* live."

"Describe her. Um hum. Um hum. A'ight den. What's her address?"

McGuire wrote it in his notebook and thanked the caller before hanging up.

"Who was that, Mac?" Cortes asked.

"Someone who didn't want to be identified, but he identified two of our victims and gave me an address for one of them. We gotta go make a notification. The house is not that far from here."

"This would be a good time to shut it down anyway," Cortes said. "We've been at it all day."

"You ain't lying. I'm tired as fuck."

After posting two uniformed patrol officers to safeguard the scene, McGuire instructed lab personnel to meet back there at 7:30 a.m.

He and Cortes took separate cars to the address provided by the anonymous caller. The location was a small, one-story house in Carson. Every light in the house was on. They knocked on the front door, careful not to disturb the numerous pairs of shoes lined up neatly along the wall.

The person who opened the door immediately started wailing, creating a chain reaction among Vanessa's numerous extended family members. They had already heard the news from street sources, but victim survivors always harbor hope, regardless. Two homicide detectives showing up at their door after midnight was confirmation enough without anyone saying a single word.

Death notifications are the worst duty for homicide investigators to perform, but they are necessary—not only to notify the loved ones of a victim, but also to gauge their reactions. There have been occasions when the person receiving the death notification was the reason for there being a need for one. Not this time, however, as was apparent by the overflowing of grief. It was the same as when the coroner's office notified LV's wife and kids.

Nothing travels faster than news on the streets. It is comparable to when enslaved people had their own form of communication during the Civil War called the "grapevine," or when inmates pass along information, known as "word on the yard." More times than not, the information from both sources is as close to confirmation as possible, pending physical corroboration, and the streets were already saying that LV had been the target. He was "no good in the hood" because he had testified against a D-13 gang member. This was all fine, but the scene still had to be properly processed. Word on the yard and the grapevine don't win cases. Evidence does.

McGuire and Cortes were exhausted when they left the house. When McGuire got home, he went in through the attached garage. He had no idea what may have gotten on his clothes while he was searching in all that filth, so going in through the front door of his house was not an option. Cain met him, licking his hand and sniffing him.

"Hey, buddy. Papa has had a long day."

McGuire walked past his beautiful Gold Wing motorcycle. He knew that before this case was over, he was going to put more weekly miles on it than usual.

It was now a little before 2 a.m. Cain wagged his tail and watched silently while McGuire stripped down. He left his clothes in the laundry room and took a quick shower. He was glad Kim was asleep. He knew she had seen everything on the news. Now he wouldn't feel the need to talk about it. Although she never asked him about his cases, he had never had one like this before.

Setting his alarm for 6:30 a.m., he knew he had to *sleep quick*, a common saying among older Black folks when working sixteen-to-eighteen-hour days back-to-back. He put his gun on the nightstand and was asleep before his head hit the pillow. Cain walked to the front door and lay down, keeping silent vigil for dragons.

CHAPTER EIGHT

MCGUIRE GOT BACK to the scene at 7:30 a.m.

Cortes was already there. He was holding two Styrofoam cups of steaming coffee, one black and one decaf. Like McGuire, he was wearing jeans, boots, and a black windbreaker with "LBPD" emblazoned on the back in white letters.

Cortes had turned out to be an outstanding homicide detective. He could be stubborn and sometimes had a bit of a temper, though. Early in their partnership, they caught a murder at a local bar. A cartel member shot a man in the head because he thought the man was laughing at him. He then calmly walked out of the bar, got into a car, and drove off. A witness got a partial license number. Before killing the man, the cartel member had been reading a magazine and having a drink in a booth.

McGuire and Cortes ran every variation of the plate and came up with six possible addresses in Long Beach. Cortes wanted to knock on every door, but McGuire did not think this was a sound strategy. They would possibly be getting themselves into an unnecessary armed confrontation at each location. He shut Cortes down, using the cliché of walking down the hill to fuck all the cows instead of running down and fucking only one.

"Hugo, for the last time, the crime lab is fingerprinting the magazine and the glass that he fingerfucked. All we gotta do is wait and get warrants for whoever the prints come back to. Let's fuck all the cows, my brutha."

51

Cortes was furious and accused McGuire of not letting him run investigations on his own. He believed that the senior partners of other new homicide detectives were letting them do whatever they wanted.

On the way to interview a witness on another case, he brought the subject up again. Finally, McGuire had had enough.

"Look, Hugo. You and I are minorities. We don't get to make mistakes. We get one shot. The white detectives? They get to make mistakes. Someone will always take care of them. No one looks out for us. We gotta be perfect. We can't mess up. You need to listen to me."

"That's why nobody in the unit likes you, Mac. You're an asshole. You always have to have everything your way."

"Let's get one thing straight, Hugo. I don't give a fuck if nobody in that unit likes me. But they *are* gonna respect me."

As soon as McGuire finished talking, his Blackberry rang.

"What? Really? Okay. Print that information out and leave it on my desk."

He ended the call and glanced at Cortes.

"That was the crime lab. They got a hit on prints from that magazine. The guy lives in one of the houses you wanted to door knock. You happy now, bitch?"

When the department's Career Criminal Apprehension Team (CCAT) served a search warrant the next day, the cartel member was armed with a gun.

"What did you do, bitch? Sleep in your car?" McGuire asked as he took his cup.

"You know, the first time you called me a bitch or a motherfucker, I wanted to kick your short ass," Cortes said. "I was insulted. I thought, *Who is this little* pendejo *calling me a bitch?* And then I found out that's how you talk to people you work with when you like them. The more insults, the better, I heard, so I said fuck it. Let me reciprocate the love, motherfucker."

"That's because if I call someone out of their name who I don't like, there may be some fists coming next," McGuire said before taking a sip of his coffee.

"Well, we don't need to see *that,* but to answer your question, no. I didn't sleep in my car. I went home. I couldn't really sleep, though. I just lay in bed for a few hours and then got up and took a shower and headed back in."

"Shiiiid. You gotta learn how to sleep quick. I slept like a baby."

"That's because something is wrong with you, *pendejo.* I still can't believe you quit playing drums for Barry White to do this job. I knew you were screwed up then. Everything you've done since has only confirmed it."

"You know why I quit, bitch. I had a wife and two daughters that needed medical and dental benefits. Didn't you join up for the same reasons? I mean, getting married at eighteen years old and having three fucking kids within the next four years had to be rough."

"Yeah," Cortes said. "But if I had been traveling the world with Barry White and meeting every kind of exotic woman imaginable?" He kissed the fingertips of one of his hands with a loud *'mwah'* before flinging it to the wind. "You? You're a dumbass."

"Priorities, muthafucka. Priorities. Come on. Let's get this out of the way."

Cortes nodded, and they both went to the trunks of their cars just as crime lab personnel drove up. They got paper booties for their boots, surgical gloves, and face masks to put on. Once pleasantries were out of the way and everyone else was outfitted in the same manner, they all descended back down to hell.

THE SEARCH WAS COMPLETED SIX HOURS LATER.

McGuire and Cortes went through everything that they possibly could. They knew that it was the little things that made the biggest cases. They had learned long ago not to overlook a receipt for 9mm ammunition just because someone else found an AK-47 with a 100-round drum magazine—especially when your victim was killed with a 9mm pistol. Murder weapons are rarely found. Most of the time they are torched or at the bottom of a large body of water somewhere, so circumstantial evidence is paramount.

McGuire and Cortes had collected various items for fingerprinting. It was just good housekeeping. They didn't really think that the killer or killers had stayed around too long. This had the appearance of an "in quick, out quick" deal. There would have been no need to touch anything. Simply come in, blast away, and get out of Dodge. But someone had taken the time to rifle through LV's pockets. Maybe he had dope or money on him, or maybe he didn't have anything.

It was possible that McGuire and Cortes would never find out one way or another, though. And whomever had gone through LV's pockets targeted him specifically; Vanessa had meth on her, Kat had a syringe containing heroin, and there was a meth pipe still in the tent with at least two hits left under Kat's leg near her buttocks.

"Hey, Hugo. One of the calls I got at the scene was from someone who said LV was a member of the D-Thirteen gang."

"That's a Carson gang, isn't it?"

"Yeah, they bleed over into our city sometimes, but not much. They're small-time compared to what we got here. I know some of the guys that work OSS at Carson Station. They've helped me out with cases before. I'll give them a call when we get to the office and see what they have on LV."

McGuire and Cortes worked on the fifth floor of the Long Beach PD Headquarters building, located just a few blocks away from the boardwalk and the Queen Mary. The entire floor was dedicated to gang, homicide, and other violent crime investigations. McGuire and Cortes sat at adjoining desks. There were several other investigators in their office space, and the secretary's desk was just a few feet away. There were no windows, as the office was in the middle portion of the floor, but the vending machines weren't far away, which the investigators often took advantage of to purchase drinks and snacks for witnesses.

McGuire picked up his desk phone and dialed.

"Carson OSS, can I help you?"

"Yes, ma'am. This is Detective McGuire from Long Beach PD Homicide. I was wondering if any of your detectives are working today."

"Mark Wedel is the only one in the office right now," the secretary said. "I'll transfer you."

"This is Wedel."

"Hey brutha, it's McGuire from Long Beach."

"What's going on, brother? What can I do for you?"

"Shaking trees, my friend. My partner and I caught the five murders in the homeless encampment."

"Damn, that's your case? Been all over the news. How can I help?"

"One of the victims is Lorenzo Villicana. They call him LV. We were wondering if you guys have anything on him, or if you've heard anything from any of your informants about what happened."

"LV, huh? Yeah, we know—knew that fool. He used to go by Lyncho when he was banging. And he had no problem whatsoever dropping a dime on somebody. He was mostly a tweaker, but he did sell a little from time to time. He hadn't been banging for a while. He was dating a chick from the Malaepule family. I think her name is Vanessa."

"Was. *Was* Vanessa."

"She was one of the victims, too?"

"Yeah. You knew her?"

"Her family is well-known in Carson. Nobody fucks with them."

"Do us a favor and keep your ears open, huh? Any information you guys get will be greatly appreciated."

"Will do, my brother."

"Thanks, Wedel. Peace."

McGuire was optimistic about getting information from Wedel and the Carson OSS team. OSS, an acronym for Operation Safe Streets, was one of the premier gang units in the state, if not the country, and the Carson OSS team was one of the best teams in the entire unit.

Not long after McGuire hung up with Wedel, a man claiming to be Frederick's cousin called the Homicide desk from the lobby. His name was Karl. McGuire caught the elevator down, introduced himself, and offered his condolences. Karl burst out crying and hugged him as people looked on.

"Let's go somewhere where we can talk," McGuire said. "Please, follow me."

McGuire led him to an office where he asked the usual questions:

"Do you know who would do this to your cousin? Did he have any enemies? When is the last time you saw or talked to him?"

According to Karl, Frederick wouldn't hurt anyone, and he didn't have an enemy in the world. They were estranged, but Karl loved Frederick and was devastated that someone had murdered him. He had seen the incident on the news and, knowing that Frederick sometimes lived in an encampment there, came to the police station fearing the worst.

McGuire gave Karl his business card and the number to the coroner's office, where he could get more information about what to do next. The office had already notified Sammy's next of kin, who were devastated as well. No matter how estranged someone is, their family still loves them and is in pain when something happens to them. Even if they didn't want them in their home, or if they used drugs and stole from them, or if they prostituted themselves, death always brings forth the unconditional love that one family member has for another.

McGuire and Cortes were less than forty-eight hours into the investigation. There is a cliché when it comes to investigating murders; if they aren't solved within forty-eight hours, they become infinitely more difficult to solve. It is a great catchphrase for a reality TV show, but this is not altogether true. It *is* true that investigators often get a lot of information in those first two days. It must be vetted, however, and weighed and corroborated with the evidence. Whoever came up with that time frame for solving murders hasn't worked very many. They are often like 10,000-piece jigsaw puzzles, and there is no time limit for finishing them. Most of them take much longer than two days to solve.

CHAPTER NINE

NOVEMBER 3

A Long Beach PD patrol unit stopped a van close to noon for a traffic violation near Fantastic Burgers. When the driver and passenger mentioned that they knew the homeless murder victims, the officers brought them to McGuire and Cortes.

"Detectives? My partner and I stopped these guys not far from the scene. They say they knew your victims, but we think they might know a lot more than that."

"Beautiful," McGuire said as he stood up in front of his desk, "We got it from here."

"I'm McGuire," he said to the two men as the officers walked away. "This is my partner, Cortes. And you are?"

"They call me George Bush."

"A'ight. I can see that. I voted for the other guy, though."

"So did I. This is my friend, Agapito."

"Nice to meet both of you. Have a seat and tell us what you know."

George Bush knew Kat and Vanessa. He was having an on-again, off-again love affair with Kat. He had seen her the night before the murders at about 10 p.m. at a friend's house where they got high before she took a shower and left.

"Vanessa and her boyfriend had to move because they were having problems with somebody, and the next thing you know, this shit happens," he said. "Agapito found them. He came running back screaming that everyone was dead, and we had to call nine-one-one. I drove to the freeway, and he called from one of those yellow boxes."

Agapito was still shook about what he saw in the tents, only mentioning that there was "blood everywhere," and "crows were near LV's body." He confirmed what George Bush said and didn't have much to add other than his ex-girlfriend might have some information about the murders.

"She has deformed hands," he said. "Everybody calls her Lobster Girl. She knows who the three guys are that beat up LV about a week before the murders. The word on the streets is that LV snitched on somebody, or he fucked over somebody in the past, and it finally caught up with him."

The community of those experiencing homelessness is extensive but closely knit. Everyone knows everyone. Not many of them use last names, though. They call each other by abbreviated names, like Kat, or base them on a physical characteristic, like Lobster Girl.

"A'ight den. Thanks for the information. If you hear anything else, get in contact quick as you can. Here's my card."

"Thanks, Detective McGuire."

"No problem. Be safe. Before you guys leave, what are your real names?"

"LO? THIS HOMOCIDE?"

It was a little over two hours after George Bush and Agapito left. A terrified woman had just been transferred to McGuire's desk phone. He waved Cortes over and put the call on speaker.

"Yes, this is Homicide. I'm Detective McGuire. Are you okay? How can I help you?"

"I'm fine. But I seent something last night."

"Okay. What's your name and where are you?"

"Juanita. I'm at Angel Food."

Cortes called dispatch and had a patrol car respond in the event one was in the area.

"Don't move," McGuire said. "My partner and I will be right there."

They pulled up to Angel Food less than five minutes later.

"There she is, Mac. That's gotta be her. She looks scared as hell."

"Juanita?" McGuire asked as they pulled next to her.

"Uh, huh. I'm Juanita."

"Get in the back seat."

Hello, Mrs. Beck, McGuire thought as he noticed her missing teeth. *Your husband and children miss you.*

A patrol unit drove up as they were about to leave. Cortes held up four fingers in the universal cop signal of Code 4, indicating that everything was okay. The driver nodded before pulling into the drive-thru.

"I was there that night," she said as she slumped down low in the backseat. "I heard somebody axe Sammy where LV was. They left and Sammy never came back. I know'd something was wrong, especially after all the gunshots and screams."

McGuire looked at her through the rearview mirror as Cortes turned in his seat.

"Go on, *amiga.* You're safe now. Do you know who took him?"

"No. I never seen him, but they say he half-Samoan and half-Black. They call him Lucky. 'Bout a week before the murders, a light-skint nigga bought him to LV's old spot. LV beat Lucky's ass and another nigga with Lucky took Sammy's money."

Juanita was much more relaxed when they got to the station. Cortes treated her to a bag of Doritos and a can of Pepsi. She scarfed them down and chugged the soda as if she hadn't anything to eat or drink in days.

"On the night of the murders, me and my boyfriend Elmore was laying in our tent. I heard a voice say, 'Yo!' and Sammy axed if it was Elmore. Somebody said, 'No. Show yo' face, G.' Just like that. 'Show yo' face, G.' Then somebody else axed where LV was, and then they all left."

"When did this happen, Juanita?" McGuire asked.

"'Bout midnight."

"A'ight. We'd like to talk to Elmore at some point."

"Fo' sho.' I'll make sho' he talk to y'all."

"What does Lucky look like again?"

"He a big ole' nigga, Detective Cortes. Half-Samoan. Lease that's what I heard. Real stout, and tall. And he wear glasses. Them lil bitty ones that make you look smart."

"How do you know what Lucky looks like if you weren't there?"

"Sammy told me. That's what the guy who LV beat up look like, anyway. I never seent who took Sammy. Oh, I almost forgot. I heard that George Bush went to the camp and fount the bodies. He drive one of those lil vans."

"What kind of little van?" McGuire asked as Cortes rolled away in his chair back to his desk, grabbed his portable radio, and called the two officers who brought George Bush and Agapito in.

"You know. Like a Scooby-Doo mistry van. Except it ain't painted like that."

Cortes rolled back over to them.

"The officers said it was a VW, like what hippies drove to Woodstock."

"Woodstock? What's that?"

"Something from another lifetime, Juanita," McGuire said as Jimi Hendrix's "Star-Spangled Banner" reverberated in his head.

"Where would you like us to take you?"

"Where y'all picked me up is just fine."

"You sure?"

"Yeah. That's where my peoples at. I'm cool now. I just had to talk to y'all 'bout what I heard. Sammy was cool peoples."

"A'ight den. Let's go."

"Listen to this, Mac."

Cortes pushed play on the Homicide main line recording system.

I got information on the murders. They happened because of a hit on some guy named LV. His girlfriend got killed, too. LV had gotten into an argument with a Black dude named E the day before. He went back looking to kill LV and ended up shooting everyone there. He is supposed to be homeless, and he gets around on a bike.

"It came in last night after we went home," Cortes said. "She called from a blocked number and didn't leave her name."

"A'ight, den. Let's go find a Black dude named E."

They took Cortes's car and drove toward the L.A. riverbed, stopping and talking to various homeless people and giving out business cards. None of them appeared shaken by the fact that a murderer was loose in their community. They were still sitting in front of liquor stores and 7-

Elevens, still standing at intersections with cardboard signs, still pushing shopping carts down the street.

"You seeing this, right Hugo?"

"Yeah, I am. Homeless people going on about their lives as if nothing happened."

"They are awfully comfortable to have a serial killer preying on them, ain't they?"

"I guess there aren't any *chupacabras* lurking in these parts, huh?"

McGuire remembered when the bosses first brought up the possibility of a serial killer being behind the murders. It was almost as if they *wanted* it to be true. Scaring off the homeless to another city would get rid of that political football in Long Beach, at least. Maybe they would join the herd of people on skid row or at that other beach in Venice.

He and Cortes had told the bosses then, that there was a feeling of something personal involved with one of the victims. The others were probably killed because they were witnesses. The homeless in the area not being afraid and conducting business as usual was sort of a confirmation of this theory, at least in his mind. Still, at least two or three times a day, someone either in the department, at city hall, or in the media would mention the possibility that the victims had been targeted because of their social status.

Homeless people were the very definition of survivors. Had there been a serial killer in their midst, they would have fled to other areas. These people may not have known who the killers were, but they knew that whatever had happened was all over now.

McGuire and Cortes continued handing out business cards. They were able to find someone who told them that a girl with deformed hands might have some information about the murders.

They found her in less than ten minutes. It wasn't hard. She was the only person walking around wearing mittens. After introducing themselves and promising to feed her if she accompanied them to the station, she got in their car. They gave her hot coffee and junk food from the vending machine when they arrived.

"A'ight, den," McGuire said to her as she took off her mittens, and began pouring sugar into her coffee. "What do you prefer that we call you?"

"The same thang er' body else do," she said, still pouring. "Lobsta' Girl."

"Okay, Lobster Girl. We understand you might know something about some guys LV had a problem with a week before the murders—"

"I don't know where you heard that from," she said as she finally stopped pouring. "Did Agapito tell y'all that? Asshole."

"No, ma'am," Cortes said. "He never said anything about you, other than you and him were good friends."

"That's all he shoulda' said, 'cause I wasn't there. I just heard some guys came looking for LV and he got in a fight with one of them. Some Samoan named Lucky. Er' body know that."

"You know who was with him?" Cortes asked.

"No. Just two other dudes is all I heard."

"Okay," McGuire said. "How about the murders. Do you know anything about what happened? Did you know any of the victims?"

"Yeah, I knew the people who got kilt. I was there that night, but all I seen was two men walk to the camp. Then I heard shots, and they left walking to Wardlow. I didn't see nothing else. What's yo' name again?"

"McGuire."

"Right. And I cain't identify nobody. I wasn't wearing my glasses at the time."

"But you're not wearing glasses right now."

"I lost them."

"When?"

"'Bout two years ago."

"Two years ago? How have you been getting along without glasses for that long?"

"I'm—how you say? Resourceful. I do okay. Most of the shit that happen, I don't wanna see no how. But I *did* hear that Fred seen who did the murders."

"Fred? Freddy's dead."

"Freddy's dead?"

"That's what I said."

"No, not White Fred, McGuire. I know *he* dead. I'm talking 'bout Black Fred."

"There's a Black Fred?"

"Yeah! Dark-skint nigga with big crusty lips."

"We need to talk to him. You know how to get ahold of him?"

"Er' body know him. You prolly can find him hanging 'round somewhere down the way."

"A'ight, den. Thank you for coming in. I would shake your hand, but..."

"It's cool. I get that a lot. Hey, y'all thank y'all could run me for warrants? I would really appreciate it if y'all arrest me. I need to take a shower."

"Sure. We'll see what we can do."

"Thank you, Detective Cortes with an *s*."

"You got a second, guys?"

McGuire and Cortes hadn't been back in the office long when the criminalist who analyzed the ballistic evidence walked in.

"*Sí, amigo*. What you got?"

"A total of thirteen nine-millimeter shell casings were collected as evidence from your scene. That would surely be enough to kill five people, but there were also several spent bullets found."

"Wait," McGuire said. "Our victims got plugged nineteen times."

"I'm sure, Mac, seeing as how two guns were used. Some of the bullets were from a thirty-two-caliber revolver, so your suspect is either ambidextrous, or there were two shooters."

"You know what ambidextrous means, Hugo?"

"Screw you, Mac. A thirty-two revolver, huh? You don't see those much."

"No, you don't," the criminalist said. "The good news is that if you guys find the guns, it will be easy to match the ballistic evidence to them. All the casings and the projectiles are in excellent condition."

"Beautiful! Thank you, my brutha."

"You bet, Mac. Take care guys."

After he walked out, McGuire grabbed his jacket.

"Come on, Hugo. Let's go see if we can find some more witnesses. Maybe we'll come across Black Fred."

While sitting at a red light not far from headquarters, Cortes pointed at a young Caucasian man standing in an intersection near a McDonald's with a *help wanted* sign in the window. He was wearing a pair of clean sneakers, a white T-shirt, and sagging blue jeans. He didn't appear to be older than twenty-one. He was holding a sign that read: *Homeless veteran. Please help with a donation.*

"Check out the sign that guy is holding, Mac."

"Get me out of here, Hugo, before I get out of this car and put my foot in his behind."

Cortes glanced in the rear-view mirror as they drove off. A woman had pulled over and handed the man some money.

"You see that? That's the kind of thing that pisses me off," Cortes said. "My mother and father brought us to this country for a better life, but they knew that meant working hard. And they did, too. Every day. My papa in construction and as an electrician, and my mama cleaning houses. And then you got this lazy guy right here. He probably grew up in a house that my mama cleaned."

"Some people really do need help, Hugo. But *he* ain't one of them."

"True. But I gotta admit, I will give a person money from time to time, if they look like they really need it. That *pendejo* back there? He can easily get a job somewhere."

"Yeah. He can start by walking into that fucking McDonald's. Hey, pull over, Hugo."

Cortes pulled into the parking lot of a 7-Eleven located at Long Beach Boulevard and 10th Street. Two men were sitting near the entrance begging for money. Neither one was dark-skinned or had big lips.

"Hey," McGuire said after getting out of the car. "Either one of you heard anything about those five people who got murdered a few days ago?"

One of them shook his head and the other one said, "No. Nothing. You got two dollars?"

"You know Black Fred and where I can find him?"

"No, Detective. That's what you *is* right?"

"Sometimes I wonder. Too bad you don't know Black Fred, though. I might have found a couple dollars for you."

McGuire stepped over the man and went in the store to buy a bag of potato chips. A tall Indian man with a full white beard and a turban gave him his change and pleaded with him to make the two vagrants leave. McGuire looked out the window and saw Cortes handing one of them a few dollar bills. The cashier stared at McGuire with a *what the fuck* look on his face.

"I'll have a patrol car come by and make them leave, sir. Forgive my partner. He's got a kind soul."

When McGuire got back in the car he said, "Hugo, that clerk almost took my head off when he saw you give that guy money. What the fuck is wrong with you?"

"Yeah, I know, but he looked like he really needed something to eat."

"Did he at least tell you where we can find Black Fred?"

"I didn't even ask him."

"You're a bleeding heart, Hugo. I guarantee he's in that store right now grabbing a bottle of wine out of the cooler, and that clerk, who wanted him gone so badly, is taking his money. I mean, *your* money."

"Ah, who cares. At least it makes me feel a little better."

"That ain't why you do it. You think that by giving that guy a few dollars, you're gonna score some points to help you when you get to the gates of heaven. But you don't have to worry. You won't be the only one sweating as Saint Peter goes over his short-ass list. All of us are constantly trying to unload the heavy wages of sin that we carry by giving somebody we don't even know a few dollars while we shit all over our neighbors."

"Well, my wife and I like our neighbors. She takes them enchiladas every Christmas, and they give her a gallon of Tequila."

"Quit trying to be funny. That's not what I'm talking about. You knew goddamn well what that guy was going to do with that money. They get food out of the trash. America throws away more than some countries produce. These homeless people spend the money they get from begging on drugs and alcohol. It's a mean thing to say, but it's the truth. If it's so hard for them to eat, then why are so many of them so fucking fat?"

"But giving that guy something made you feel good, didn't it? Bought you a little goodwill for later, right? I'm trying to tell you that you don't need to do that. None of us are perfect. We've *all* fallen short. The only thing that comes close to perfection is grace for others, not supporting their habits. Now, I need a cup if you don't mind."

They stopped at Angel Food and got two, one decaf and one black, before continuing their search for Black Fred.

"How you drink that shit like that, Hugo? No cream, no sugar, no nothing."

"I like it like you."

"You trying to be funny?"

Cortes laughed and said, "No, my friend. I like it straight-up, like you. That's why you're so good at this job. People can sniff out bullshit. With you, what you see is what you get. But more importantly, why ruin a good cup of coffee? Personally, I don't see how you drink decaf. Defeats the purpose if you ask me."

"I drink it for the taste, bitch. Regular coffee fucks with my heart. You know my people have a problem with hypertension, right?"

"Decaf is for *putos*. I bet you drink those non-alcoholic drinks with the little umbrellas in them, too."

"Whatever, muthafucka. Hey, look at that guy. Pull over."

Cortes stopped next to a dark-complected gentleman with noticeably large lips.

"Hey *amigo*, are you Fred?"

"Who wanna know?"

"I'm Detective Cortes, and this is my partner McGuire. You mind taking a ride with us to the station? We'll bring you back when we're done. It shouldn't take long. Plus, we got donuts."

"Okay. I got no problems with that."

"Cool," McGuire said before getting out and walking over to him.

"Lift your shirt to your tits and spin around."

"For what? I ain't done nothing."

"It's for our safety, sir. We don't know you, and you're gonna be in our back seat unhandcuffed."

It was something McGuire had done countless times. He only did it when someone was wearing clothing that could easily conceal a gun or knife. There had been multiple occasions where someone in the back of a police car had shot or stabbed the officers in the front seat. The man did as McGuire asked, performing each task as if he had done them a million times before.

"A'ight. Now lift your pants legs up."

"I'm clean, sir. I ain't got no weapons."

"Just being cautious. Turn your pants pockets inside out. All four of them."

After confirming that he didn't have a weapon, McGuire opened the back door.

"Get in, Black Fred. Let's take a ride."

CHAPTER TEN

BLACK FRED KNEW all five victims by name.

He believed that they were killed around midnight. A couple named Juanita and Elmore came to where he was sleeping on Santa Fe under the freeway overpass and told him what happened. They said someone took Sammy from his tent. Shortly afterward, they heard a bunch of gunshots, and he never came back.

"Juanita told me she thank whoever took him was a Samoan or Black dude called Lucky. They had a fight 'bout a week before the murders. Er' body know 'bout that fight. LV owed Lucky some money, supposedly. I guess he was hiding out and nobody could find him, but E took Lucky over there."

"Who is E, *amigo*?"

"Oh, that's my niece boyfriend. He a French nigga."

"What's his real name?" McGuire asked.

"Hell if I know. I don't fuck with him like that."

"Anything else?"

"You might try talking to this crazy white bitch name'a Flora Belle. She always pushing 'round a shopping cart. She see everythang. And if she don't see it, she hear 'bout it."

"A'ight, den. You've been extremely helpful. Grab a couple of donuts, and we'll take you back into the world. Where do you want to go?"

"Can y'all drop me off at the boardwalk by the Queen Mary?"

"I was hoping you'd say the steps of City Hall," McGuire said. "But the boardwalk it is."

Afterward, McGuire and Cortes discussed what they had learned so far. They had several possible motives for the murders. They had received information from an anonymous informant that some guy called Lil Man from D-13 killed LV because he testified against Leonard Lloyd. The gang revenge scenario was a promising lead. Snitches got stitches, for sure. But no one from the Carson OSS team knew who he was when McGuire called over there to ask about him, so that lead was still open. And then there was the fact that Kat had a white supremacist tattoo on her back, another possible motive that had to be checked out.

The best lead they had, however, was the drug debt angle, where Lucky killed LV because he owed Lucky money, and the other four were killed because they were witnesses. They put out word to patrol and the QOL (*Quality of Life*) team that they needed to find a homeless man called E. Then McGuire called the Carson OSS office to see what information they had on a Samoan gangster named Lucky, but no one answered the phone.

Once word got out that the cops were giving coffee and donuts to people that they interviewed about the murders, the homeless descended on the police station in droves. McGuire and Cortes were now inundated with them wanting to give statements, and one interview would quickly lead to another:

"Detectives, I heard there was a fight and LV got beat up. The guys who beat him up kilt him 'cause he was a snitch."

They looked at the shoeless, unshaven man who was wearing three pairs of socks and McGuire said, "Thank you, sir. Take a donut with you. And by the way, you're clear of warrants."

"Goddammit! How you know so fast?"

"We got new technology at the station," McGuire said. "When someone with a warrant walks in, red lights start flashing."

"Damn! That's some high-tech shit! Thanks anyway."

Cortes shook his head and laughed at McGuire as the man walked out. Then he turned to Mary, the unit secretary, and asked her to send the next one in. He grinned and grabbed a donut before sitting down.

"Help yourself, my brutha, please," McGuire said, his voice dripping with sarcasm. "Do you have any information about the murders?"

In between bites, the man nodded and said, "Um hm. Yeah. I heard that there was a fight and LV got beat up. The guys who beat him up killed him because he was a snitch."

McGuire stood up and extended his fist for a fist bump.

"Thanks, brutha. And in case you were gonna ask, our warrant system is down."

The man took another donut and shuffled out the door.

"Send in the next one, Mary," Cortes said. A few minutes later, the young white kid they saw panhandling near McDonald's walked in.

"Hello. I'm McGuire and this is Cortes—"

"With an *s*, not a *z*."

"—my partner. Okay my friend, what can you tell us?"

Pointing at the donuts, he sat down and asked, "May I?"

"Sure, help yourself."

"Thank you, Cortes with an *s*. Anyhow, there was a fight and LV got beat up. The guys who beat him up also killed him because he was a snitch."

"Enough of this bullshit," McGuire said as he stood up. "Y'all are only coming in to eat and drink coffee and maybe get arrested. Let's go. We'll walk you out."

When they got to the lobby, the man walked toward the restroom, donut and Styrofoam cup in hand. Cortes whistled softly and said, "Look at all these people, Mac. Didn't we give out business cards to most of them in the field? They didn't have anything to say, then."

"Yeah, but we didn't have free donuts and hot coffee then, either."

McGuire cleared his throat and said, "Is anyone here who has information about the homeless murders?"

A dozen hands went up. McGuire pointed to one of them, and a dark-skinned man with long dread locks and a beard almost as long walked over.

"We're the detectives handling the murders by the freeway," Cortes said. "Do you have any information about what happened?"

"Pleased to make your acquaintances, detectives. And yes, the information that I have accumulated indicates that there was a quarrel sometime before the murders, and LV was bested. The victors came back well within a fortnight and terminated LV because he was an agent for the government."

"Aight, den. I didn't understand half of what you said, but I think I know what you meant. Thank you for coming in."

"What, no beverages or other refreshments?"

"No," McGuire said, weary of the game being played. "We are fresh out. Go fight with the crows in the dumpster behind Angel Food."

"Talk about not judging a book by its cover," Cortes said as the man walked away. He then put two fingers in his mouth and whistled to get the attention of the rest of the people in the lobby. They turned almost in unison, waiting for him to say something.

"Is there anyone here who knows anything else besides LV getting beat up and killed because he was a snitch?"

As they all started mumbling and filing out the exit door, Cortes looked at McGuire and stifled a laugh. It was funny, but not really.

NOVEMBER 4

A woman by the name of Ruthie Wilson was in custody on a citizen's arrest.

She told the jail officer that she had some information on the murders and wanted to talk to the detectives. McGuire and Cortes walked to the jail, introduced themselves, and escorted her to the Homicide office.

"Detectives, I live a hard life. It's rough out there, you know? Well, I been on the streets for about six years, and I knew all of them—Kat, Sammy, LV, Vanessa, and White Fred... Can I have one of those donuts?"

"Sure, *amiga*."

"Can I have that big one? That bear claw?"

McGuire and Cortes hadn't bought these donuts. Another detective by the name of Watkins had. He brought in a dozen almost every day. Bear claws were his favorite. Those were for him. Everything else was fair game.

Cortes disliked Watkins because he was always making jokes about the way Mexican people talk and the way Black people live. He also made crude remarks about women and gays and lesbians. Cortes didn't care what color a person was, what sex they were, or what sexual preference they had. All he cared about was if a co-worker was honest and competent. *Fuck Watkins*, Cortes thought as he smiled at the woman.

"Help yourself."

"Thank you, Detective Cortes. Like I was saying. I knew them all. I was at a house with Kat the night before. There was a Samoan guy there with a tribal band tattoo on his left bicep, and he had a gun on his lap. I don't know why he had it, and I don't know what his name is. I never asked anybody, either."

"How long were you there?"

"About four or five hours."

"And you weren't frightened? That this clown had a gun on his lap?" McGuire asked.

"He didn't have it there the whole time. He was sleeping at first and something startled him, and he woke up. Then he put it away, and I didn't see it again."

"What about the murders? Have you heard anything about who was involved?"

"Oh, no. I don't know who did that. I just heard the same thing everybody else has. LV got in a fight with some dude named Lucky and next thing you know LV and the others got killed."

"I think you know more than you're telling us."

"That's all I know, Detective McGuire. I promise."

"A'ight, den. Thanks for your cooperation. Come on. We'll take you back to your cell."

Ruthie grabbed another donut and walked between them to the elevator. They heard Watkins yelling about his bear claw as the doors were closing.

When McGuire and Cortes got back to their desks, he asked them if they knew anything about his missing donut.

"I only eat healthy," Cortes said.

"And I'm diabetic," McGuire added. "With borderline high-blood pressure."

Watkins stormed out of the office, muttering under his breath. Sergeant Vince Nielsen, the supervisor of the Homicide Unit, walked in a few seconds later. A corpulent man with a sweep-over hairstyle, he was a quintessential paper-pusher who constantly strived to please his superiors.

"What are you guys laughing at?" he asked.

"Nothing, boss. Mac's just telling one of his juvenile jokes again."

McGuire rolled his eyes and turned to the phone ringing on his desk.

"Homicide. Detective McGuire speaking."

McGuire took out his notebook and started writing. "Uh huh. Uh huh. Okay. Okay. Really? Alright, do me a favor and forward your report to me and Detective Cortes when you're done. And thank you."

McGuire hung up and swiveled his chair around to Cortes.

"Who was that?" Nielsen asked.

Ignoring him, McGuire said, "That was a CCAT officer, Hugo. He and his partner found a witness. It's Juanita's boyfriend. He said some men took Sammy *and* Kat. He didn't actually see anyone because he and Juanita never stuck their heads out of their tent. They just stayed quiet. A little while later, they heard gunshots and ran and told Black Fred."

"Well, that corroborates Juanita's story."

"It's a good thing they played dead. The killers would have murdered them, too. As a matter of fact, they would have killed anyone they came across in those homeless encampments that night."

"What's seven, Mac?" Cortes asked.

"Huh? Seven what?"

"You know, like five is a quintuple. What's seven?"

"Septuple. Seven is septuple," Nielsen said, pleased that he could contribute to the investigation.

"Thank you for that, Sergeant," McGuire said before turning back to Cortes.

"I'ma run out and vote, Hugo. I'll be right back."

It was an historic day in America. A Black man had a better than average chance to become the 44th President of the United States. After years of oppression, Black people stood on the cusp of vindication in the eyes of many.

"Okay, Mac," Cortes said. "I already voted. I stopped on my way in."

McGuire judged everyone based on their character, and not the color of their skin. He had been all over the world with Barry White and had interacted with people of all nationalities. When they played Monte Carlo, they were treated like absolute royalty. Good people were good people, regardless of anything else. He often said, *Fucked up ain't got no color. Fucked up ain't got no gender, or no race. Fucked up is just fucked up.*

To McGuire, it was as simple as that. And that was the way he policed. Everyone was his "brutha" or his "sista" until they weren't.

When he got back to the office, him and Cortes fielded calls and questions from reporters until 8:35 p.m. They had been at work since 7:30 a.m.

and were dragging. Still, before leaving for the day, they decided to contact Ruthie again. McGuire grabbed the last donut out of Watkins's box, and he and Cortes walked to the jail.

"We're out of here for the day," McGuire said when they got to her cell. "Have you thought of anything else you might want to tell us?"

"Try Lobster Girl and George Bush," she replied, never taking her eyes off the donut. "They might know something. And this crazy white bitch, always pushing a shopping cart."

"That it? Nothing else about the guy with the gun?"

"I told you guys everything I remember about that, Detective McGuire."

"A'ight. Thanks."

She watched as McGuire took a bite of the donut before he and Cortes walked away.

"That was cold, Mac. How about a little grace, huh?"

"Fuck you, Hugo. *And* her. She's fucked up. She could've told us that the first time we talked to her."

"You're right."

"Damn right I'm right."

"Hey, I forgot to tell you happy birthday! How old are you now, partner?"

"I'm old, Hugo. Just fucking old. I'll see you in the morning."

NOVEMBER 5

It was the day after McGuire's fifty-second birthday and the historic election of America's first Black president. He and Kim had stayed up late watching the results, crying when they were announced. When Cortes asked him how he felt about it, all he said was, "Long overdue."

Neither of them asked who the other one voted for. They usually preferred to honor the sanctity of the voting booth and never discussed politics, but this election was extraordinary. With election euphoria over now, it was back to the business of being the murder police. They were going over their plan of attack for the day when the phone rang.

"Homicide. Cortes speaking. Can I help you?"

"Yes. I have some information on the murders."

"Okay. Can I get your name, ma'am?"

"No, you can't. I just want to give some information. I don't want to be involved, though. Can I do that?"

"Yes, ma'am."

"Alright, look. Someone I know overheard what happened because he was at the next camp over. He said it sounded like two Samoan guys did this, and it was over money owed by the one they called LV."

"Okay. Go on."

"The person I talked to told me the men said, 'Come out! Come out and show your faces!' and then they started shooting."

"Anything else, ma'am?"

"No, that's all I heard."

"Thank you. Please feel free to call back if you hear anything else."

Cortes hung up and pulled his cooler from under his desk.

"Anything good, Hugo?" McGuire asked.

"Same old stuff about Samoans killing LV over a drug debt."

"Well at least they called your line with that bullshit for once."

"You heard back from Carson OSS?"

"Not yet," McGuire said just as his phone rang.

"Homicide. McGuire speaking."

Cortes grinned at McGuire and took a bite out of a protein bar.

"Hey sir, I work on the QOL team. I have a guy here who flagged me down. He says his name is Eric, but everyone calls him E. Says you guys been looking for him."

"Beautiful. You mind bringing him in?"

"He has his girlfriend with him. You want me to bring her, too?"

"Absolutely."

Less than twenty minutes later, two QOL officers escorted a man and a woman into the office. McGuire and Cortes stood up and nodded at them. McGuire looked at the officers and said, "Thanks, guys. Can you have this lovely young lady have a seat in the waiting area while we speak with Mr...?"

"Baudelaire. Eric Baudelaire. I'm French."

"Hello, sir. I'm Detective McGuire, and this is my partner, Detective Cortes."

"Nice to meet y'all."

"You can call me Mark. Can I call you Eric?"

"E is fine."

"A'ight, E. Have a seat."

A rail-thin, light-skinned Black man with straight black hair in a pony-tail, Baudelaire was in bad shape. He was missing several teeth and reeked of urine and alcohol, much to the dismay of the other detectives in the office. He also fidgeted a lot during the interview, no doubt due to an addiction to something other than the contents of liquor bottles.

"We've been hearing some things, E," McGuire said.

"Like what?"

"Like you took Lucky and some other guys to LV's camp about a week or two before the murders."

"Yeah, I did. We went in Motor's black Hyundai. There was another nigga with us. I don't know if he was Mexican or Black. He had a faded tattoo on his face. I cain't remember what it was."

"Who is Motor? And why did you take them over there?"

"Well, Detective—Cortes, right?"

"That's right. With an *s*."

"I don't know Motor's real name. 'Bout a week before the murders, I was at Lucky's house with him, Lucky, and that dude with the tattoo on his face. They was rapping and getting high. Lucky said some nigga named LV owed him money, but he couldn't find him. He offered to give anybody who knew where he was a hundred dollars. That's a lot of fucking money, man. Just to point somebody out? Shiiiid! I told him I knew where he was and we hopped in Motor's bucket. I stayed in the car, and I guess Lucky and the other two got in a fight with LV."

"You knew LV?" McGuire asked.

"Er' body knew LV. He was from Dominguez."

"Do you know what they call the other dude?"

"Nah."

"You mean you didn't hear anyone call him by name or nickname, *amigo*?"

"Nah."

"You said you stayed in the car, right?"

"Yeah."

"Then how do you know what happened in the camp?"

"I heard 'bout it later. Lucky threatened to come back in a week and shoot up the camp if LV didn't have his money."

"A'ight, den. Where does Lucky live, E?"

"I thank he live with his daddy in Moreno Valley or Perris most of the time."

"Wow, that's a long way away, *amigo*."

"Yeah, but his homies live down here."

"Is he in a gang?"

"I don't know, Detective Cortes. Prolly! Ain't all these young mutha-fuckas rappers or in gangs? Or both? I'm kinda' scared, though. Er' body know I took Lucky to LV's camp, and Vanessa family looking for me 'cause they thank I had something to do with what happened."

"Well...did you?"

"Hell naw, Cortes with a *s*! I gets high. That's it! I ain't with all that gangsta shit!"

"Where can we find Motor, E?"

"I don't know where he live exactly, Detective McGuire. I only know he from Long Beach, and he friends with Lucky."

"A'ight den. Thanks. Give me a minute. I want to show you something before we talk to your girlfriend. Then we'll get an officer to take you guys back into the world."

McGuire looked up the moniker of Lucky on the computer. He found a booking photo for Maleko E. Laki Jr., dated April 30, 2007. It was from an arrest for a shooting in Carson. Laki was on felony probation, but not for that. McGuire printed out the photo and showed it to Baudelaire.

"Yep, that's him," he said.

McGuire and Cortes talked to Baudelaire's girlfriend next. She knew all five victims, but she didn't know anything about what happened or who killed them. She had never heard of anyone called Motor, nor did she know anyone with a tattoo on his face. But she did know Lucky, and iden-tified him from the booking photo.

"Er' body know Lucky," she said.

"Okay, *amiga*. Thanks for coming in. The officers who brought you in will take you back to where they picked you and E up. Call us if you hear anything else."

"You thinking what I'm thinking, Mac?" Cortes asked after Baudelaire and his girlfriend were gone.

"Probably. Is it that Lucky and the guy E is scared to identify are prob-ably our killers?"

"*Sí, mi amigo.*"

"I love the way you think, Cortes with an *s*. But why identify Lucky, and not the other guy? And why give us Motor's name, and tell us what kind of car he has?"

"Maybe he's hoping we'll tell Vanessa's family that he cooperated so it will keep them off his ass. Or maybe he really doesn't know who this other guy is."

"Well, Lucky is on parole. After I go get something to eat, I'll contact his parole agent and get all the information they have on him. If they have a good contact number for him, I'll get started on a warrant. We can use it as a template for the rest of the phones we write warrants for. I have a feeling we're gonna be writing a lot of them. I would love to be able to put Lucky's phone at the scene at the time of the murders. And remind me to follow-up with OSS."

"Will do. See you when you get back," Cortes said, pulling an apple and a peanut butter sandwich out of his cooler as McGuire walked out.

Saint Michael was looking out for them over the lunch hour.

They had been able to eat in peace without being disturbed by any phone calls. The respite was over as soon as McGuire balled up his empty In-N-Out bag and shot it toward the trash can, missing like he always did.

"Detective McGuire speaking. Can I help you?"

"Yes. My name is Tim Cratchit. I have some information on the homeless murders."

"Go ahead, Mr. Cratchit."

"There were two campsites. Two men took Kat and Sammy from Sammy's tent and made them tell where the other campsite was, and that was where the murders happened."

"How do you know this, sir?"

"That's the talk on the street. And there was a fight at the other campsite earlier that day or some other time between the killers and somebody who lived there."

"Okay. Thank you very much. Can I get your call back number? Uh huh. Uh huh. Thanks. We'll be in touch if we need anything else."

McGuire hung up and repeated what the caller said to Cortes.

"This version of what happened is getting a lot of play, Mac."

"No shit. Only Elmore and Juanita are obviously telling everyone that Kat was with Sammy when he was kidnapped. Neither one of them ever saw or heard her. They are making assumptions. Hey, do me a favor and catch my line if it rings. I gotta hit the head."

"You got it partner. Don't fall in. You know your feet barely touch the floor when you're on the toilet."

McGuire flipped Cortes off before he disappeared around the corner of the office. Within two minutes, his phone rang again.

"Long Beach Homicide. Cortes speaking."

"Hey Hugo, it's Wedel from Carson OSS. I was returning a message from McGuire. Sorry it took so long. We've been swamped over here. The 190 East Coast Crips are going at it hot and heavy with Stevenson Village."

"Shit never ends, huh? Mac's away from his desk right now—wait. Here he is now."

"McGuire."

"Sorry I'm just now getting back to you, Mac. Like I was just telling Hugo, we've been swamped."

"No worries. What's up?"

"That guy Lucky?"

"What about him?"

"I got a lady here who I have known for years. She has some interesting information for you. She was Vanessa Malaepule's best friend, and LV's first cousin."

"A'ight, den. We'll be right there."

CHAPTER ELEVEN

THE CARSON SHERIFF'S Station was less than ten miles away.

McGuire and Cortes got there about twenty minutes after McGuire hung up with Wedel. The station would be familiar to most people, even if they had never been there before. It was used to film parts of the movie *Colors* and was also used to film the sit-com *Reno 911*.

McGuire and Cortes walked across the parking lot past a huge open area used for one of the many helicopters the L.A. County Sheriff's Department had at its disposal. The OSS team operated out of a double-wide trailer at the very end of the lot. Wedel was standing on the small porch just outside the door.

"Hey, Rhino," McGuire said, greeting him with the nickname he had been given years ago after head-butting a violent criminal into submission. Wedel was stocky now, middle-aged and with a beer-gut that he called his "boiler," but in his younger days he was a baseball player so skilled that he was signed out of high school by the San Diego Padres.

"Hey guys," Wedel said, shaking their hands. "Good to see you. Come on in and have a seat."

There were several desks with computer monitors on them lined up along the walls, which displayed gruesome framed photographs of dead gang members at crime scenes. There were also several large cork boards on the walls. They had facial shots of deceased gang members stapled to them. Their names and gangs were written underneath each photograph. Known as "dead boards," there were at least 200 photographs on them, and each person depicted had either been killed in Carson or were members of a Carson gang who were killed elsewhere. The purpose of the dead boards was to stimulate conversation among witnesses and suspects when the gang investigators interviewed them.

The team supervisor worked in an office at one end of the trailer. The desk closest to the office was occupied by the team secretary, a vibrant Filipino woman who brought her little white designer dog named Sugar with her to work every day. She got away with it by saying that it was her "support" dog.

"This is Ms. Judy Ray, fellas," Wedel said as he pointed to a hefty woman with a dour look on her face. She was sitting at a desk close to one of the dead boards.

"Judy, these are the two detectives I was telling you about."

"How do you do, Ms. Ray. I'm Mark McGuire, and this is my partner, Hugo Cortes."

"Nice to meet y'all."

"We understand you have some information for us?"

"Yeah, Detective McGuire. About this bitch ass nigga name Lucky. Last year, he came to my house looking for LV. When I told him that LV wasn't at my house, he pulled out a gun and threatened my kids. Then he shot up in the air and left."

"That's terrible," Cortes said. "Did you make a report?"

"Hell yeah, I did! I talked to a gang detective named Niloc, but nothing ever happened. Lucky still running around after all this time."

"Okay, Ms. Ray," McGuire said. "I'm sure something will happen with your case. Sometimes these things take time. Have you heard anything about who murdered LV and your friend Vanessa?"

She looked up at LV's photograph on the dead board and said, "Before Vanessa got kilt, she told me that Lucky and two other dudes came to her camp. Lucky wanted money from LV and they got in a fight. She told me that she didn't know the other two, though. After that, Vanessa and LV moved to the other camp."

"What about the night of the murders, *amiga*? Have you heard anything about that?"

"Yeah. The same three muthafuckas went back and made some homeless man named Sammy show them where LV's new camp was, and that's when everybody got kilt. And there was some hood rat hiding in the cut that the killers didn't see. She saw Sammy get taken away and then heard shooting at the other camp."

"How do you know all this, Judy?" McGuire asked. "LV and Vanessa couldn't have told you."

"This lesbian chick who fucks with my sister told me. Her brothers are from D-Thirteen. Good luck getting her to talk to y'all, though. She fucking hates the po-leece. I hate most of y'all, too, but Wedel cool. Oh yeah. Some Black French nigga with good hair supposedly showed Lucky where they were at, too."

"Thanks, Ms. Ray," McGuire said.

"Y'all gonna arrest that bitch-ass Lucky?"

"Well, that's a Sheriff's case, but I'm sure they're gonna look into it."

"Thank you, Detective McGuire."

"Mac, the detective who handled the case is Tsicar Niloc."

"We'll need to speak to him, Rhino. You mind if we check out the file?"

"How about you guys get it from Niloc when you meet with him."

"Oh, I gotcha. A'ight den. No worries. Thanks for everything. And thanks again, Ms. Ray."

"Just catch the son-of-a bitches who kilt my people! And arrest Lucky! Or put his picture on one of these goddamn boards! That's how you can thank me!"

"We can't make you any promises," McGuire said. "But we will do everything in our power to try—to arrest the people responsible for the five murders, that is. Everything else that you requested is in God's hands —and Deputy Niloc's."

When McGuire and Cortes got to their car, Cortes adjusted the rear-view mirror, watching as a helicopter prepared to land.

"What was that all about, Mac?"

"I think Niloc fucked that case up. Wedel doesn't want any part of it."

After the helicopter had safely landed, Cortes pulled out of the parking lot. As they got on the 405 Freeway to head back to Long Beach, McGuire thought back to when they did a background check on Lucky. He had been arrested for assault with a deadly weapon. It had to be the Judy Ray incident, but there was no court disposition. This meant that nothing was ever presented to the DA's office for filing. McGuire suddenly realized that if Lucky was involved in the Quintuple, then it was Niloc's fault because he should have been locked up at the time.

THE NEXT DAY, MCGUIRE AND CORTES WENT BACK TO THE OSS trailer.

"Detective Niloc, why didn't you follow up with this?" McGuire asked after reading the case file.

Niloc was a bald white man who carried an empty soda bottle to spit his chewing tobacco into. He sneered, spat into the bottle and said, "The family didn't want to prosecute, so I let it go."

"Well, I don't know if that's altogether true. Me and my partner talked to the victim yesterday, and she seemed upset that no one was ever arrested."

Niloc spat into the bottle again.

"You calling me a liar, Detective?"

"Wouldn't dream of it. Just trying to put a case together, that's all. Perhaps she didn't want anyone prosecuted back then. Maybe she's changed her mind now. But your bad guy? Lucky? He's walking the streets with a gun, shooting it in the air, and threatening kids with it. Why didn't you at least try to get him prosecuted for discharging a firearm and being an ex-felon with a gun? You don't even need a victim for those charges. The state is the victim."

Niloc spat, Cortes glared, and McGuire stood.

"I would like you to arrest him on your case, please, because he may be a suspect in a quintuple murder," McGuire said.

As if on cue, Sugar ran to the door, sat down, and started barking. The secretary stopped typing and took her outside. Niloc shrugged but didn't offer an answer, looking like he had to take a shit, too.

"Sure thing," Niloc answered. "I'll take a look at it again."

"Thank you, Detective. Let's get out of here, Hugo."

"Can you believe that?" Cortes asked McGuire as they walked past the secretary while she stooped down with a plastic bag, Sugar watching patiently. "What a lazy *pendejo*."

"I've worked some great cases with that gang team, Hugo. They are solid. They helped me solve a murder on the 91 Freeway in 2005."

"And here you are with another freeway case, working with them again."

"Not exactly, but close."

"What about this Niloc guy? Do you know him? He seems like an asshole."

"No, I don't know him. He wasn't on the team when the 91 Freeway case happened. He has got to be sweating bullets right now, though, thinking that he let a guy go who went on to murder five people. If Lucky is involved, old Detective Niloc is gonna have a whole lot of explaining to do."

NOVEMBER 11

It was Veteran's Day; the day America celebrates those who have served in the protection of the nation. The date was allegedly picked because on the eleventh hour of the eleventh day of the eleventh month in 1918, a peace treaty was signed marking the official ending of World War I. It is without irony, or perhaps with divinity, that angel numbers were so omnipresent in the ending of a war that killed over 8,500,000 soldiers and as many as 13,000,000 civilians.

"Excuse me, sir?" McGuire asked a man who was digging through a dumpster in one of the grimiest areas in Long Beach. He and Cortes had just parked next to him.

"Yes, sir?"

"I'm Detective McGuire, and this is my partner, Detective Cortes. Are you the man who left a message with my secretary for us to meet you here about the homeless murders?"

"Yes, sir."

"What's your name?"

"Soldier Boy."

"What's your real name?" Cortes asked.

"Soldier Boy is fine. That's what everybody calls me."

"No worries. Talk to us," McGuire said.

Soldier Boy had certainly seen better days, having gone from the clean pressed uniform and spit-shined boots of the US Army to a dirty camou-flage jacket and filthy tennis shoes. Still, he had maintained a sort of mili-tary bearing despite the reality of his bleak situation now.

"Thank you for that, sir. I knew Vanessa since I was a kid. About a week before she got murdered, she told me that LV and a Samoan or Black dude named Lucky got into a fight because LV owed him three-thousand dollars. Two other guys were with Lucky, a Black guy and another guy who looked mixed with Black and maybe Samoan or Mexican."

Soldier Boy's voice trembled as he spoke. He was clearly upset about the murders.

"Did she say anything else about that day?" Cortes asked.

"Yes, sir. They told LV that if he didn't have the money when they came back, they were gonna pop him. And I seen LV a few days before he got killed. He had a few bruises on his face."

"A'ight den. Have you heard anything else?"

"Yes, sir. Lobster Girl may have been there during the shooting. The grapevine is that she may have also taken the dudes there to kill every-body. Vanessa's family is supposed to be looking for her. Anyhow, LV and Lucky had been having problems over money for a while. Word is that a Samoan and two Black dudes killed everybody, and LV was killed because he snitched on somebody from D-Thirteen. It makes sense for Lucky to have killed LV, but I don't understand why he had to do that to everybody else. This ain't combat."

"Okay, *amigo*. Here's my card."

McGuire leaned over and whispered, "For Saint Peter" in Cortes's ear before giving him a twenty-dollar bill. Cortes removed the same denomi-nation from his wallet and gave both bills to Soldier Boy.

"Take this, too. If you hear anything else, let us know."

"Alright, detectives. God bless both of y'all. Y'all be safe out there, ya' hear?"

"You, too, sir." McGuire said. "Oh yeah, Happy Veteran's Day."

They drove off, Cortes looking at his rear-view mirror, McGuire looking through his side view mirror, the two of them watching silently while one of the nation's heroes started digging through the dumpster again.

As they continued their quest for additional witnesses, they saw the fallout of America's war on drugs. Numerous people—not all of them experiencing homelessness—high on either meth or crack were every-where. There was no mistaking them, especially by seasoned police offi-cers who had spent much of their careers dealing with drug addicts. Just as obvious were the people nodding off from heroin highs in the doorways of abandoned buildings and in alleyways.

"Some war, huh, Mac?"

"Which one?"

"The war on drugs. You know. The one started by Nixon."

"Yeah, it may have been started by Tricky-Dick, but George Bush—not W, but the old man—took it to a whole new level."

"He just took all the rhetoric out of it. He made a cold war hot."

"Fuck that asshole, Hugo. He made an enemy out of entire inner cities across the country, which was where the biggest drug problems were. And if you think about it, he didn't really do shit until his wife got pissed. She was 'appalled at what was going on in her great nation,' when all she had to do was look at the muthafucka sleeping next to her to find the root cause of the devastation."

"It's always the wives, huh *amigo*? Then Nancy Reagan got on TV and said, 'Just say no to drugs,' like it was that easy to do for those people in ghettos. Next thing you know, her husband authorizes local PDs to deploy armored vehicles. They called them battering rams, but you and I both know they were just tanks without guns. That had to be some scary shit for kids to see rolling past their schools and playgrounds."

"We got all these presidents declaring war on the wrong enemies, when they should've declared it on the the people bringing that bullshit into our country. But that would've meant following the money, and we both know where that would've led to."

"*Sí.* 1600 Pennsylvania Avenue."

"How about the collateral damage from the 'war?' Our morgues and prisons have been filled ever since. We got battering rams crashing down doors, drive-by shootings over drug turf, prostitution, and kids who don't know who their fathers are all over the goddamn place. They grew up walking to school seeing dead bodies in alleys, junkies in doorways, and crackheads giving blowjobs in parked cars. And they wouldn't even mention it to their teachers. Telling teachers was like talking to cops. It was snitching. Those kids learned it from a very early age."

"Well, what do you expect? When you call something a war and tell cops that they are fighting one, then they are going to act like soldiers instead of peace officers. And like you said about the kids, they've been left behind, their only memory of cops making their older brothers lie on the ground at gunpoint and tanks crashing down doors. Like my *abuela* always said: '*Los pollos siempre vuelven a casa.*'"

"What does that mean, bitch?"

"Chickens always come back home."

"Well, your grandma stole that from Malcolm. Besides, a friend of mine had another saying. And it had to do with cops who cross the line."

"What?"

"Brutality and cowardice are shepherds of unwell flocks."

"That's *muy bonita, mi amigo.* Too bad you ain't as smart as your friend. You would be dangerous. Now you're just short."

"I'm big where it counts, bitch."

They both laughed a little before they grew quiet, watching the vestiges of collateral damage all around them, hookers and gang members alike staring malevolently at them as they drove past. The so-called war on drugs had absolutely created a generation of cop-hating kids in America. The chickens were home indeed.

McGuire leaned back and looked out his window. About ten minutes later, he saw a white woman pushing a shopping cart filled with plastic bottles and aluminum cans on Santa Fe Avenue.

"Pull over, Hugo."

"Excuse me, ma'am. I'm Detective McGuire and this is my partner, Detective Cortes. What's your name?"

"Why?"

"We're investigating the murders that happened over this way not long ago."

"Oh. Okay. I'm Flora Belle."

Flora Belle, who suffered from bipolar disorder, lived a nomadic existence, moving from the riverbed to city hall to the encampments.

"You mind if we talk to you for a minute?" McGuire asked.

"Sure. I don't know how much I can help, though."

"No worries. We really want to find out who did this. You guys may think no one cares about you, but we do. What happened was horrible."

"Yes, it was, wasn't it? What's your name again?"

"McGuire."

"McGuire? That's a white man's name. How'd you get it?"

"It's a long story. But back to the murders. Can you tell us what you know or heard, if anything?"

"This guy everybody call E pumped up a Samoan dude everybody call Lucky, or maybe they call him Snow? Or is it Lucky Snow? Snow Lucky? Or Rain? Or Summer Rain? I get so fucked up over weather. You know I hate when it rains. Snow ain't that bad, though, but I prefer spring—"

"Relax, ma'am. Lucky? Or Snow, you said?" Cortes asked, easing her back into reality. She pressed her fists against her temples while closing her eyes so tightly it looked like she was in excruciating pain. She began huffing and puffing.

"I don't know! I don't know! He a Samoan, I know that! I know that! I know that! I know that!"

"It's okay, you're doing fine. Just slow down a little. You have no idea how much you are helping us right now," McGuire said, thinking that the name Snow sounded familiar to him.

After a few seconds Flora Belle started breathing normally and calmed down.

"Where was I, again?"

"E pumping up Snow, Flora Belle," Cortes said. "You got this."

"That's right. I do got this, don't I? Well, E pumped that Samoan up to go beat up LV. Then he told LV he was coming back to shoot up the place —what time is it? I gotta go feed those black birds soon, you know. They remember—"

"Flora Belle," McGuire said. "We're almost done. The birds ain't going nowhere. You were saying? About E and LV?"

"Yeah. E. Everybody call him that because he got a long last name. French, I think. That's funny, huh? Another Black man with a white man's name. Everything is so confusing—"

"It's okay, Flora Belle," McGuire said. "What were you gonna say about E?"

"Oh, yeah. That's right. He got guns. Two of them. A nine-millimeter and a forty-five. I seen both of them before. A Mexican who walks with a limp saw him standing there when the shooting happened. He was shooting the gun."

"Who was shooting the gun, *amiga*?"

"I know what that means. Friend, right? I gotta a lot of wetback friends—"

"That's great. And you and me? Friends, for sure," Cortes said. "Now who'd you say was shooting the gun?"

"E was. Ain't you paying attention?"

"Please forgive me, *señora.*"

"I don't know what *that* word means, though."

"It means ma'am. It's a show of respect. Let's go back a bit. Are you saying that someone saw E kill LV and the others?"

"No, I ain't saying that."

"What else do you know about the guy named Snow, Flora Belle?" McGuire asked.

She started huffing and puffing again and said, "I don't know who that is! Look. I gotta go. Find that Mexican with a limp."

"A'ight den," McGuire said. "We'll let you go feed your birds. Thanks. And here's my business card. Call me if you hear anything else. There are still a few pay phones around."

"Can I use this card to get out of jail free if I get arrested? Can I tell them you said it's cool?"

"No, ma'am. Don't do that. How about you try not to do anything that will get you arrested, huh?"

"Poor lady."

"You ain't pissed that she said wetback, Hugo?"

"Not any more pissed than you are, 'Black man with a white man's name'. She was toeing the line, huh?"

"Fuck her. She's fucked up."

"She doesn't know any better. I feel sorry for her."

"You *would*, muthafucka."

"You know I gotta a big heart, *amigo.* But as far as E is concerned? I don't believe what she said about him. That *pendejo* wouldn't hold onto one gun, let alone two, before selling it as soon as he got his hands on it."

"You ain't lying about that. This guy Lucky keeps coming up every day, though. There's something there. We definitely gotta talk to him. And

Snow. I know that name from somewhere, Hugo. I just can't place it right now."

Their attention was drawn to a homeless man walking near Cabrillo High School on Santa Fe. He was gesticulating wildly and talking as if someone was walking next to him, his voice going from a whisper to a roar without warning. He had long dreadlocks and was wearing at least two pairs of trousers and a hooded sweatshirt underneath a large jacket. He was using black trash bags as shoes, which were tied at his ankles to keep them from coming off.

"What about him, Mac?"

"Hell, no. I think we're gonna pass on him. Shit, he could be an eyewitness and know where the murder weapons are, and the judge wouldn't even allow him to testify."

"And you think a judge would let Flora Belle testify?" Cortes asked.

"Good point. I wonder what this poor bastard's story is. He can't be older than twenty-five. What the fuck is he? White? Black? He's so dirty I can't tell."

"He's a white boy, *amigo*. Homelessness doesn't discriminate."

"Neither does mental illness."

"Should we be concerned that he's so near a high school?"

"Are you for real? Cabrillo students? Shiiiid. We should be concerned about *him*. Those kids would chew him up, spit him out, and take his fucking trash bags."

Twenty minutes later, they saw a man walking with a limp near Angel Food. Cortes pulled over, and they got out of the car.

"Hello, sir. I'm Detective Mc—"

"No *habla ingles*. Sorry."

"I got it partner," Cortes said.

McGuire walked to the order window and bought three cups of coffee. The Korean lady inside never charged cops for it and always gave them a discount on the donuts. Places that gave free stuff to cops were known as "pop spots," but unless it was coffee, McGuire always paid.

Cortes spoke to the man in Spanish. His name was Joadano Tomás. He had crossed the Rio Grande years ago and now survived by panhandling, stealing, and sometimes standing near Home Depot Centers seeking employment as a day worker.

He told Cortes that he lived in a tent near the Metro rail on Del Amo not far from where the murders occurred, but he didn't see anything and had no information about what happened. Cortes offered him a business card. Tomás showed his palms and said that he couldn't read or write.

"*Tu sabes Flora Belle, Tomás?*" Cortes asked.

Tomás put his right forefinger to his temple and made circles with it and said, "*Muy loco, El jefe. Muy loco.*"

McGuire walked up with the coffee and several packets of sugar and cream in a cup holder. He gave one of the cups and all the sugar and cream to Tomás. McGuire had learned that almost all the homeless people he and Cortes contacted during this investigation loved sweet coffee.

Cortes tucked a business card in Tomás's shirt pocket as he tore open the sugars with his mouth and poured them in his coffee.

"*Gracias, amigo. Adios.*"

Tomás nodded and walked toward the back of the donut shop where the dumpsters were as McGuire gave Cortes his coffee.

"Well? Did he have anything good to say?"

"No, partner. Just someone else chasing *the dream*, that's all."

CHAPTER TWELVE

NOVEMBER 12

A message to dispatch had come in on the non-emergency line overnight. A female with a raspy voice who wished to remain anonymous said, "About those five homicides, you wanna look for a Samoan named Snow."

The caller hung up before the operator could ask any questions.

After McGuire heard the message, something clicked. *Now I remember. The guy with Sammy on that case years ago was named Snow,* he thought. He and Cortes had gotten sidetracked on other leads, and he hadn't had a chance to do a computer search for that moniker. Now, with this latest information, he immediately turned to his computer. In just a few minutes, he handed Cortes a printout containing a photograph of Kekoa Rongomaiwenua, aka Snow, with his physical description.

"Damn, Mac. Big boy."

"Yeah, he is. And he's from the Sons of Samoa gang. He was with Sammy when I handled that case in 2004. I hadn't tracked down the report yet because I don't think Sammy was the target of the murders. Everything is pointing to the killers just using him to find LV and then murdering him because he was a witness. As I remember, Snow was not a threat to Sammy during the case that I handled with them. He was just an asshole who loved to fight. He didn't even want to give me his real name."

"I don't blame him. You see how long it is?"

"No shit."

"I know you said he loves to fight, but murder is a whole different ballgame. Could he be good for this? You think he has the balls?"

"*Hell* yeah! Looks like he's on felony probation for assault right now. He lived in a tent behind a junkyard in Wilmington when I dealt with him and Sammy. He probably still lives there."

"Let's sic the dogs on him, then. By the way, how the hell are you on parole and you live in a tent? How does your PO keep track of you?"

"Not our concern, Hugo. Let me call probation and confirm his status. *Then,* we'll sic the dogs on him. If he's home, we'll bring him in."

Several members of CCAT found him several hours later and called McGuire and Cortes. A parole search of his tent had revealed nothing out of the ordinary. When McGuire and Cortes got there, McGuire walked over to the team leader.

"We're gonna take him to the office and interview him. You mind watching his stuff until we get back? I would hate for somebody to steal his shit because we took him away. The interview shouldn't take long."

"What if you guys end up arresting him?"

"Then somebody gets a whole shit-load lot of bottles and cans without having to hustle for them."

SNOW WAS NOTHING LIKE MCGUIRE REMEMBERED. HE WAS POLITE, AND courteous.

He stood next to his chair in the interview room, towering over the two detectives. Cortes was the kind of investigator who, while interviewing a man who found his wife with a bullet hole in her head and a gun in her hand, would glance perspicaciously at the man's oddly clean hands and fingernails sticking out from sleeves with tiny drops of high velocity blood spatter, and smile. Snow's tribal band tattoo peeking out from his short-sleeve shirt hit him like a slap in the face.

"A'ight den, have a seat. What do you prefer? Snow, first name, or last name? Please say Snow."

"Snow is cool."

"Beautiful. Okay, Snow. Like I told you when we were at your house,

I'm McGuire and this is Cortes. Before we start talking though, I want to read you your rights."

"I already know them. If I want a lawyer here, I can have one. For free. And I don't have to say anything if I don't want to. *If* I do say something, y'all can use it against me in court."

"I'm impressed," McGuire said.

"I ain't got nothing to hide. Ask your questions."

"Okay, for starters, what do you know about the murders? Did you know any of the victims?"

"Sammy was my best friend. I knew Vanessa and her *aiga*, too."

"Hold up, *amigo*. Her what?"

"Her *aiga*," McGuire said. "Means family in Samoan."

"That's right, sir," Snow said as he nodded. "And I'm sorry I didn't want to help when me and Sammy had that case with you. It was business, you know. Street shit. Sorry if I was a *solofanua*."

"Unless that means asshole," McGuire said. "I don't know what the hell you just said."

Snow laughed loudly. "But for real though. I had nothing to do with those murders. I don't know what happened or who was involved, either. I only found out about them from a guy I know named Black Fred. He come by my spot every now and then."

"How about rumors?" Cortes asked.

"I heard three rumors about why the murders happened. One: Word on the yard is that some dude got burned for some dope, and he came back and shot the place up. Two: Whoever the Mexican guy was who got killed had testified against somebody and sent them to prison. And three: A big-time drug dealer known as Snow went there and killed everybody."

"We thought *you* were Snow, *amigo*."

"It must be another one, 'cause it damn sho' ain't me. Oh, I almost forgot. There's a rumor going 'round that some *alii uli* from Compton did it. They call him E. And one of Sammy's neighbors supposedly seen the murders. A skinny bitch with fucked up fingers."

"Black man, Hugo," McGuire said when he saw the confused loo on Cortes's face. "That means Black man."

"Okay, got it, Mac. Anything else you can think of??"

"Yeah. You got access to any guns, Snow?"

"Nah," he said as he smiled. "That would violate the conditions of my parole."

"And we *know* you would never do that, right?"

Snow smiled again and asked, "How you learn Samoan, Detective McGuire?"

"I picked up a little bit from the guys I played football with when I was in high school."

"Yeah? Where did you go to school?"

"Narbonne."

"Gauchos, huh?"

"That's right."

"I was a muthafucking Colt!" Snow said as he thumped his chest gorilla-style.

"Carson High? I'm glad you're way younger than me. I would've hated to run against your big ass. Come on. Let's get you back home, *fa'auō*."

NOVEMBER 24

McGuire and Cortes had eliminated one possible motive: The Swastika tattoo was bullshit. The rose was a cover-up Kat had gotten years ago. It was supposed to be some type of runic tattoo with a name, a cover-up of a long-forgotten lover.

Other than LV, none of the victims had any known enemies. There was simply no motive to kill them that Cortes and McGuire had been able to uncover. They had the CCAT and QOL teams looking for Lil Man, but they still hadn't been able to find him. The Carson OSS team was in the planning stages to arrest Lucky, and pending Lil Man being located, McGuire and Cortes decided to work another case that they had just got a fresh lead on.

In July of 2007, a drug dealer with a bullet in the back of his head had been found dead behind the wheel of his car at 28th and Chestnut Avenue. He came to this untimely demise because he had been making unauthorized tax pick-ups for La Eme, better known as the Mexican Mafia.

"What the hell are you guys doing?"

Sergeant Nielsen loomed in the doorway, demanding to know why they were not working on the homeless murders. He had regularly asked for updates for the series of press conferences that had been held since the murders occurred.

McGuire and Cortes were always careful about what they gave him, making sure to safeguard their "hold back," which is information that only someone with first-hand knowledge of a crime would know. Hold back info shreds bullshit confessions and statements from informants seeking money or consideration on pending charges they might have.

"Hello, Sergeant. We have teams looking for one of our subjects, and an OSS team has an open case on one of our possible suspects. We don't have enough to charge him yet, so we're waiting for OSS to arrest him on their case. We also have workable information on another one of *our* open cases, so instead of sitting here with our thumbs up our asses, Hugo is writing a search warrant for several houses, and I am doing the workups on the locations."

"I don't care about that, McGuire. The bosses are on my back about making an arrest on the homeless case, and you know the direction that shit rolls on a hill!"

"Sergeant, are you telling me you want us to forgo arresting three dangerous individuals and drum up fake leads on a stalled case so the bosses can feel better?"

Nielsen started to say something before turning sharply and storming out of the office.

"What the fuck are *you* laughing at, Hugo?"

"You know you said drum, right? You always get pissed whenever I say it. Now you said it. That's funny, *si?*"

"No. It ain't. And stop fucking around. We got a lot to do to get this warrant ready."

There are two days a year when a cop can always catch a criminal at home: Christmas morning and Thanksgiving. Most cops don't like to work on those two days, which is why criminals are always home. They feel secure. McGuire and Cortes weren't most cops, however. They served their warrants bright and early, and all three of their suspects were in handcuffs long before turkeys were being carved.

McGuire refused to let Cortes eat the food he brought to work in his Igloo that day. He could eat dinner with his family later, or have left-overs tomorrow, but today, while they were in Long Beach catching murderers on a day when everyone else was giving thanks for something, there was no way they weren't eating some of Kim's turkey and banana pudding.

Cortes kept his personal life private, for the most part. Other than knowing that he was married with three kids and lived in a beautiful house, McGuire didn't know much else. He enjoyed talking about his kids, but he hardly ever talked about his wife. If he brought something up, McGuire would listen, but he never pried, even when he sometimes overheard them arguing on the phone. But all married couples have their ups and downs, especially cops. McGuire didn't give it a second thought when Cortes readily agreed to eat at his house.

CHAPTER THIRTEEN

THE QUINTUPLE WAS starting to wear heavily on McGuire and Cortes.

They had little time at home with their families, what with the maintenance of cases in trial, catching fresh cases, and trying to stay on top of the older ones. That was when the job started to wear on personal relationships, when a strong bond with spouses was paramount to the survival of a marriage. It was difficult to separate; on the one hand, the pursuit of cold-blooded killers, and on the other hand, spouses and children who required quality time. Some marriages survived. Others didn't.

And maybe that was why some cops ate their pretty retirement guns while sitting in an empty apartment surrounded by pictures of children whom they never got to see grow up.

The job weighed heavily in other ways as well. Homicide investigators needed to find some type of outlet. They needed time to deflect, time to stop dwelling on the parts of their career that broke them down, that made them lose faith in humankind. Cortes was an avid runner and conscious of his diet. Sometimes, after a trying day, he would run up to ten miles, using the peacefulness and tranquility of his New Balance shoes softly pounding the pavement as therapy.

McGuire's mental distraction was his Gold Wing. Or, in a slap in the face to racial stereotypes, swimming. It didn't matter whether it was in pools, fresh water, or the ocean—which he was loath to do because of his healthy respect for the Great White—he was a fantastic swimmer at a time when Black people weren't supposed to be. It was another thing he owed to his father, who threw his sons in a lake when they were just boys and told them to sink or swim.

Investigators carried their cases like luggage that never got unpacked. Each new case added to the overall weight of it, the stench of blood and death lingering in their nostrils and saturating their clothes. Even when engaged in activities to help them unwind, their cases crept up on them, like a woman wearing the same shade of lipstick as a victim in an alley found with her throat cut and legs spread apart for shock value, or a name called out by a hostess in a restaurant that was the same as a suspect, victim, or witness.

That was the burden of being entrusted to solve the most heinous crimes, to protect communities from the vilest of murderers. The trauma and devastation of surviving friends and families of victims was always with them. No matter how numb against the sorrow of a loss of life a homicide investigator thought he or she was, they all cried at some point.

Not in public, or in front of their partners or peers, though. They waited until the sound of a hot shower could drown out their agony while everyone else in the house slept, or for the privacy of a parked car in the wee hours of the morning. It didn't matter how tough the cop was or how many dead bodies they had seen, an emotional breakdown was the inevitability of being the murder police.

Even now, McGuire had a feeling of sadness as he looked at the crime scene and autopsy photographs of the victims spread out on his desk. There was Kat, a huge burn against her throat and underneath her chin; Vanessa, blood-matted hair and polished nails; LV, eyes rolled back one final time; Sammy, face down in the dirt, and finally Frederick, denied his chance to choose his demise, all five suffering from that ubiquitous raccoon-eye effect and purple, bulbous lips.

McGuire also had other pictures of them—smiling DMV photographs of Kat and Vanessa, emotionless booking photos of Sammy and Frederick, and an old parole photo of a scowling LV. The images breathed life into the dead. If he looked at them long enough, he could see things, the small stuff that makes a person alive, like a toss of the hair, the wink of an eye, a hearty laugh, or a tearful goodbye, even the sensuous drag of a tongue across crimson-colored lips.

Those things were all gone now, replaced by figures no more alive than a Ken or Barbie doll. Yet McGuire studied them all. It was the way he kept everything in perspective, the way he reminded himself that he wasn't working for them in death, but as they were in life.

"Detective McGuire?"

He looked up and saw the secretary holding out a small, pink piece of paper with a phone number on it.

"Thank you, Mary. Wait. There's no name. Do you know who the number belongs to?'"

"No, Detective. Sergeant Nielsen just told me to make sure you get it."

Not a minute later, he walked in.

"Hey, Sergeant. Do you happen to know who this message is from?"

"Yeah. It's from some woman named Madame Lavigne. She's a psychic. Actually, she called herself a medium. She says she knows who killed the homeless people. She's supposed to be really good with serial killers."

"I'm not calling a psychic. I don't believe in them. We'll solve this with good old-fashioned police work. And for the last time, this is not the work of a serial killer. This is some straight up street shit, that's all."

The other investigators in the office started snickering.

"There you go, McGuire!" Watkins said. "Finally, a lead! Hey look, you think you could ask her why my wife never tells me when she comes?"

"*Vete a la mierda!*" Cortes said. "You just keep sitting at your desk doing what you do best—beating off and eating bear claws."

"Knock it off!" Nielsen said. "McGuire, you and Cortes call this lady. That's an order!"

Two hours later, they found themselves in a corner booth at the Fish House on Pine Street in downtown Long Beach waiting for Madame Lavigne. They spotted her as soon as she walked in. A rotund white woman in a black muumuu and Air Jordans, she had on an afro wig that stretched down along the sides of her face and hid her ears. It looked like she had a horseshoe on her head. She was wearing white eye shadow and lipstick, which accentuated the wig.

"That's gotta be her, Mac."

McGuire waved to her. She smiled and walked over.

"Hello, gentlemen. You must be Detective Cortes, and you, obviously, are Detective McGuire."

"Correct. And you must be Madame Lavigne. Please, sit down," McGuire said.

"Don't mind if I do."

She sat down and picked up a menu that had been left on the table for her. She went to the wine portion right away. "No Chateau Lafite?" she said after scanning it. "What to do, what to do? Do pardon me, gentlemen. Unfortunately, I have been cursed with oenophilia."

"With what?" McGuire asked as he tore open several packets of Splenda and poured the contents into a coffee cup in front of him. "I don't know what that is. I'm just a dumb cop."

"Is that contagious, ma'am?" Cortes asked.

"Oh, you silly geese! It means that I have a love of wine."

She laughed as she continued scanning the menu. Cortes took the lemon from the rim of the glass sitting in front of him and squeezed it into the water inside. McGuire grabbed a piece of bread from the basket in the center of the table, tore it apart, and slowly spread butter over one of the pieces.

"Ah, yes! Here we are," Madame Lavigne said, apparently finding something to mitigate her curse.

McGuire took a bite of his bread and looked at her, hoping that his disdain wasn't evident on his face. Cortes got the attention of the waitress. She knew both detectives from their frequent visits. They always tipped her well. She smiled broadly as she took the order from their table. Cortes had a house salad. McGuire had more bread. Madame Lavigne had an appetite. After her order arrived, she told them that she had had a dream about the murders.

"It was quite vivid, gentlemen," she said in between bites of filet mignon, lobster tails, and sips of Chateau Canon Saint-Emilion.

"I saw a black van pull up next to the L.A. riverbed. Four men wearing all black got out. They were armed with twenty-two caliber revolvers with silencers on them, like mafia hitmen. They shot the victims to death and then ran through the riverbed and out of sight."

"A'ight, den. What happened to the van?"

"I beg your pardon?"

"The van. What happened to it?"

"Oh. Oh! There was a fifth person involved. Did I not say that? Please accept my apologies. That ruffian drove off. If you tell me where the victims are interred, I can visit them and use my sixth sense that way. The dead are quite strong in the afterlife."

McGuire and Cortes glanced at each other before getting up.

"We don't think that'll be necessary," McGuire said. "Thank you, Madame Lavigne. You've been quite helpful. If we make an arrest off the information that you provided, you'll be the first to know."

"Don't trouble yourselves. I will know *before* you and Cortes do. And thank you, Detective," she said as she looked down at the check and then back at him.

McGuire grabbed it, and he and Cortes walked out of the restaurant.

"What kind of *caca* was that?"

"I don't know, Hugo, but we're putting in for ten hours of overtime today no matter how long we work. You see how much this bill is? By the way, what kind of a witch was she? Black or white?"

"I don't know what she was. If I had to guess, I would say a little bit of both."

Sergeant Nielsen could barely contain his optimism when they got back to the office.

"How'd it go? Arrest is imminent, right? I have heard good things about her!"

"From where, Sergeant? The National Enquirer?" McGuire asked as he took off his jacket and hung it up. "It went nowhere. She was a cordial lady with a taste for the finer things in life, but her information didn't match our evidence."

As Nielsen's smile evaporated, Cortes pointed at Watkins.

"She did confirm one thing, though. She told us to have *you* call your wife at home when we got back to the office so you could actually *hear* her coming."

THE CARSON OSS TEAM ARRESTED LUCKY AT HIS HOUSE DURING THE last week of 2008.

Detective Niloc called McGuire after they got back to Carson Station.

"We took his cell phone," he said. "You want it?"

"Absolutely. Hugo and I'll come by and get it later today, or next week at the latest."

"Okay. Contact Wedel or my sergeant."

"What's up? You going on vacation or something?"

"Nah. I'm going back to Palmdale Station where I belong. Oh yeah, I almost forgot. Lucky wants to confess regarding the Judy Ray incident. He's terrified. He thinks he's gonna get caught up in your case. It doesn't even sound like he wants to go to court."

"A'ight den. Peace in the hood."

McGuire hung up and looked at Cortes.

"That was our friend Niloc. Lucky is in custody, and they have his phone."

"Cool. I guess I can thank him in person when we go get it."

"Not unless you go to Palmdale to do it."

"What? He's going to another team?"

"More like running away."

"You think he's embarrassed?"

"No. I think he's scared."

McGuire and Cortes got the warrant returns a few days later.

The records showed that Lucky, or at least his phone, was in Moreno Valley at the time of the murders. It couldn't be ruled out that he left it there while he did the murders, but he would have a rock-solid alibi if someone confirmed he was in that area when they happened. If this was true, then maybe the other two people who went with him to LV's camp the first time were the killers. Lucky could still be in involved in another way as well. It was possible that he hired the killers.

The warrant wasn't a complete waste of time; the return provided a number for someone named Kenny Richardson. His moniker was Motor. McGuire quickly wrote a second warrant. From the interview with Baudelaire, he and Cortes knew that Richardson drove a black Hyundai. Other than that, they knew nothing about him, but Long Beach PD had access to an Automated License Plate Reader system.

With the color, make, and model of a particular vehicle entered into the system, cameras, which were placed all over the city, could capture the

plates of all vehicles matching that description. One matching the description of Motor's car frequented the area where the murders took place. It
was registered at an address in Long Beach not far from there. Although
not in Richardson's name, it was the same address on the subscriber information for his phone.

Someone by the name of Saint was listed as a contact on the phone.
His number showed up quite a few times. It was obvious that he and
Richardson were tight. McGuire then entered the number into CalGang, a
data tracking system for gang members in California. It came back to
David Ponce, a South Side Nut Hood Watts member, but his moniker in
the system was D-Nutt, not Saint. Gang members often use each other's
phones. Ponce and Saint most likely were two completely different
people.

Something that didn't make sense was that Motor had a contact for a
Nut Hood member in his phone. The gang was in Watts, miles away from
Carson and Long Beach, and they were bitter rivals of D-13. A Nut Hood
being in that area would put him in a dangerous situation, but by all
appearances, the men who went with Lucky to the homeless encampment
were comfortable in the environment. And they weren't armed at the
time, or else there would have been gunplay.

Officers from the South Gate Police Department had stopped David
Ponce in a car several months before the murders. McGuire pulled up a
booking photograph of him as well as one for Kenny Richardson. Ponce
had "Nut Hood" tattooed on his face.

"Check this out, Hugo. We could be looking at the face of death right
here."

"It could be why Baudelaire was so evasive. Or, maybe another gangster
from Carson or Long Beach with a tattoo on his face went with him and
Lucky. It would be pretty bold for an unarmed Nut Hood gangster to be so
close to D-13's neighborhood."

"Well, let's show his picture to Baudelaire."

"Okay. What about Niloc?"

"What about him?"

"Well, it looks like Lucky wasn't one of the shooters. Should we call
him and let him know? Put his mind at ease?"

"Fuck that guy. Let him sweat. Besides. We can't rule Lucky out just
yet. Just because he wasn't there doesn't mean he wasn't involved. Let's

bring Baudelaire back in. I'll get busy on a warrant for the phone number connected to this 'D-Nutt' fool."

Cortes picked up the phone and called a member of CCAT. A few days later, the team found Baudelaire and brought him in. He identified Richardson as Motor, and the black Hyundai as the car they took to LV's encampment. He did not identify Ponce. He was either still vacillating between his loyalty to the streets and his allegiance to humankind, or Ponce really wasn't there. There could also have been another factor at play.

Fear.

CHAPTER FOURTEEN

THE YEAR 2008 was brutal for LA County.

There had been 838 murders, with 666 of them, an inauspicious number to be sure, committed with the use of a firearm. Most of them were committed in Compton and South L.A. The politicians may have changed the name of the area, but the killings continued at an even higher rate and at one point there were 180 bodies stacked up in the morgue at the coroner's office waiting to be autopsied.

And 2009 picked up right where the previous year ended, the promise of a breather for McGuire and Cortes dashed almost immediately. In January, a Long Beach patrol officer interrupted a robbery and got into a shootout with two armed men. Known as a "red ball," this was the kind of case where all hands were on deck, overtime was not an issue, and people in power were paying attention. The Quintuple was the epitome of a red ball.

Four days later, McGuire and Cortes got another one, a double murder that occurred at a Masonic lodge during a birthday party for twin teenagers. Two people dancing were shot dead through a window by gang members who had been denied entry.

McGuire and Cortes put the Quintuple aside and worked non-stop on the lodge murders. They were doing a tremendous amount of work, and except for submitting extra overtime so they could pay for the expensive meal that that onyx and alabaster quack ordered, they earned every penny. Needless to say, they had the highest clearance rate in their unit, particularly with the so-called "unsolvable ghetto murders," which were murders in zip codes that didn't count.

On January 31, they were sitting at their desks going over lab and evidence reports from the Masonic lodge case. It was close to 10 a.m., but other than Mary, they were the only ones in the office.

"Where the hell is everyone?" Cortes asked.

"Fuck if I know, Hugo. Maybe they went to a party that we weren't invited to."

"Ah, who cares. Hey, I forgot to tell you. One of those *gringos* asked me what our secret was."

"Secret to what?"

"Clearing our cases. I never thought of it as having a secret, did you?"

"That's because it *ain't* no secret. It all comes down to treating people how you would want to be treated. Some of our peers like to call law-abiding citizens who end up on the wrong side of a knife or gun 'true victims.' They call crooks, the homeless, and dope-heads deserving of what they got if they get killed. And it's bullshit. We don't get to pick who the true victims are or who is deserving of police service. Humanity does. Even if there wasn't a law against murder, we would know instinctively that it's wrong.

"There's an old saying when it comes to saving money: *If you watch the pennies, the dollars will take care of themselves*. It applies to police work, too. Especially when it comes to investigating murders. If solving one is like putting together a 10,000-thousand-piece jigsaw puzzle, then those most in need are the corner and edge pieces. The rest of the pieces always fall into place once you take care of them first."

McGuire got the warrant return for the number connected to D-Nutt the next day.

On the night of the crime, that phone was nowhere near the scene. McGuire and Cortes turned to David Ponce next, thinking that he was possibly D-Nutt, too. Perhaps he had given the Southgate cops a bogus moniker. It wouldn't have been the first time gang member did something like that. Ponce had a tattoo on his face, and his moniker was Saint, which was the name of a contact in Richardson's phone. Baudelaire was most likely lying when he said he couldn't identify Ponce as one of the men who went to LV's camp with Lucky. There were just too many coincidences.

They were in the office brainstorming about how they could get Ponce and Kenny Richardson into the station as something other than "witnesses." New leads had long ago stopped coming in, but now they had an address for Richardson, who, along with Baudelaire and Lucky, was one of the four men who went to LV's campsite a week before the murders. McGuire and Cortes suspected that Ponce was the fourth man, but they had no proof. They put Lucky on the back-burner for the time being. He had taken a deal for nine years in state prison for the Judy Ray case. He wasn't going anywhere anytime soon.

"Hey, Hugo. Let's find out who Ponce and Richardson hang out with. Ponce is on parole, so we should be able to get something on him as far as where he is laying his head."

"That's not a bad idea. I'll call surveillance."

"I got the parole officer. It's a woman," McGuire said as he smiled and winked.

"Well alright, Mac Daddy. Go ahead and work that old Love Unlimited magic on her, then."

"You know I'm strictly business, Hugo."

"That, and Baby would put her foot in your ass."

McGuire turned his back to Cortes when the line was picked up.

"Hi, this is Detective Mark McGuire from Long Beach PD Homicide."

"Hello, Detective. What can I do for you?"

"Please. Call me Mac."

"I WANNA TALK TO MCGUIRE AND CORTES. I HEARD THEY LOOKING for me."

It was Monday morning, February 4, and a huge Hispanic man had just walked into the lobby of the Long Beach PD headquarters. He was dressed in the attire favored by street gang members and tattooed everywhere except for his face. The desk officer fingered the gun on his waistband despite the presence of bulletproof glass protecting him.

"And you are?" the officer asked.

"Lil Man."

"Okay. Have a seat. I'll let them know."

A few minutes later, McGuire and Cortes introduced themselves.

"Thanks for making this easy, *amigo*."

"I ain't tripping. I ain't got nothing to hide."

"A'ight den. Follow us."

When they got to an interview room, Lil Man stood next to one of three chairs around a table. McGuire nearly strained his neck as he looked up.

"You are one big muthafucka. Why they call you Lil Man?"

"'Cause I was a lil muthafucka when I got jumped in. And all'a sudden, I just started growing. Yo' hood name is yo' hood name. You can't change it. Only the big homies can. Now it's one of ah those—what you call that shit?"

"An oxymoron."

"Yeah. That's the name ah that shit."

"A'ight den, Lil Man. Have a seat so you can tell us about LV and Hoodlum."

McGuire and Cortes sat down after Lil Man, listening to the strain he was putting on his chair.

"Nobody in the hood liked LV. He was a *rata*, but I didn't kill him. Nobody know anythang, far as I heard. And Hoodlum? Ain't nobody from D-Thirteen rolling with that fool no more. He dropped out. Ain't like he ever had that kinda' juice anyway. And he was always doing stupid shit, like that stupid shit he done at that party. He was always trying to score points."

"Where were you on the night of the homeless murders?" Cortes asked.

"I was at my baby mama's. And it was a house fulla' niggas there, you know, just in case y'all need some—what you call that shit?"

"Corroboration," McGuire answered.

"Naw, that other shit—"

"Alibi. Alibi witnesses."

"Yeah. That's the name ah that shit. I got me a buncha' those."

"That it?" Cortes asked. "You don't know anything else?"

"That's it. Y'all gotta look somewhere else. I can tell ya'll this, though.

Whoever smoked them fools some real ones. That was some straight-up gangsta shit. Ain't too many muthafuckas out here getting down like that."

"Okay. Thanks for coming in, *amigo*."

McGuire and Cortes followed up on his story and found out that he was right. His alibi was solid. They still didn't have any evidence tying anyone to the murders. So far, all they had was grapevine and yard talk.

"We need to go about this another way, Hugo. My gut is telling me that Lucky and those dudes he brought with him to LV's camp are involved somehow, someway. I hate that word."

"What word?"

"Coincidence."

"Me, too. It's just another word for lack of proof."

"Sammy got robbed, right?"

"Yeah. What are you thinking?"

"We gotta get them in here and get them talking. Stimulate them with interviews and then throw them in wired cells and record whatever they say. But we need some teeth behind it. How about we try and get warrants on them for robbery? It's a stretch because the victim is dead, but maybe we can get a DA to sign off on it anyway. Then we'll put the surveillance team on them."

"What do we got to lose? That's a great idea, *Big Man*."

"That's an oxymoron. You, my friend, are just a moron."

They took the warrant application to the filing Deputy District Attorney at Long Beach court the next day. They were seeking arrest warrants on Motor and Baudelaire. Lucky was already in custody, and since no one had identified Ponce as being present when Sammy was robbed, their names were not included. It didn't matter. The filing DA refused to charge anyone, citing a lack of sufficient probable cause and no victim.

When they got back to the office, McGuire picked up his desk phone receiver.

"Who you calling?" Cortes asked.

"The detective who handled the Leonard Lloyd case. We gotta eliminate that bullshit rumor sooner or later.

SHERIFF'S HOMICIDE INVESTIGATOR MARK LILLIENFELD WAS A personable man.

He was middle-aged and clean-shaven with well-groomed dark brown hair, and he loved sucking on hard candy or breath mints. He had a dry sense of humor and an affinity for calling people "donkeys." With a sharp mind and a sharper tongue, he had been a homicide investigator for almost twenty years, and the only thing he loved more than working murders was his dog.

McGuire knew him well because he had helped investigate the murder of Maria Cecilia Rosas, an off-duty deputy murdered in the driveway of her Long Beach home in 2006 by two gang members looking to rob someone. She was killed less than a mile from where the Quintuple occurred.

"What's up, Mark?"

"Hey brother! How's it hanging?"

"Low, my brutha."

Lillienfeld laughed and asked, "What can you do for me?"

"I'm on the hunt for dragons."

"I hear ya', my friend. Ain't we all?"

"You had Leonard Lloyd, right?"

"Yeah. That Carson OSS team helped a lot with that. What's up?"

"My partner and I caught the homeless murder case. One of my victims was in the same gang and testified against Lloyd."

"You caught that clusterfuck, huh? God bless you. Yeah, I remember that guy who testified in my case. Real dirtbag, but he got on the witness stand and laid it all out. Wasn't worried about retaliation, either. The only thing I can tell you right now is that Lloyd ain't got nothing to do with it. That donkey ain't got that kind of juice."

"Are you sure?"

"Brother, if I thought he did, I would have called you first thing."

"A'ight, den. Thanks. We gotta get together soon. Peace in the hood."

"You betcha. Kiss the dog and pet the wife and kids, and good luck with your case. Sounds like you're gonna need it."

ON FEBRUARY 5, THE SURVEILLANCE TEAM MET MCGUIRE AND CORTES in the Homicide office.

After getting briefed on the facts of the case, one half of the team left to initiate surveillance on Richardson's house. The other half had the responsibility of finding where Ponce truly laid his head. Almost all parolees had two addresses: the one they give to their PO's, and the one where they slept.

Later that evening, the team returned to the office.

"How'd it go, guys?" Cortes asked.

"It went like clockwork, sir," the first team leader said. "Your guy, Richardson, drove his black Hyundai to the registered address. He was with some older woman, his mother, if I had to make a guess. They went into the house and stayed until Ponce pulled up in a dark green Buick Century."

"Interesting. Anybody in the car with him?" McGuire asked.

"Yeah. Two women and another guy. One of the women had a baby."

"The same group that was with him when he met his parole officer," the other team leader said. "That's the car they were in. Apparently, the other people in the car were uncooperative with her, and Ponce gave a home address in Long Beach even though a registration sticker in the window showed a Lancaster address. And it was in Ponce's name."

"What happened when Ponce got to Richardson's house?" Cortes asked.

"Nothing, really. He went into the house while the rest of the people stayed in the car. Five or ten minutes later, he and Richardson came out, hugged, and he got in the car and left. We followed him all the way to an apartment in Lancaster. Everybody in the car got out and went inside."

"Thanks, guys," McGuire said. "You can leave your surveillance logs and any pictures that you took with us."

McGuire and Cortes looked over the logs after the team left the office.

"Ponce and Richardson are tight, Hugo. There might be something here."

"I agree. Now we know where they both lay their heads, at least. You want to do some parole and probation searches?"

"No. If we don't find anything, we will have given our case away. If they are involved, they will slip up eventually. Remember? Bottom of the hill? We want them all, right?"

"The hell with you and your cows, Mac."

"Now that you mention it, I'm hungry, bitch. For something medium rare, to be exact. Let's go. Bring your little cooler."

"Hey, partner. What are you reading?"

It was the morning of March 7, and Cortes had just gotten to the office.

"An assault report," McGuire said, leaning back in his chair and putting his feet on his desk. "Lobster Girl got beat up yesterday by Vanessa's sister. She was in jail at the time of the murders, so I guess she just got out. Apparently, she believes that Lobster Girl set up LV and her sister to get killed."

"But she didn't have anything to do with it."

"*I* know that. *You* know that. But that Malaepule family doesn't know that. And I ain't trying to piss *none* of those big muthafuckas off. Thankfully, Lobster Girl doesn't want to press charges, but apparently, she has taken to carrying weapons to protect herself."

"Weapons? Like what kind of weapons?"

"Mace. And brass knuckles."

"What? Brass knuckles? Like brass knuckles that go over your fingers brass knuckles?"

"Yep."

"I'ma leave that one alone, *amigo*. Too easy. Should we be worried, though?"

"I wouldn't sweat it. By now, if Lobster Girl does know who the shooters are, she has id'ed them from a six-pack line-up to the Malaepule family."

Cortes laughed and said, "Oh yeah, by the way. I heard you're getting an award, *sí*?"

"Yeah, that's what I'm hearing, too. Don't really know why, though. Hey, did Lobster Girl have a cell phone?"

"Yeah. Why? And how the hell does she even dial?"

"Probably the same way she wears brass knuckles. She's resourceful. In any event, I'm gonna write a warrant on her phone. See who she was talking to around the time of the murders."

McGuire had never believed that Lobster Girl was involved. She may

Sell your books at World of Books!
Go to sell.worldofbooks.com and get an instant price quote. We even pay the shipping - see what your old books are worth today!

00088418253

have been ornery and spiteful, but she was no killer, just pissed off at the world because of her lot in life.

"It's a long shot, but you never know. I've been wrong before. Not often, but it does happen from time-to-time."

"Yeah, partner. You're a regular *leyenda* in your own mind."

The warrant return yielded nothing. Several calls were made from her phone that night, but none of the numbers had a connection between Lobster Girl and David Ponce, Motor, Baudelaire, or Lucky.

CHAPTER FIFTEEN

THE QUINTUPLE WAS anointed the "Homeless Massacre" by the media.

They love sensational names: "The Hillside Strangler." "The Night Stalker." "The Scoreboard Killer." They thrive on arousing fear in the general populace. It sells papers, and that is their bottom line. If McGuire and Cortes caught the killers, the press would call them the "Homeless Slayers," or some other corny shit like that.

The police bosses called the killings the "Homeless Murder" case. McGuire and Cortes never called it by either of those terms. It was just the "Quintuple." Period. They didn't see the victims as homeless people. To them, they were just five innocent people who had been murdered. And if they caught the killers, they would just be like any other assholes who needed to be removed from society.

McGuire and Cortes couldn't care less about the press, or what their bosses wanted. It was a big case, but they had to work it just like they worked the rest of their cases. The only difference was that there were five coroner's case numbers instead of just one. They weren't going to let anyone pressure them into putting together a sloppy case. Whenever a detective tried to force pieces into places where they didn't fit, the final picture was always fucked up. The corner and edge pieces had to be in place first.

McGuire and Cortes had other responsibilities as well—other murders to work on, court cases to deal with, trials and autopsies, even funerals and wakes to attend. Although not required as part of his duties, McGuire felt it sometimes necessary to attend the last rites of some of his victims, not only because it was respectful, but also because attendance demonstrated to the family that he cared.

He received his award on March 12. He was being recognized by the West Los Angeles AME Church of God in Christ for work he did as the lead detective on the Masonic lodge double murder case. LAPD Assistant Chief Jim McDonnell attended the ceremony. He was a longtime resident of Long Beach and had closely followed that investigation as well as the Quintuple.

A few days later, McGuire got the 2009 Peacekeeper Award. It was one of the most prestigious awards given to Long Beach police officers. He and Cortes were walking to the ceremony at City Hall and discussing the impact murders have on surviving family, friends, even the investigators, when Cortes brought up Officer Daryle Black, murdered by gang members in 2000.

His services had been held at the Long Beach Convention Center near the Queen Mary. Over 15,000 cops from all over the country in addition to Officer Black's family and numerous friends were in attendance. There was not a dry eye in the house when McGuire sang "It's So Hard to Say Goodbye" by Boyz-to-Men.

"That was the first time I ever heard you sing," Cortes said. "I knew you were a world-class drummer. But to also be able to sing? How does somebody so little get blessed with all that talent?"

"Kiss my ass. But as far as the impact murders have? They all affect me. I have stopped trying to figure out why some people die horrible deaths and others die in their sleep, why some people live to be a hundred years-old and others are born dead. It's the baby deaths that get to me, though, and the murders of police officers. The pain is a thousand times worse when the police officer is a close friend.

"When Daryle got killed, I thought about it every day. I would ask myself, *When is this feeling gonna be over? When am I gonna feel better? When am I gonna stop thinking about it all the fucking time?* And I asked those questions of a buddy who had gone through the same thing, only he lost *two* cop friends at the same fucking time.

"He was sympathetic, in the way that only a muthafucka like him could be. He told me, 'Look, bitch. You'll know when it's over. When something terrible happens, like the breaking of your heart by someone who you may have thought you were in love with, or the loss of a friend, your gut hurts like your appendix burst. You feel like you want to curl up in a ball and die. But one day, you will realize that the incident or person hadn't crossed your mind all that day. And that's when you'll realize that you are better.'

"And you know, Hugo, one night not long after that my mind was fried after working a long-ass crime scene, my back and feet hurt, and all I wanted to do was curl up next to Baby. I got in bed, turned off the night lamp, and closed my eyes. Then it hit me. It was almost midnight, and I hadn't thought of Daryle all that day. I smiled, kissed Baby on her forehead, and fell asleep. From that point on, other than the anniversary of his murder, all I think about now are the good times that we had."

McGuire's award that day was for recognition and appreciation of a "Distinguished law enforcement officer for his outstanding service for the past eighteen years."

It read as follows:

As a Long Beach Police Department Homicide Detective, you are sensitive to the families of your victims, treating every case as if it happened to a member of your own family. You found your niche working as a Homicide Detective, and several families within the community are grateful for your expertise. You were quoted as saying, 'Every case is solvable, we just need the right piece of evidence or the right person who cares enough to take a stand.' You exemplify outstanding values and ethics, and it is all together fitting and proper to honor you with this most esteemed award.

It was signed by Mayor Bob Foster, one of the muckety-mucks McGuire had kicked out of his crime scene on the 405 Freeway on-ramp.

PART THREE

CHAPTER SIXTEEN

"Yo, cuh! Put on some of that Lil Wayne shit!"

It was about 4 p.m. on Tuesday, March 23, 2009, and Tony Bledsoe was at a barbecue party. He had just requested that the DJ play the newest album by the raspy-voiced rapper with long dreadlocks. Bledsoe loved rap music and considered himself worthy of being given a shot at fame. He had the perfect stage name, given to him because of his beautiful light-green eyes.

"Hold on, Cat Eyes," the DJ answered. "I'ma get to that shit, cuh."

Bledsoe hugged his girlfriend Rhonda and began rapping the lyrics to "Pussy Monster," his lips close to her ear as if he was crooning a love song instead of begging her for oral sex. The other twenty or thirty attendees at the party joined in while some of them began Crip-Walking. When the song was over, Bledsoe told Rhonda that he was going to Tupac's, a local liquor store named after the rap legend.

He gave her a quick kiss on the cheek and then got on his bicycle. He was feeling good; the blunts and liquor had been flowing freely. He looked forward to getting back to Rhonda after picking up a couple of 40-ounce bottles of beer, but his thoughts were interrupted by a car pulling in front of him when he was a few blocks away from the party.

"Yo, what's up with my money, my nigga?" the driver asked.

Bledsoe put his feet on the ground, steadying the bicycle as he peered into the opened front passenger's window.

"What up, G?"

"We need to talk. Get in. Leave your bike."

"A'ight. Let me tell my girl I'm going with you."

"Nah, nigga. Get in the car. She already know. I'll bring you right back. Ride with me to the store. We can talk about that money you owe me on the way."

The man was coming from a friend's house where they had drank a bottle of Hennessy and some Cisco. His voice was slurred, but steady and calm. Even still, there was something menacing in the tone. Bledsoe knew that he was talking about the proceeds from the quarter pound of marijuana he had given him to sell. The problem was that Bledsoe had spent the money and smoked what little he had left. He thought about pedaling away or jumping off and running, but either of those choices would surely cause the man to turn him into human roadkill.

I'll reason with him, Bledsoe thought as he got in the car, leaving his bicycle lying on the sidewalk. He would rather lose it than his life, and this man was nothing to play with. *He's dangerous, but all he wants is his money. And he can't get it from a dead man.* The two of them drove off, both sounding like gang members hanging out on a corner in what used to be South Central L.A, one of them desperately trying to survive.

"Go get me a bottle of Cisco," the man said as he stopped in front of Tupac's.

He was familiar with the store—more popular because of the name than what it sold—and he knew there was no back door accessible to the public. There was only one way in and one way out for customers. Bledsoe got out and walked inside. He came out with a bag and handed it to the man, who threw it on the backseat. Bledsoe got in the car, and they drove off. A few minutes later, the man pulled out the biggest gun that Bledsoe had ever seen.

"You think you can fuck me? I been looking for you and you ain't even qualified to have a muthafucka like me looking for you. Where's my money? It's been three months already."

"I only got thirty on me right now, G, but I'll get the rest by tomorrow, I swear."

The man didn't reply. He didn't have to. He had a way of smiling that was intimidating rather than ingratiating.

Thirty dollars for a quarter pound of high-grade marijuana is insulting, he thought. *Hell, you could barely get one blunt for that. Is this nigga serious?*

Although he had told Bledsoe that he was going to take him back to his bike, he kept driving toward Lake Los Angeles. Bledsoe relaxed a little when the man put the gun down.

"Where we going, G?"

"Relax, homie. I got some new John Blaze shit. We can get high and talk about how you gonna make my money right."

Most people still referred to Lake Los Angeles as Lancaster, although it was a separate city. Its origins had been dubious; it was founded on a real estate scam when unscrupulous developers took a small natural lake in a basin and made it into a larger pair of man-made lakes. The developers then named the area Lake Los Angeles and advertised it as a resort destination with mentions of a country club and lakefront luxury lots.

They subdivided the land into thousands of lots, many of which were bought by absentee landlords. The original speculators eventually sold their interests and problems arose within the community over where the money was going to come from to keep the artificial lakes filled. By the 1980s, they had evaporated. Now it was an empty basin surrounded by buttes.

Lake Los Angeles was a place where dreams went to die, and the man was driving Tony Duane Bledsoe directly there.

It had been over three hours since Bledsoe left the barbecue.

The store wasn't that far away. He should have been back long before now, but his friends and girlfriend weren't worried. They just thought he had decided to do something else or went to get high at someone's house. They still weren't worried when he didn't come back after the barbecue was over. Bledsoe didn't have a place of his own and his girlfriend knew that he sometimes slept over at different houses in the area. She didn't hear from him that night, but she figured he would come to her house when he was ready.

Three days later, on March 26, he still had not been seen or heard from. His friend, José Salamanca, who had also been at the barbecue, was concerned. They had known each other for at least four years. Bledsoe would call to check in or they would see each other almost every day. Salamanca found out that he had last been seen getting into a green Buick with either a dark-skinned Mexican or a Samoan who looked Black. But he had left his bicycle on the sidewalk. Salamanca found it unusual and was so concerned by now that he reluctantly went to the Lancaster Sheriff's Station to file a missing person's report.

Being in the lobby of a police station or sheriff's station was an unusual position for Salamanca. He usually came in handcuffed through the back door. He walked to the front counter where an older white deputy glanced at him with disinterest. The deputy looked like he had been around for a million years and was just whiling away time until he could retire and move to a quaint little house, someplace quiet, maybe close to a body of water with wildlife coming close to his front porch.

"Can I help you?"

"I wanna file a missing person's report on my friend."

"Have a seat. Someone will be right with you."

After twenty or thirty minutes, a much younger deputy, one who was probably more concerned with getting to OSS or Homicide than retiring, came to take the report. He took out his notebook and started writing.

"Do you remember what he was wearing?"

"He wears Timberlands a lot, but I think the last time I saw him he had on a pair of blue Nikes, a tan shirt, and blue jeans. And he had an earring in his ear."

"What kind of earring?"

"One shaped like a lil barbell with a fake-ass diamond."

"Anything else?"

"No. I just think something bad might've happened to him."

The reporting deputy and another one took Salamanca to the location where he thought Bledsoe last lived. The woman there did not know him. Then they contacted Rhonda. She had not seen nor heard from him since he left the barbecue. One of the deputies wrote a number on two business cards and gave them to her and Salamanca.

"I'm sure he'll turn up," the deputy said. "Sometimes people just need to get away, you know? If you hear anything, call the station, and reference that file number."

The next morning, the deputies faxed their report to the Missing Persons Unit at Homicide Bureau. One of them also called Detective Laverne Howard and briefed her about the matter. The first thing she did every morning when she got to her office was to grab the reports that came in overnight. Then she would sit at her desk with her coffee and review them. After speaking with the Lancaster deputy, she casually thumbed through the reports until she got to the one regarding Tony Bledsoe:

Name: Bledsoe, Tony Duane
Race: W
Sex: M
Eye color: Greenish Blue
Gang: 60s
Moniker: Cat Eyes
Jewelry description: Clear stone earring shaped like a barbell worn in left ear
Missing: Suspicious circumstances

"Well, that's different," Howard said to herself. "A white Crip."

AT A LITTLE AFTER 1:30 P.M., RHONDA ALSO FILED A MISSING PERSON'S report. Howard called Lancaster Station and detailed an OSS deputy to conduct interviews regarding the incident. Then, she put the reports in a file cabinet and closed the drawer, effectively closing the case.

CHAPTER SEVENTEEN

THE L.A. COUNTY Sheriff's Homicide Bureau was one of the finest in the country.

In 1977, an L.A. Times reporter interviewed a deputy district attorney who had high praise for the investigators. The DDA credited their success to their dedication and tenacity and likened them to *bulldogs* because they never let go of a case no matter what.

They would wear the mantle with pride. The Bureau mascot had been an English bulldog since that day, and their logo was the head of the dog smoking a cigar and wearing a gray fedora. Protruding from the fedora's band was the "dead man's hand"—black aces and eights, the playing cards Wild Bill Hickok held when he was murdered in a saloon in Deadwood, Dakota Territory in 1876.

The investigators worked out of a nondescript building and were broken up into six teams of eight. A lieutenant supervised each team. They wrote evaluations, approved reports, overtime, and responded to murder callouts to handle the press. The Missing Persons Unit was not part of the teams; they worked in an office in the back of the building.

The phone lines at the front desk, also known as the *barrel*, were manned by a security officer and two investigators twenty-four hours a day. There was a white grease board on the wall behind the desk with the names and cell phone numbers of the investigators next up for callouts.

All six Homicide teams worked in tandem, as "sister" teams. Team One paired with Two, Three with Four, and Five with Six. When they were on call, one of them was available for callouts while the sister team worked the desk and answered phone calls.

On Tuesday, September 8, 2009, Teams One and Two were up.

"WHAT'S THAT, BOY? WHAT YOU GOT?"

It was 7:25 p.m. Forty-three-year-old Lucinda Dujardin was riding her horse along the trails behind Challenger Middle School in Lancaster, something she did almost every night. Her dog, who always accompanied her, became agitated and started barking and running in circles around something. Dujardin looked closer and saw that it appeared to be a human hand.

"HOMICIDE. HECHT SPEAKING."

It was 8:30 p.m., and Investigator Peter Hecht had just answered one of the phones at the front desk. Assigned to Team Two, he was a tall, slim white man who had a love for art and could tell the difference between a Cezanne and a Gaugin from a mile away.

"This is Lieutenant James Burrell at Lancaster Station. Lookit, a citizen riding her horse on a trail up here found a human hand. We need Homicide to respond."

Hecht took down as much information as he could before hanging up. Then he looked at the grease board. Rodriguez and his kid were up next. After calling their team lieutenant and speaking with him briefly, Hecht called Rodriguez.

SERGEANT MARTIN L. RODRIGUEZ, WITH A Z, NOT AN S, WAS ASSIGNED to Team One.

A tall, well-built Mexican man with huge hands and feet, he was well-read but liked to keep that part of himself hidden, preferring to be as smart as he needed to be, depending on his surroundings. By 2009, he had been a Sheriff's deputy for over twenty-five years, almost half of them at Homicide.

He was a prototypical bulldog, with highly polished shoes and well-fitted suits purchased from downtown L.A. in the garment district. He kept his head and face clean-shaven and often had a wooden toothpick in his mouth. He had an intimidating presence until displaying a disarming, cherubic smile that revealed deep dimples. His friends and co-workers called him "Marty."

"Marty. It's Pete. You and your partner got a call-out. Some lady on a horse found a hand in Lancaster."

Rodriguez groaned as Hecht brought him up to speed on the situation. The Homicide Bureau was close to eighty miles away from Lancaster. Investigators, unless they lived in the Antelope Valley area, hated responding there for callouts. Rodriguez lived close to twenty-five miles from the Bureau, so a callout to Lancaster from his house meant a trip of over one hundred miles.

"What kind of hand, Pete?"

"A human hand, Marty. Fuck kinda' hand you think?"

"Relax. I'm fucking with you. Did you notify the Lieutenant?"

"Yeah, I did. He said there was no need for him to respond. It's just a hand."

"So, he thinks somebody just left their hand in the road and walked off?"

"What do ya want me to say, Marty? Maybe there's a one-handed person still alive somewhere telling fucking war stories about how he lost the other one. Maybe he's got a hook now and he's a fucking pirate! Maybe the fugitive is chasing him—"

"The fugitive was being chased *by* the guy with one hand...well, actually he was missing his whole arm—"

"Who gives a fuck, Marty? And how the hell do I know why there's a hand in the road? I agree with the lieutenant. It's better that he stays available in case a *real* murder happens somewhere else."

"You mean somewhere other than fucking Lancaster. And what's with you? You got an evaluation coming up or something? Get your head outta the Lieutenant's ass."

"Why you gotta always be such an asshole, Marty?"

"Relax, Pete. I'm still just fucking with you. I'm gonna make it up to you. I'll take a picture of the hand so you can hang it up in your house. You can call it, 'Hand in Desert,' by unknown artist."

"God, you're fucking hilarious, Marty. You know that?"

When Rodriguez stopped laughing, he requested that Hecht have a cadaver dog handler and someone from the coroner's Search and Recovery Team respond. Then, Rodriguez called his kid.

SERGEANT ROBERT GRAY WAS BEING "BROKEN IN" BY RODRIGUEZ.

Although Gray had been a Sheriff's Deputy for twenty-two years at that point and at Homicide for over four months, he was still considered a kid by Homicide standards, and Rodriguez was considered his daddy.

Gray was a keen investigator and had an eye for what others sometimes missed. While everyone else on a search warrant was tearing apart a house with an underfed dog chained to a tree in the back yard, Gray would be the one turning over a full fifty-pound bag of dog food and retrieving the gun that fell out.

"What took you so long to answer the phone, Bobby?"

"It only rang four times."

"That's three times too many. I assume you got a call from the desk?"

"Yeah. Some poor bastard in Lancaster is walking around with one hand."

"Stop being a smart ass. Get your head outta your ass and get dressed. Meet me at the Bureau."

A small, slim man who looked good in his clothes, Gray wore expensive designer prescription glasses and sterling silver bulldog cufflinks and tie pins. He was already dressed when Rodriguez called. All he had to do was slip on his Bally shoes and straighten his silk tie and he would be out the door.

"I'll be there in thirty. And my head ain't in my ass, although I was about to call someone so I could put it in theirs."

"Stop dreaming and get to the office."

Gray laughed after he hung up. It was always funny to him whenever Rodriguez tried to play his daddy. Gray was a former US Marine. Hazing that he couldn't handle didn't exist. Not only that, growing up on the rough streets of Orange, New Jersey, had prepared him for anything life could throw at him, including that bullshit about addressing him only as Bobby, or Gray, even though his peers in OSS called him Bobby G, or Bobby G-Ray.

"No one is gonna call you anything other than your first or last name until you prove you're a bulldog," Rodriguez had said to him when he first got to Homicide.

Gray grabbed his Beretta 9mm pistol from the kitchen countertop. Other than his rescue dog, a Border Collie and Pitbull mix that he named Bandit because he was all white except for black patches around his eyes, Gray lived alone. His only daughter lived with her mother, so he didn't have to worry about his gun not being locked in a safe.

He had developed chronic back pain after years of wearing the heavy leather gun belt that street cops wear. Now that he was a detective, he seldom wore his duty weapon on his waist unless he was in the field. Whenever he was in the office, his pistol was in his desk drawer or on the seat next to him if he was in a car.

Holstered gun in hand, he kissed Bandit, touched the Star of David that he always wore under his shirt, and rubbed his autographed Eli Manning football for luck. He then got in his county-issued Chevy Malibu and put his beachfront home in Huntington Beach in his rear-view mirror.

"Did you grab a poor boy, Bobby?"

"What?"

"A poor boy. Did you get one?" Rodriguez asked again, referring to the accordion-like brown folders that investigators used for holding reports, photographs, and investigator notebooks.

"No, I thought you grabbed one."

"Why would you think that? You know that's a job for kids."

"I'll get one when we get back. It's just a hand for god's sake."

"Now you sound like that fucking Pete Hecht."

"Huh?"

"Never mind," Rodriguez said while tuning the radio to the Dodger game.

He and Gray had had a few good cases since they partnered. They bickered like teenaged siblings, but they genuinely liked each other. When they weren't talking about their cases, they talked about mundane things, like sports, or if J-Lo had the best ass in the entertainment industry. They also often reminisced about their patrol days, which they were doing on the way to Lancaster.

"Hey Bobby, you know why cops never sit down on calls when they're inside a house in the ghetto?"

Gray slid off his Bally's and got comfortable in the passenger seat, preparing to answer Rodriguez with a derogatory word in Spanish. His daughter's mother was from East L.A. She was a beautiful Mexican woman whom he had fallen hard for the first time he saw her. Their relationship didn't last, and the only things Gray got out of the deal were his daughter and Spanish curse words.

"Who cares, *pendejo*? Have you seen the *culos* on these chicks wearing yoga pants and biker shorts lately? God, whoever invented those things should win a Nobel Prize."

"No, seriously, Bobby. Do you know why cops don't sit down in houses in the ghetto on calls?"

"No shit, Marty. Every cop knows that. It's so they don't take any fucking bugs home with them when they leave."

"That's exactly right. They're afraid of taking roaches home with them, you know, especially those little brown ones, the ones that always seem to have an egg attached to their ass. But I didn't care. I sat down anyway. I wanted the people to feel comfortable. That funky little apartment I lived in when I got hired? Shit, I would've only been taking home companionship for the legion of pregnant little fuckers who already lived there. You know those little fuckers didn't even have the courtesy to try and hide after I turned the lights on?"

"I bet you won't sit down now. Your wife would kick your ass if you brought roaches to that beautiful house that you live in. Besides...did you ever once think that those people had roaches because you were *bringing* them from your shitty apartment? Maybe people in the ghetto had them because of *you*. Smooth as butter Marty Rodriguez...the man responsible for all the roaches in the ghetto. Fucking fuhgeddaboudit."

"Whatever, Bobby. Your horny ass wouldn't even know there was a roach *on* you unless it was wearing biker shorts."

Gray laughed so hard he couldn't catch his breath as he scrambled to retrieve his gun, which had fallen on the passenger side floorboard and slid under his seat.

As they drove along the Interstate 5 Freeway, Rodriguez listened to the end of the Dodgers and Diamondbacks baseball game on the radio while Gray bitched about his New York Mets losing to the Florida Marlins 4-2. But Rodriguez was happy. His Boys-in-Blue beat the Snakes 5-4.

The post-game report became nothing more than white noise as Rodriguez settled in for the long drive still ahead. He always felt that the Bureau should be broken down into two offices: North and South. There were plenty of investigators who lived close enough to only respond to calls up north. The other ones who lived down south could then handle the other callouts.

There were many more callouts down south, but that just meant more overtime. And with two daughters—one of whom was autistic—to put through college, Rodriguez had no problem with that at all. *After God weeps, he smiles*, as his mother always said whenever the sun came out after a heavy rain. Out of every tragedy, there was always profit for someone else. And he meant to give those who suffered from tragedy the best service money could buy.

One of the first cases he and Gray caught was in Lancaster. On October 7, 2008, they were called out to a dirt road on the outskirts of the city. Maurilio Ponce, a thirty-one-year-old Hispanic man who owned a trucking business was found dead on Avenue I East of 110 Street West, about six miles from his residence.

Three men, including Anthony Duane Smith, a retired Los Angeles Raiders defensive end, were arrested not long after. They had been in business with the victim and were hijacking and selling truckloads of merchandise. Apparently, Smith and his associates felt that the victim had cheated them out of their share of profits from a heist.

Rodriguez and Gray solved the case by using the latest cell phone technology, tracking Smith and Ponce's cell phones to the crime scene, and back down to L.A. But Ponce never made the trip. He was still lying in the desert sand, shot to death and beaten so savagely that a shoe print was embedded in his face.

Well over six feet tall and three hundred pounds of pure muscle, Smith was menacing at times during a subsequent interrogation. Gray wasn't starstruck or intimidated by the hulking man at all. When he told an obvious lie during the interrogation, Gray leaned forward, looked him in the eye, and said, "I like you, Tony, but you're a liar." The way that Gray, a wisp of a man, handled Smith had impressed Rodriguez.

The case led to the LAPD being able to solve three cold case drug-related murders in their jurisdiction, including the murders of two brothers who were abducted from their business in L.A. in 1999 by Smith, who posed as a cop. One of the brothers was dumped on Greenleaf Boulevard in Compton near a cemetery, the other one in an alley eight miles away. They were both handcuffed and had multiple gunshot wounds to their duct-taped heads. One of them had also been tortured with a hot clothing iron.

Two years after that, Smith, again posing as a cop, kidnapped another man from the area of Pacific and Centinela Avenue in L.A. The man was later found in his own vehicle, dead from a gunshot wound to the head.

And now, less than a year after Maurilio Ponce was brutally murdered, Rodriguez and Gray were going back to that fucking hell hole in Lancaster.

CHAPTER EIGHTEEN

RODRIGUEZ AND GRAY pulled up to the scene at 11 p.m.

An L.A. County Coroner's Search and Recovery Team was already there. It wasn't considered a full team because a forensic anthropologist didn't respond, but a K-9 handler with her dog "Indiana Bones," was present. The found hand, dehydrated, and discolored with some tissue still attached to the bones, was laying on the dirt roadway not far from Challenger Middle School at the edge of Lancaster. The bones did not appear to have been severed by mechanical means; there were teeth marks present.

The hand was about seventy feet from the fenced property line of the school. Yellow tape cordoned off the area, which consisted of a desertscape with dry brush, loose dirt, and sand. The CSI's took photos and measurements of the hand and surrounding area while the SRT team and the K-9 conducted large-scale searches for additional human remains.

Wild dogs and coyotes have a ranging area of several miles. Because the hand had signs of animal activity, a safety hazard existed for the dog, who now had to remain on a leash. It was also getting dark, cold, and the terrain was rough. Taking all these factors into consideration, the leader of the SRT team made the decision to have a full team respond back to the scene on Friday morning at 7 a.m. The team leader took possession of the hand and transported it to the Coroner's Office where it was designated as specimen #2009-52, a number revealing a grim reality that with three months still left in the year, there had been fifty-one other body parts found in L.A. County.

It was Thursday, about 2:30 p.m.

"Did you guys hear they found a hand not far from here yesterday? I'll bet the rest of the body is somewhere around here, too."

The twelve-year-old boy was giddy as he spoke to three of his classmates near Challenger Middle School. The boy had seen a news truck and reporters as he was about to go home and, curious, like most boys his age, he asked one of them what was going on. His eyes widened in surprise when the reporter told him that a human hand had been located nearby.

"Let's go see if we can find it," he said to his friends.

The four of them then walked off into the desert like minions of Indiana Jones in search of what Indiana Bones had been unable to find. A little over a mile away from the school, they found something that would stay with them for the rest of their lives.

Rodriguez and Gray met at the office after getting four or five hours of sleep.

They contacted Laverne Howard's partner, Detective Denise Fine, in the Missing Person's office. Rodriguez filled her in on the circumstances of the hand and asked if she had any missing person reports out of the Lancaster area. She opened a file cabinet and pulled out a stack of reports. After thumbing through several of them, she stopped.

"Here we go. Tony Duane Bledsoe, aka 'Cat Eyes'. A white Crip, if you can believe that. He was reported missing in March of this year."

"Okay. Thanks, Denise," Rodriguez said. "Our case might tie into this Bledsoe thing."

"I also remember my partner telling me that she had some Lancaster OSS deputy canvass for witnesses and write a supplemental report. I don't see any supplemental reports with follow-up interviews, though."

"No worries. If one was written, we'll find it. Maybe the deputy didn't have it forwarded to Homicide."

"I'm sure that's it."

"We gotta do lunch one day, Denise."

"Sure thing, Marty. You know I got nothing but time. And please let us know if your case ties in with Bledsoe so we can close ours."

"You got it. Oh, one more thing. Did you guys do a flyer seeking information on this kid?"

"I know I didn't, Marty. And there isn't one in the file."

"Okay. Thanks, Denise."

"Maybe you guys should do one now, huh?" she said.

Rodriguez and Gray forced smiles at her when she gave this untimely bit of advice. They weren't happy. Bledsoe had gone missing under suspicious circumstances, and little to no work had been done. They knew that if a little kid, a white woman, or an affluent individual had disappeared under the same circumstances, a Homicide team would have been called out. But since it was only a gang member with a criminal record, no one gave a shit.

The MPU was responsible for notifying a team lieutenant whenever someone was missing under suspicious circumstances. Otherwise, none of the teams on-call would know. Similarly, when an investigator on barrel duty responded to a dead body call and something appeared to be amiss, in almost every situation, the Lieutenant would have a team respond to the scene.

Despite the Homicide Bureau having a glowing reputation overall, the MPU had been turned into a dumping ground for lazy investigators, those about to retire, or those who didn't have the overall aptitude for the assignment. The unit had become a place where homicide investigators went to die.

There were hundreds of reports in the file cabinet, just put away until the missing person was found, dead or alive, or returned home. Then the investigator would write a follow-up report and close the case. They almost never conducted any actual follow-up investigation. Except for going to lunch, they rarely left the office.

Gray sat quietly for a few minutes after reading the reports. Then he slammed them on his desk.

"Marty, this kid was fucking abducted. Nobody abandons their bike willingly to get into a car. This case should have come to the floor as soon as it happened. 'Make a flyer,' she says. I guess she thinks she's giving us case advice, huh? I'd rather get relationship advice from a promiscuous ex-girlfriend with cauliflower herpes on her fucking mouth. Why didn't *they* do a flyer?"

Rodriguez seldom lost his temper; if he did, it was hard for him to find it again. But he had learned to control it in recent years. Supreme patience was required when raising an autistic child. As a result, he had mellowed out considerably in his older years. At most, he would just squint his eyes and chew toothpicks when he was annoyed.

"You're right, Bobby," he said as he put a fresh toothpick in his mouth, squinted, and shrugged. "It's all fucked up. They need to do something with that missing person's unit. It's missing."

Gray, too angry to reply, cooled off by going to the supply room to get a poor boy.

THE FOUR CURIOUS AND ADVENTUROUS BOYS WALKED INTO THE DESERT.

They separated and began searching in different directions. As luck would have it, the ringleader made the find. It was like something out of one of those movies he'd watch with his siblings late at night after their parents went to bed—only this time, he was all alone, and he wasn't eating popcorn while peeking out from underneath a blanket. This was real. As his jaw dropped and his eyes bulged, he gasped at the sight of the lower half of a human body. The upper half lay a few feet away. The head was missing.

The ringleader immediately ran off to get his friends. He didn't want to be alone anymore, his bravado as fleeting as several nearby tumble weeds rolling farther into the desert. He and his friends were silent when they looked at the discovery. Except for one of the boys who nudged a portion of the remains with his shoe, no one touched anything. Then they sprinted back to the school and told the reporter what they had found. The reporter called personnel at the Lancaster Sheriff's Station, who, in turn, notified Homicide.

RODRIGUEZ AND GRAY HAD DECIDED TO HAVE A NICE SIT-DOWN MEAL before going home.

The next day, they would have to get up early and meet the SRT team in Lancaster to continue searching for body remains. They chose John Corina's steakhouse, the unofficial home of Sheriff's Homicide investigators. It was cozy with a soothing ambience; the perfect place to relax and unwind for men and women who routinely saw the worst humanity had to offer. On any given day, one could find investigators, both active and retired, on-duty and off-duty, having a delicious steak while indulging in an alcoholic beverage.

It was 3 p.m., and Rodriguez and Gray were about to leave the office when a security officer working at the front desk caught them.

"Excuse me, Detectives. Some kids just found parts of a body in Lancaster. The coroner's office and the SRT team are already on the way up there."

Rodriguez and Gray looked at each other. Nothing in life is absolute, but a good homicide investigator doesn't believe in coincidences. They didn't know, but they *knew*.

"Get the poor boy, Bobby. We're not gonna be able to sit down and eat. Let's take separate cars. Grab something and I'll see you in Lancaster."

After going through the drive-thru at a local fast-food restaurant, Gray got on the freeway, trying to eat his burger and grabbing a few fries every now and then as he fought stop-and-go traffic for the next hour and a half. He stopped by the Lancaster Sheriff's Station to relieve himself when he got to the city, having drank almost 64-ounces of Coke. When he got to the scene afterward, personnel from the Coroners' Office were already there.

Lancaster patrol deputies had put up crime scene tape to secure a portion of the desert about two miles from where the hand was found. There were no paved roadways, only dirt roads created by off-road vehicles. Other than Challenger Middle School to the north and a Church of Latter-day Saints to the east, there were no other buildings nearby.

Rodriguez arrived about fifteen minutes later. He walked to a black and white patrol car where Gray and two uniformed deputies and a sergeant were waiting. One of the deputies was responsible for the crime scene log. The other deputy and Gray, having already been briefed, brought Rodriguez up to speed while the sergeant just stood around with his thumb up his ass.

After the briefing was concluded, one of the deputies escorted Rodriguez and Gray to the center of a thirty-by-thirty-foot area surrounded by four dirt roads. There were footprints and tire tracks interwoven in all directions, a disappointing confirmation of the apathy of humankind. It was obvious that other people had seen the remains at some point and never bothered to alert the authorities.

"I think we found Mr. Bledsoe, Bobby."

Gray touched his Star of David as he nodded and looked skyward, seeking an answer from a higher power. He closed his eyes before looking back down at the devil's reply.

On top of a raised portion of sand and dirt just east of a Joshua tree were the skeletonized remains of the lower half of a body. Clad in blue jeans, the entire left leg was present throughout the pant leg, ending with the left foot in a blue Nike tennis shoe. The right shoe was close to the empty right pant leg. The right femur and the ilium, ischium, and pubis bones were a few feet away from the pants. Various other foot and arm bones and a sock containing more foot bones were scattered about in the area.

The upper half of the torso was in a prone position about twelve feet away from the lower half, a tan shirt keeping most of the bones in place. A few ribs bones were close to both halves. The skull was all but obliterated, with numerous pieces spread out not far from the upper torso.

A portion of a jawbone with teeth intact was found a foot or two away; a piece of a human scalp with hair still attached about forty yards from there. Wild dogs and coyotes had fought over the body, pulling it in opposite directions, engaged in a grotesque game of tug of rope until the body split in two while Turkey vultures patiently waited until daylight.

"You see that, Bobby?"

"What? Oh, yeah. There's something shiny on the ground."

Gray walked closer and squatted like a baseball catcher.

"What is it?" Rodriguez asked.

"It's an earring. A small one with a fake diamond in a barbell."

"Same description as the jewelry on Bledsoe's missing person's report."

"That's right, Marty. The same goddamned description."

Gray was solemn as he took everything in. His father had died when he was just six years old. He worked menial jobs instead of concentrating on school to help his mother, who had almost been broken by the death of her husband. Gray felt that he had to help, even if he was only a child. This need that he had to try to always fix broken things had followed him into adulthood. He didn't know anything about Tony Duane Bledsoe, but something deep inside told him that Bledsoe had spent his entire life as a broken thing in need of fixing.

Darkness was quickly approaching. Although the Sheriff's Department had an Emergency Operations Bureau equipped with several motor homes and portable stadium lighting, it made more sense to conduct a search of the area and excavate the remains during optimal daylight hours. The decision was made to have uniformed deputies hold the scene overnight.

With no confirmed identification, the Coroner's Office designated the remains as John Doe #2009-160. It was merely a formality. Rodriguez and Gray were 99-percent sure of who it was. They didn't want to wish death on anyone, but they needed it to be Bledsoe. Otherwise, they had an even bigger problem in Lancaster.

CHAPTER NINETEEN

THE MOOD IN the car was somber the next morning.

"What do you think, Marty?"

"About what?"

"Life. And death. I mean what's the point? And what do you think happens when you're dead? No one fucking knows if there is an afterlife or if angels and demons are real. But just because it can't be proven, it doesn't mean they don't exist. If a motherfucker truly believes in them, maybe they can become a reality to them if not to anybody else. You believe that Marty?"

Most of the time, Rodriguez would blow Gray off when he started getting philosophical. However, this time, based on what had happened to the Bledsoe kid, he was reflective as well.

"I wish I knew, partner. We see so much shit that is just *so* fucking evil. I find myself often wondering that as well. What do you think?"

"Well, obviously no one knows. Ain't nobody coming back to tell the tale. My faith tells me there is *something* after death, though. But the way some of us act? Fuck. *Is* there something after? For all of us? Even the fuckers so evil they should never have been born? Or is it just an ending? Does it all just go black like the last episode of the Sopranos? Even *that* had people divided as to what really happened. I think most homicide dicks knew what that was about. When the lights go out, they go *out*, you know? I wonder what that poor kid in the desert was thinking right before his went out."

"Like you said, Bobby, we'll never know. My belief tells me there is something after death as well. And that's all we have. Our beliefs—whether it's your Star, or my crucifix, a Buddha, or a jamming ass choir at a Baptist church, or even fucking witchcraft, or Satanism, or Scientology—are all that we have, and that's gonna have to be enough. Even atheists. Their belief is *no* belief. But it's still a belief."

"True. But do you think death is random, though? Or is it divinity? You think it's all preordained, or is it random how we go?"

Rodriguez shrugged and turned on the CD player. He was tired of the conversation. Before long, he was lost in thought about the fickleness of life and death while listening to the *Greatest Hits of Journey*, one of his all-time favorites.

THEY GOT TO THE SCENE AT 7:45 A.M.

The Coroner's Office had sent out a full SRT team consisting of a scene investigator, Indiana Bones and his handler, a criminalist, a forensic anthropologist, and two students working on their degrees in forensic anthropology. Clearly out of their league, Rodriguez and Gray stood by solemnly while the people with all the letters behind their names did their thing.

The team found more bones and skull fragments as they sifted through the sand. The skull was all but destroyed, but one of the larger pieces bore the unmistakable sign of murder: a bullet hole.

The remains were positively identified on September 14. In a process known as "re-hydration," a saline solution was inserted by syringe into the fingers of the found hand, which caused them to take shape and expand. The fingers were then rolled in ink, and the prints put into the Automated Fingerprint Identification System. Two hours later, the identity of John Doe #2009-160 was confirmed, leaving 159 bodies in L.A. County still unidentified.

"HOMICIDE, RODRIGUEZ SPEAKING. CAN I HELP YOU?"

An hour after Bledsoe was identified, Rodriguez was sitting at his desk when his phone rang. Gray was standing next to the wall behind him, supporting himself with one hand while he held one of his shoes under an electric shoe buffer.

After listening for a few seconds, Rodriguez said, "Okay. Not exactly earth-shattering news, but at least we can put a face to the body now. More importantly, we don't have a serial killer running around in the desert. That we know of, at least. Thank you very much for the update."

Rodriguez hung up and sighed.

"Bledsoe, right?" Gray asked as he switched shoes.

"Damn you're a smart motherfucker, Bobby."

"No shit. I coulda' told you that."

Rodriguez sighed again, picked up his phone, and dialed.

"Missing Persons. Detective Fine speaking."

"Hey, Denise. It's Marty. Our John Doe in Lancaster was just positively identified as Bledsoe."

"No shit, huh? Thanks for letting me know. You guys got any leads?"

"Nah, not yet."

"Bummer. Well, good luck on the case."

"Thanks, Denise."

Rodriguez hung up, stuck a toothpick in his mouth, and squinted.

"I guess there's no need for a missing person's bulletin now, huh Marty?"

Rodriguez chewed on the toothpick and said, "We need to find the report that Lancaster deputy was supposed to have written. What's his name again?"

"Who? You mean Bumpus? He works OSS up there."

"Bumpus? What kinda' name is that?"

"I don't fucking know, Marty."

"Well, can you please call him?"

"Gimme a minute. I'm almost done with this shoe."

A few seconds later, Gray picked up his desk phone and dialed.

"Lancaster Station. Can I help you?"

"This is Sergeant Gray from Homicide. I'm trying to get ahold of OSS Deputy Bumpus. He's not? Okay. Can I leave my name and number for him? Thanks."

Gray hung up and turned to Rodriguez.

"He's off today."

"Fuck it. Let's go eat. How about a steak from Corina's? My treat."

"Oh, my god. He has a conscience after all."

"What are you talking about?"

"You think I didn't smell steak on your breath that day you were late to Lancaster? As fucking tight as you are, the only way you're offering to pay is because of a guilty conscience."

"Just the perks of being your daddy, my friend. You are right, though. Those Jack in the Box wrappers on your front seat had me feeling kinda' bad. But I got you today, Bobby G-Ray."

As they were leaving the building, Detective Fine was in her office pulling out her Bledsoe case file. She marked, "Closed, MP found dead" on a supplemental report and put it in a basket for supervisor approval. Then, she went to "Case Assignment" in her computer and cleared her portion of the case as, "Solved, MP located. Case transferred to Homicide."

GRAY AND RODRIGUEZ GOT IN EARLY THE NEXT DAY.

They wanted to talk to the graphic artist about preparing a "Murder—Information Wanted" poster for Bledsoe. Just before noon, Gray's cell phone rang as he and Rodriguez were heading out the door to grab lunch.

"Oh, hey Deputy Bumpus. My partner and I caught the found remains case in Lancaster. We're looking for a supplemental report you wrote for a Missing Person's case back in March. We can't find it. The found remains have been identified as—what? Yeah? Did you ever fax it over? You don't remember? Well, give me the reader's digest version. Uh, huh. Uh, huh. Cool. Thanks, Deputy."

Gray ended the call and put his phone back into the holder on his waistband.

"What was that all about, Bobby?"

"Shit for brains never even wrote a report until June 29th."

"Did he say anything good?"

"No. Only that he contacted some people who live on Lingard Street, and none of them knew anything about what happened to Bledsoe. He listed their names and DOBs in the report."

Rodriguez looked at his watch.

"Let's go to King Taco in East L.A. for lunch. My treat again."

"Oh, fuck you. You know fucking well they pop. But let's go! And don't stop at any red lights, ya *putz*."

"Relax, partner. What's the hurry? You just remember to grab your gun before we get out of the car. A toothless sheepdog ain't no good to nobody."

SEPTEMBER 17

It was 8:50 a.m., and Tony Bledsoe's autopsy was about to begin. Rodriguez had court, so Gray went alone. There were at least six other bodies in the room—which smelled like someone had put decomposing flesh, urine, feces, and rotting fruit into a blender and made a smoothie. Gray stood near the table bearing Bledsoe's remains, listening to two pathologists discuss the likely cause of death in medical terms. Gray had no idea what they were talking about but knew they would break it down for him in layman's terms when they were done. As he listened, he looked at Bledsoe, his skull a jigsaw puzzle put together without using the corner and edge pieces first.

Gray was with Rodriguez the first time he ever attended an autopsy. Rodriguez told him to take note of everything and listen to whatever the pathologists said. Rodriguez knew everyone at the morgue. The men joked with him, and the women smiled at him. He was a regular fucking rock star in the house of the dead.

After seeing all the bodies lying on stretchers, Gray thought about his father as he walked past all the bodies on stretchers lining the walls outside of the autopsy room. Born Heinrich Graubart, he was Jewish and had escaped to the United States in 1936 amid the rising antisemitism movement in Poland. When Gray's grandfather was killed in a concentration camp, his father changed his first name to Henry, and the family name to Gray Beard—English for Graubert—which he later shortened to Gray.

As Gray listened to the sounds of the autopsies and looked at the bodies in waiting, he imagined that brutal Nazi doctors may have operated on his people the same way, albeit for different purposes. The sounds were eerie, each one coming together to form a creepy consonance; the intermittent cracking of ribcages and buzz saws peeling caps as flying bone chips stuck face shields worn by the pathologists, who at times whistled, hummed, and even talked to themselves as they went about their business. The pathologist assigned to Rodriguez and his case was cordial with him but elated to see Rodriguez, and they talked about sports with a sprinkling of gallows humor while a portable radio played classical music in the background.

Bledsoe's autopsy was the first one Gray attended without Rodriguez. He meshed imperfectly with the two pathologists assigned to the case, bragging about his Super Bowl winning NY Giants while they discussed what they were doing as calmly as if they were talking about a play on Broadway.

It was a fairly short autopsy. In addition to brain removal, a normal autopsy consists of the decedent's torso being cut open, known as a "Y-incision," before all the organs are removed, examined, and then put back into the body. Bledsoe had no organs left, and his remains were skeletonized. Twenty-five fragments of skull had been found, but a partial reconstruction the day before the autopsy had revealed at least four penetrating gunshot wounds and four perforating wounds. There was also damage to a portion of the base of the skull, as if it had been struck with an object.

The cause of death was ruled a homicide, with the manner of death due to gunshot wound to the head. Sometimes, death by gunshot wound is formally listed as exsanguination, a fancy way of saying that the deceased simply bled out because of holes in his or her body.

Based on the condition of Bledsoe's skull, the weapon had been huge, likely a .44 or a .50 caliber. Only one gunshot wound to the head is necessary to kill. Even a .22 caliber bullet, which is the smallest available, would have been sufficient. Bledsoe didn't have time to bleed out. The first shot almost blew his head completely off. The next shots would have been into whatever was left as he lay lifeless on the desert floor.

Whoever killed Tony Duane Bledsoe, aka Cat Eyes, was a monster.

PART FOUR

CHAPTER TWENTY

"NOTHING STOPS A BULLET like a job."

It was the last part of 2006, and David Ponce had just reiterated the motto of Homeboy Industries to a beautiful teenager named Tatsuo Hitomi. Father Gregg Boyle stood next to him, smiling with his arm around his shoulders.

"That's right, David. Nothing stops a bullet like a job," Boyle said before turning to Tatsuo, a receptionist at the organization. "David just got out of prison. He's turned his life around and now wants to live right, a saintly life of good, if you will. And I need you to train him for his new job."

She smiled and extended her hand to Ponce, staring at the words *Nut* and *Hood* tattooed on his face, each word beneath an eye. She tried not to make it obvious, but she couldn't help herself. She knew what it meant when gang members tattooed the name of their gang on their face. He put her at ease by smiling back and shaking her hand.

He was a rough-looking man, with the typical appearance of the many street gang members whom she had grown up around. She had expected him to be gruff when he shook her hand, to squeeze it tightly so that he could show her how strong he was. Instead, he shook it delicately, as if he was handling something precious.

"Nice to meet you, Tatsuo," he said, looking into her eyes and holding her hand until she pulled it away. His voice was totally at odds with his appearance. It was high-pitched and whiney, almost as if Mike Tyson was just hitting puberty. She couldn't help but notice his eyes, the tattoos on his face a neon sign advertising their sublimity.

"Nice to meet you, too, David."

Tatsuo knew that Nut Hood had to be a gang, but she had never heard of it. She had grown up in the White Fence and 18th Street gang areas, two of the largest and fiercest Mexican gangs in L.A.

She didn't know if Ponce had turned his life around or not, but she knew that this *mekishiko hito gyangusuta,* as her mother called Mexican gang members, had more on his mind than learning how to answer phones. She had seen the same look in the eyes of other men too many times to count. Ponce asked her out on a date the very next day.

"I don't date people I work with," she said to him.

"Oh, c'mon baby. You don't really mean that, do you? There's gotta be another reason. Is it 'cause I'm older than you?"

"You don't even know how old I am."

"You're right. But I know you not old as me. What are you? Eighteen? Nineteen?"

"Seventeen. How old are you?"

"I'm twenty-seven. But that don't mean shit. Age ain't nothing but a number."

"I don't care how old you are. I've dated older guys before. I just don't want to date anymore gangsters. The last one I dated stole a car and I got caught in it with him. I went to juvenile hall for a whole year. And Father Gregg might think you're getting out of gang life, but as long as you have your hood blasted on your face, you're still in it. It doesn't matter what *you* think. The only thing that matters is what everyone *around* you thinks."

"It's for real," Ponce said. "I don't bang no more. Let me have your phone number."

"Nope," she said, her desk phone ringing. "Especially not while you have that on your face. And get back to work. I need this job."

She picked up the receiver and said, "Homeboy Industries. Can I help you?" as she watched Ponce smile at her and walk away. When she got home after work, she found his phone number in her purse, next to her wallet containing her grocery money.

David Ponce was exactly the type of man her mother had always warned her about.

She knew that her mother was right, but Tatsuo was attracted to him, perhaps *because* he was that kind of man. When she saw his number, she smiled. She could have just thrown it away, just like he could have stolen her money. She would have never known. *Maybe he isn't all bad,* she thought. *One call can't hurt.* The one call became several, and eventually she agreed to go out with him.

Ponce usually wore oversized trousers that sagged off his buttocks, and either brown or traditional L.A. Dodger baseball caps. But on their first date, he was dressed in a long-sleeved collared shirt, freshly starched pants, and clean sneakers. If the gang tattoo hadn't been on his face, he would've looked like any other law-abiding citizen.

He opened the car door for her before getting into the driver's seat. The car reeked of marijuana, and she counted at least ten smoked blunts in the ashtray. She didn't have a problem with it, though, especially since she smoked as well.

"What's Nut Hood? Is that your gang?" she asked as she buttered a slice of bread from the basket on the table. They were in a booth at the rear of a dimly lit restaurant with soft opera music playing. Their booth was close to a large window that offered a spectacular view of the scenic L.A. skyline, an ignis fatuus concealing the human suffering and wanton violence of a city that averaged over five hundred murders every year.

"Was, Tatsuo. *Was* my gang. I used to be from Varrio Nuevo Nut Hood Watts, hundred and eleven clique."

"Boy, is that a mouthful. I'm glad you didn't get all *that* on your face."

Ponce noticed one of the other diners staring at them. The diner quickly averted his eyes when Ponce looked at him. Most of the people in the restaurant were white. Still, Tatsuo was pleased that they chose this location to dine. She knew that there was little chance of them running into a rival gang member here.

Ponce turned back to Tatsuo and smiled. "For reals? Oh, you got jokes, huh? But listen, I really have turned my life around, Tatsuo."

"That's what you say. I know you have a hood name. What is it?"

"Why?"

"Just curious."

"Saint. Big Saint," he said, a hint of pride in his voice as if letting a crowd of fight fans know that he was champion and not challenger.

"Saint? Why Saint?"

"If I had my choice, it woulda' been Clown. I fucking love 'em. Not the happy ones. I love the scary ones, like the one in that movie who used red balloons to get the little kids down in the drain."

"You mean Pennywise from *It*."

"Who?"

"The clown. His name was Pennywise. And it was a TV series based on a Stephen King book."

"For reals? Okay, okay, okay."

"You forgot to tell me why your hood name is Saint."

His attention was suddenly drawn to the skyline, shining like jewels in a dragon's lair, a direct contrast to the horridness he had grown up in. He didn't belong in a fine restaurant like this, with rich fucking mummies eyeballing him. Tatsuo's question had flung him back to the drive-by shootings and gang fights, the only thing close to jewels being broken beer and wine bottles glistening under red and blue lights of cop cars. That was where he belonged. He belonged to what lay beneath the facade, the evil stretching from vast metropolises to small neighborhoods to the prison system, where he had earned a nickname that Tatsuo didn't yet know—Bloodbath—due to his participation in numerous prison gang wars.

"David? Are you okay?"

"Wassup?"

"You were about to tell me how you got your hood name."

"That's right. Sorry. It's 'cause of my brother, Danny Boy. He was a big OG. I did my share of dirt, no doubt. But they said that back in the day he was so ruthless that I was a saint compared to him."

"I hope you ain't too much of a saint."

"Why? I thought you said you was done with gang bangers."

"I am. But I still like guys with a little edge. Girls like bad boys."

"Yeah? It's like that?"

"*Just* like that."

"Okay, okay I feel you. But on the for reals? I'm never going back to prison."

"I'll believe that when you get that tattoo taken off your face. That's the only reason these fucking people keep looking at you."

"I'm getting it off the first chance I get. I swear. Even though it's supposed to hurt like hell, according to Father Gregg. Well, he ain't say it like *that*, you know."

They both laughed at his verbal faux pas. Tatsuo found herself attracted to Ponce. He was funny, and had an undeniable charisma. She knew he had done things in the past, probably violent things. He had an aura of danger about him, but she felt strangely comfortable and safe with him.

"Why'd you get it, anyway?" she asked.

"Dumb. Stupid. I got it in prison. I did six years for possession of crack for sale. That's a lot of down time. Most of the time I just read. And fought a lot. I also rapped. My stage name D-Nutt."

"Stage name? Boy, please."

"For real, girl. I got mad skills."

"If you say so," she said.

"If you be nice to me, I might freestyle for you later," he said as he smiled and reached across the table, taking one of her hands into his. She grabbed the glass of Coke sitting in front of her, now a mixed drink after Ponce poured some of his rum in it when the waiter wasn't looking.

I'm feeling this dude, she thought, smiling back at him coquettishly and peering over the glass before taking a sip.

"Anyway," she said as she put the glass back on the table. "As far as getting the tattoo removed, it'll be for the best, believe me. No more stares. No more *vatos* from other neighborhoods challenging you. I just can't deal with all the drama that comes with gang life. That's how I met Father Gregg. He came to juvie to talk to all the girls, mostly the *cholas* and *tintas*. He gave everybody business cards and told us to get in contact with him if we ever needed anything."

"I like Father Gregg, I really do. I think he trying to do the right thing, you know? But enough about him. Let's talk about you. I really don't know much about you. A phone conversation ain't like looking in somebody's eyes when you rapping with them, you know?"

"True. Well? Let's rap."

"Okay. First off, I ain't never seen no Asian as dark as you. What you mixed with?"

"My father is Black, and my mother is Japanese. I never met my father, though. I think he must have been in the military and met my mother when she was living in Okinawa. He brought us back to the United States and left us. I was so young I don't even remember him."

"That's fucked up, Tatsuo."

"My mom was strict about my schooling. I was in private school a lot. During the summer, she would take me to Okinawa. Her family called me *burakku utukushi.*"

"What does that mean?"

"Black beauty."

"Yeah, I can definitely see that."

"I learned a lot about Japanese customs whenever I visited. I loved it there. I had a couple of uncles who loved bonsai trees. They would prune and mist them with just enough water so they wouldn't drown, speaking to them in whispers at the same time. It was like they were making love to them. They treated them better than their wives!"

They were still laughing when the waiter walked up and took their orders. The meals were expensive, but Tatsuo didn't think to ask Ponce how he could afford such a restaurant nor whose car he had picked her up in. Maybe it was because she truly didn't want to know. What she did know was that he wouldn't be able to afford this restaurant on what they made at Homeboy Industries.

"I love those trees to this day," Tatsuo said when the waiter left. "Sometimes I miss that place. Everything was so peaceful, you know?"

"No. I don't, baby. I ain't never know'd no peace."

The mood at the table suddenly changed. Ponce grew pensive, looking back out the window. The beautiful skyline beckoned, eye-fucking him.

Tatsuo waited patiently, trying to get into his head, trying to guess exactly what he was thinking of as she looked at him and ate in silence. Despite his grim persona, she found him ruggedly handsome. She surmised that he had never had a problem getting female companionship. He was medium-complected with a shaved head, a neatly trimmed mustache, and a goatee surrounding Cupid's bow lips. He made her nervous; not a fearful type of nervousness, more like a desire to please type.

She had no way of knowing then that Ponce was beholden to his life of crime, both in and out of prison. Being a *sureño*, if one of the Big Homies, also known as *carnales,* or "made men," tasked him with committing a crime, he had to do it. There was no compromise. Do it or die. It was the goal of every *sureño* to become a made man. It was not an easy thing. A person wasn't even considered a prospect until they had murdered someone at the behest of a *carnale.* Even being related to one wasn't enough. But once made, you were untouchable.

Tatsuo straightened her skirt, smoothing it out on her legs. She normally wore pants, or jeans, but she had wanted to make a good impression. Or maybe it was because she knew she had amazing legs, and she wanted the bad boy to see them. Her head was spinning from the rum and Coke and the blunt they had shared in the car. She suddenly felt giddy and shy, like a schoolgirl, but not the kind her mother had always wanted her to be.

When Ponce turned back from the window, he looked at her, holding her gaze. His eyes were beautiful, like ballerinas in brown leotards, but for a brief second, they slowly morphed into stagnant, mosquito infested ponds. Tatsuo had an uneasy feeling until he smiled, the creases around his eyes softening them, making them dance again.

"How'd you and your mom end up in the hood?" he asked.

"I don't really know. As far back as I can remember, that's where we lived. She didn't want me to hang out with anyone in the neighborhood. All she wanted me to do was go to school. She would always tell me how she didn't want me to end up like her."

"Sounds like your moms was trying to do right by you."

"She was, but I didn't look at it like that then. I know she worked hard to pay for those private schools, but I just wanted to be like everyone else. I don't know how many fights I had with the *cholas* picking on me, calling me 'slant-eyes' and a 'Japanese nigga.' But I never backed down."

Ponce smiled. He was Pennywise now, holding out a balloon.

"Whaaaat? You was scrapping with the homegirls, huh?" he asked.

"I did what I had to do, you know? I got my respect, so I started dating one of the homies in the neighborhood. And you know how that turned out. My mom kicked me out of the house after I did my time in juvie, and I was homeless for a little while. But then I called Father Gregg, and here we are."

"Yep. Here we are," Ponce said as he slid around in the booth. Tatsuo blushed, a warm tingling sensation going through her body as he brushed up against her bare leg.

"But what about you, stranger?" she asked, trying to get her mind on something else. "Tell me about your life. How did you end up living in Long Beach?"

"My moms live in Long Beach. I had moved out and was living on Linden Street before I went to prison. When I got out, I moved back with her. It's just temporary, though, until I get back on my own two feet."

"Yeah. You and me. Survivors, right?"

"Hell yeah, baby. Hell yeah. How come you and your mom never moved back to Okinawa?"

"She always told me that she didn't want to, but I think she didn't go back because I was half-Black. Some of the elders on the island are pretty racist."

"Well, I'm glad they are."

"Why? Why would you say that?"

Ponce grabbed her chin and kissed her. It was just a short kiss on the lips, but it was electric while at the same time warm, and gentle. The ballerinas were dancing again as he looked at her caramel-colored face, a deep cleft in her chin only adding to her pulchritude.

"Because I would've never met you," he said before kissing her again.

By September of 2007, Tatsuo was pregnant.

She and Ponce were now living together in Boyle Heights, within walking distance of their jobs. Father Gregg knew the owner of an apartment building and had written a letter in support of Tatsuo moving in.

Before she got pregnant, Ponce was doing well. He was working, staying home with her, and had even started the painful process of getting his face tattoo removed. After she shared what she thought would be wonderful news with him, he changed almost overnight.

"You're gonna be stuck with me forever now!" he said. "You can't go anywhere! That's my baby in your stomach!"

At times, it was almost like he was three different people: the loving and caring future baby daddy, the hardened gang member, and the scared little boy trying to be something that he wasn't. But the *sureño* in him was in control of them all. He became abusive, and violent, something she never would have dreamed of him being—at least not with her. He would take her car and often stay gone for two or three days at a time.

She was nine months pregnant when she found out he was cheating on her. When she confronted him, he slapped her. She got a nasty cut on her knee as she braced herself to keep from falling on her stomach.

"I could have lost the baby!" she screamed at him.

"I don't fucking care. I told you I gotta go to a hood meeting. This life is driving me nuts. I can't do this. The hood needs me."

Tatsuo hated the hood meetings. They were supposed to be for discussing potential new members, rivalries, and finances, but the gang members just passed hood rats around, drank alcohol, smoked blunts, and played with guns. Ponce had taken her once, and that had been more than enough. Despite his promise that he had stopped gang banging, he got even deeper in it after they moved in together.

"Well can you please leave the stuff for the baby in case it comes while you're gone?" Tatsuo pleaded as she crawled on the ground. He opened the car trunk and threw a car seat, a stroller, and baby formula at her before driving off while she scrambled to grab the formula as it rolled toward the drain.

Ponce may have at one time tried to get his facial tattoos removed, but it was all for show. He was still Big Saint, leaving Tatsuo to wonder if jobs truly did stop bullets. He often threatened her and told her that if she ever tried to leave, his homies would find her and kill her. "You belong to me now, bitch!" became his mantra, and Tatsuo was terrified of him.

She often felt like she wanted to leave, but she didn't want to give up the respect that someone like Ponce commanded and the fear that he instilled in most people. No one dared touch her. She had found a twisted version of protection in him, perhaps even the father figure she'd never had. She would not let go of this feeling of comfort easily, so she endured the abuse and the disrespect. Now, trapped in a self-imposed prison because she believed she had no one else and nowhere to go, David Ponce became her everything, her ride-or-die, her endgame.

CHAPTER TWENTY-ONE

NOVEMBER 1, 2008

David Ponce and his companion were forcing Sammy across the 405 Freeway on-ramp at gunpoint. The darkness and fog surrounding the three men was thick and enveloping, encircling them like the interior of a casket as they crept into Frederick's encampment.

After walking past two bicycles lying on a dirt pathway, Sammy stopped a foot or two away from a plastic bag containing a cup warning of nightmares coming alive. He pointed at one of three tents that had a dim glow emanating from inside and said, "I think that's the one they're in now."

Ponce's companion put his gun to Sammy's head and forced him to walk to the tent. Kat was sitting near the entrance hitting a pookie. LV and Vanessa were sitting further inside, waiting their turns. Ponce stuck his face into the tent and smiled.

"Wassup, muthafuckas? I told y'all I'd be back with the full fit."

Using his 9mm like a baton to set the upcoming tempo, Ponce put it underneath Kat's chin. As she blew out the smoke from the last hit of meth she would ever take, Ponce began his murderous musical arrangement. A sonata of heat and flames caused a vertical burn on Kat's neck. The bullet penetrated her chin and perforated the top of her head. Vanessa screamed as Kat's dead body collapsed on her lower legs. Ponce then unleashed a barrage of gunfire, striking Kat and Vanessa multiple times in their upper torsos, faces, and heads as LV watched.

Ponce's companion had instantly executed Sammy at the sound of the first gunshot. Numerous crows took flight from the rooftop of the Kohler building, a chorus of caws joining the gunshots and screams as Sammy fell dead. Ponce's companion then turned to Frederick's tent and shot Frederick several times, that elusive white peacock finally appearing.

Ponce had saved LV for last. He was rooted in fear, his face as white as Ponce's, his eyes wild with fear and the realization that his ride-or-die had been massacred right in front of him, their endgame upon them.

"Please, Saint! Please, God! No!"

He had lied to Vanessa. He'd known the man's name all along. But he couldn't tell her that she had literally cursed out death that day when Lucky came calling.

Those eyes, he thought as the Pale Rider dismounted. *Who the hell could forget those eyes. Everybody in the game knows Saint. He is a stone-cold killer. But I had no beef with him. I only had beef with Lucky. Unless it had to do with that other vato I testified against—*

LV never even heard the shot that ended his life. Ponce then shot him three more times in the chest, face, and throat before finishing with another shot to his head. Then, in the thickening odor of sulfur and blood, Ponce waved his conductor's baton one final time, shooting Kat in the head again, completing his sanguineous symphony.

It was the last part of September 2009.

Sergeant Rodriguez was sitting at his desk reviewing Tony Bledsoe's autopsy report. He already knew the mode and manner of his death, so he went to the investigator's notes. Bledsoe had been homeless, and the product of a failed foster care situation. The notes indicated that he had possibly been involved in some type of sexual abuse situation and that his foster care providers had just moved away without providing an address.

There was no next of kin information listed. Without it, Bledsoe would probably end up in an unmarked grave at the county cemetery. Rodriguez was the product of a broken home, born and raised in East L.A., home to the notorious Maravilla gangs. He very well could have ended up in a similar situation. *There but for the grace of God*, he thought before getting back to the task at hand. He tried to concentrate, but his mind kept drifting. He truly was lucky. He had a great wife, a beautiful home, and two daughters that he adored.

Rodriguez had taken up golfing to get his mind off the job when he wasn't at work. He enjoyed smoking a cigar and walking the greens to clear his mind of the carnage he frequently witnessed at work. He didn't care about his score or a handicap. He just loved the serenity of the course. It didn't even matter if he left chunks of grass and divots everywhere. The beauty of the greens took him away from the stench of death and the wails of the victim's loved ones during death notifications.

His partner, Gray, found other ways to escape. He often watched the NY Giants and the Mets or went deep-sea fishing, but his greatest peace of mind came from playing with Bandit on the beach. Although he and Rodriguez had totally different ways of dealing with the horrors of the job, the results were the same. Zen was zen, whether throwing a Frisbee to a rescue-dog or chopping at a little white ball in a sandpit.

They caught their first murder together in September of 2008. It was related to a case Rodriguez picked up about six months before he started breaking in Gray. He solved it with the help of an eyewitness, who Rodriguez then relocated for his safety.

Unlike the federal law enforcement agencies who have enough resources and money to move witnesses to a hamlet in another country and buy them a cottage and an electric car, local law enforcement agencies can move you to another city, at best, and give you enough money for chili-cheese fries twice a week. And that is exactly what Rodriguez had done with his witness, who saw a gang-related murder in Compton, and was slated to testify.

Rodriguez had told him repeatedly, "Stay the fuck out of Compton! You hear me? Stay the fuck out of Compton!" So, quite naturally, the witness went back to Compton.

It had been Detective Rich Tomlin who called Rodriguez from the desk with the notification. Tomlin was one of the most likeable investigators at the Bureau. He had a lot in common with Detective McGuire. They were both small Black men who were outstanding investigators in an assignment not known for its diversity.

"Sergeant Rodriguez."

"You and your new guy got one, Marty."

"What's up, Rich? Where, and what are the circs?"

"Two MWG's domed your victim at a Mexican bar at 108 East Rose-crans. The body is still at the scene. Suspects are in the wind."

"Okay. Has the victim been identified yet?"

"Yeah. A Mexican guy. Name of Raul Gonzalez."

"What? Is that with an *s* or a *z*?"

"A *z*."

"Son of a bitch! That's my fucking witness! I told him to stay the fuck out of Compton! Has my partner been notified?"

"One of the security officers already called him. He's on the way."

"Cool. Thanks, Rich."

Rodriguez had gotten to the scene first. When Gray arrived shortly afterward, they were briefed by the handling deputies. Rodriguez pulled out his light-blue notebook with *Los Angeles County Sheriff's Homicide* and a drawing of a bulldog stamped on the cover. He opened it and started writing as he listened to the briefing.

Every homicide case has a notebook. They contain notes and names, dates, addresses, possible witnesses, etc. In the wrong hands, the information could be catastrophic. Some cases would encompass up to three notebooks by the time they were concluded. Then, the notebooks would be put into poor boys and filed away in the Homicide library like the Ark of the Covenant at the end of the first *Indiana Jones* movie.

A titanium-colored sedan pulled up and an OSS detective got out. He was wearing the uniform of the gang unit: blue jeans, a green sheriff's raid jacket, boots, and a nylon gun belt with his gun hung low on his right leg, held in place by two nylon straps. Holding a Styrofoam cup filled with steaming coffee, he walked over to Rodriguez and Gray.

"I got a call from an informant about thirty minutes ago," he said. "Two guys, one shooter, both from the Flats."

"Thanks, partner," Rodriguez said. "Sounds about right. Take us to the scene."

"The defendant in your other case is Compton T-Flats, too, Marty?" Gray asked.

"Yes."

"Huge gang. Violent too. We're standing in the middle of their hood right now," the OSS detective said, seeking to demonstrate his knowledge of gangs. The goal of almost every OSS detective was to get promoted to Homicide, so they bent over backward to please Homicide personnel.

He walked Rodriguez and Gray into the bar where a man was lying on his back near a pool table, a huge pool of blood on the floor surrounding his head.

"That him, Marty?" Gray asked.

"Sadly, yes."

"Shit for brains didn't listen, huh?"

"I guess these guys can't stay away, Bobby. It's the game, and it's all they know."

Tucking his tie in his shirt so that it didn't fall into the coagulated blood and the serum separating from it, Rodriguez squatted next to the man and looked into his raccoon eyes.

"How many times did I tell you not to come back to Compton? Well look at you now, you dumb motherfucker. You just had to come back, didn't you? To the same neighborhood where the guy you were gonna testify against is from. You had about as much business in this bar as a canary in a coal mine. I *cannot* believe this."

"We got the perp's description, Marty?"

"Cut it out with that 'perp' crap," Rodriguez said as he stood up and straightened his tie. "You ain't in 'Joisy' no more. And yeah, we do. Two MWG's."

"Two MWG's, huh? Well, I guess celebrations are in order then. Two Mexicans with guns in a city with sixty-thousand other Mexicans with guns. Arrest is imminent."

Rodriguez squinted, chewed his toothpick, and turned to the OSS detective.

"Anybody see anything?"

"Yeah. The security guard had a problem with the suspects before the murder. I'll go get him."

Rodriguez and Gray smiled to put the guard at ease, lest he think they were going to call Immigration.

"Tell us what happened, partner," Rodriguez said.

Relaxed, now that he realized he was safe from having to show a green card, the guard told them everything he knew. Rodriguez was pleased that the guard spoke English. Although Rodriguez had grown up in East LA and was bi-lingual, he rarely spoke Spanish. His partner, son of a Jewishimmigrant and raised in New Jersey, spoke more than he did, though most of the words he used were profane.

According to the guard, the two suspects had tried to get into the bar, but one of them was drinking a bottle of beer. The guard told him he couldn't come inside with it, and he put it down in the parking lot. He and his companion then entered the bar and shot the suspect dead. At the mention of the beer bottle, Rodriguez stopped writing in his notepad. "Show it to me," he said.

The bottle was still standing upright in the parking lot where the killer had placed it. The CSI on the scene photographed it and collected it for evidence.

A month later, a DNA hit on a T-Flats gang member came back. He was the shooter. He and his companion were friends of the person that the murdered witness was set to testify against. Gray was elated that they had solved their first murder together, but Rodriguez was quick to temper his enthusiasm.

"Look, all the cases we catch aren't gonna be like this, Bobby. We're gonna catch some that we're never gonna solve. Just be prepared for that."

CHAPTER TWENTY-TWO

IT WAS LATE August of 2008.

Tatsuo and Ponce were watching TV in their apartment. She asked him a question and when he didn't answer, she looked at him. He appeared to be in a trance-like state, almost like he was possessed.

"David! Can't you hear me? Baby, what's happening? What in the hell is wrong with you?!"

Ponce laughed and turned in her direction. He fixed his eyes on something behind her. "You don't understand," he said. "The demons are here. They trying to get me. They want me to go with them."

"There's nothing there, babe!" Tatsuo said as she turned to see what he was looking at. "No one else is here! If this is a joke, I need you to stop right now! You're scaring me!"

And just then, he finally looked at her. His eyes were dead, the corneas without sparkle, the pupils oval and fixed. He was somewhere in between heaven and hell, a blind man in purgatory.

"The demons want me to go with them, Tatsuo."

"What are you talking about? You're scaring me!"

She shook him by the shoulders. He slid off the couch like a snake, his arms and legs contorting into the shape of a swastika as he lay on the floor. He stared at the ceiling, shaking like he was having a seizure.

"They're here, Tatsuo! They're here! They trying to get me!"

She screamed.

"I don't know what to do! I'm scared, David! I'm calling the paramedics! I'm dialing nine-one-one!"

"No, Tatsuo!" Ponce said, his eyes rolling back in his head before fixating on the ceiling again. "If you do that, the demons will never forgive you! It's gonna get worse! Don't do that!"

"What are you looking at, David? What do you see?"

"It's a black face, Tatsuo! It's the devil!"

And then, as quickly as it began, it was over.

"What happened, Tatsuo?"

She broke down and cried as he sat up and put his head in his hands.

"I don't remember anything, Tatsuo. That's what happens sometimes, though. I done a lot of bad shit in my life. It's something that niggas like me go through."

She launched herself into his arms and began rubbing his head, praying that nothing like that ever happened again. Prayers tend to often go unanswered, however. A little over two weeks later, she would witness something that chilled her to her bones.

MARCH 23, 2009

Ponce turned off the paved street and began driving down a dirt road. He stopped after several minutes and pulled his gun out. He pointed it at Bledsoe and said, "Get the fuck out my car, fool."

"Please, don't kill me! I swear on my mom's and grandma that I'll get yo' money!"

Bledsoe harbored hope up until this very moment that Ponce wasn't going to hurt him, but as he looked from the black hole of the gun barrel to his desolate surroundings, despair descended and he started begging for his life.

Ponce looked at the tears streaming down his face without remorse. The more Bledsoe begged, the more Ponce wanted to kill him. Still, he remained calm, using the same tone of voice throughout, almost as if he was ordering a drink from a waitress or asking someone out on a date. The gun barrel pointing at Bledsoe didn't generate fear in him as much as the voice behind it did.

"Dawg, get the fuck outta my car," Ponce said as he shoved the barrel into Bledsoe's stomach. When he didn't move quick enough, Ponce grabbed him by his shirt, spun him around in the seat and said, "I said get the fuck out." As Bledsoe was exiting the car, Ponce kicked him in the ass which caused him to fall to the ground. He got up and started walking with Ponce following, talking to him the entire time with the gun pressed into his back.

"Say yo' prayers, 'cause you gone, homie. Yo' ass is gone. You gonna meet yo' maker, and yo' mom? Like I said, you gonna see that bitch, homie. Believe that. She gonna slap the fuck outta you for being so fucking stupid."

"Please, Big Homie. Don't!"

"This is far enough," Ponce said when they got close to a knoll near a Joshua tree.

"Get on yo' knees."

"Please don't kill me! I swear I didn't know you were looking for me!"

"What did I say? Get on yo' fucking knees!" Ponce said as he hit Bledsoe at the base of his neck with the gun.

"Ahhhhh! Please, Saint! Come on, man!"

"I ain't playing with you. You better start praying. And don't call me Saint. My name Bloodbath."

With the sun lighting up the horizon and setting an ominous stage, here they were—Cat Eyes and D-Nutt—two wannabe gangster rappers about to provide real life lyrics tailor-made for a future hit song. Bledsoe started praying as tears streamed down his face. Ponce put the barrel flush against the back of his head and cocked the hammer. All it would take now was just four to five pounds of trigger pull on the most powerful handgun in the world.

True horror isn't jump scares, or shadows that can't touch you, or something unseen like a ghost or spirit. It doesn't come from the dead. It comes from the living. It is being on the side of a lonely road, no light except for the glint of the sun or the moon's reflection off the barrel of a gun or blade of a knife. True horror comes from things you can touch, things you can taste and smell like the iron in a river of blood, like the cordite in the air after a bullet is discharged.

As Bledsoe kneeled, praying to a God that had seemingly forsaken him, Ponce started counting:

"Eleven, for the hood. One eleven block."

What does someone with a gun to their head think about?

"Ten..."

The sun was turning the horizon blood-red. Beautiful under any other circumstances, it was ugly now, foreboding.

"Nine..."

It would be all over soon; a fade to black, like what happened to Tony in the last scene of the Sopranos.

"Eight...seven...six..."

What else did Bledsoe think of as he prayed for his life?

"Five..."

Did he think of the parents who didn't reciprocate the love he had for them, or the foster care providers who abandoned him? Or Rhonda, and the last kiss they shared?

"Four...three..."

Perhaps he just prayed for a better afterlife than the life he had lived.

"Two..."

Perhaps, even, he had simply welcomed a coming peace.

"One. You up, my nigga."

Bledsoe never heard the ignition of gunpowder that propelled a large piece of metal into his head. He was dead before his body began to move forward to its final resting place, his heart still beating because of the rapidity of his death. Ponce then fired three more shots at what was left of his head as he lay on the desert floor.

To kill someone is to lose a part of your humanity. If you kill enough times, you lose it all. Ponce knew this. His tattoos were a roadmap to his slow demise—a dragon, demons, devils, masked men committing crimes, women with looks of despair, and clowns with white faces and black circles around their eyes. They all finally led to a confirmed eradication of himself, a prominent tattoo of "In memory of David Ponce" on his chest.

It was his own epitaph to anything that had ever been good about him, punctuated by his affirmation to Bledsoe before beginning his countdown. He buried David Ponce, and anything close to a saint was as dead as Ponce and Bledsoe were. He had been many names in his life: Ponce, his father's surname; David, his given name and what Tatsuo called him; Saint, in tribute to his older brother, Danny Boy; Bloodbath, as bestowed on him by the Big Homies, and D-Nutt, stage name for a dream.

As he stood there admiring his handiwork, smoke slowly rising from the barrel of his gun, he now knew without question who he was. He thought about burying Bledsoe but decided that it was too much work. He grabbed the bottle of Cisco off the back seat of his car and looked down at his blood-stained Timberlands before taking a long swig. He had no idea that a little over six months before, a man with the same last name as his had been murdered just a little over a mile away in almost the same way as he had just murdered Bledsoe.

Lake Los Angeles truly was a place where dreams went to die.

CHAPTER TWENTY-THREE

IT WAS LATE September of 2008.

Tatsuo Hitomi and David Ponce were sitting on their living room couch watching TV when Ponce started mumbling. His body suddenly became rigid as he looked at her with his palms on his knees.

"The demons want me to hurt you, Tatsuo."

Ponce was looking at her, but she felt like he was looking *through* her. She covered her mouth to keep from screaming and ran into the bathroom. She locked the door and called 911, telling the operator that her boyfriend was having a seizure.

She stayed in the bathroom until firefighters and paramedics arrived. Ponce was on the floor, unresponsive and staring at the ceiling with his limbs splayed about. One of the paramedics asked Tatsuo, "What's going on with him? Is he on drugs or something?"

"No, he doesn't use drugs. All he does is smoke weed."

"Well, there's no way that this is from marijuana. He's on something else."

"No, he's not!" Tatsuo said.

Ponce gurgled as his eyes darted from side to side, the veins on either side of his neck bulging.

"You fucked up, Tatsuo! You got no idea what you did! You messed everything up! It's gonna get so much worse now!"

Ponce's body went rigid when the paramedics touched him. They restrained his arms, put a net mesh over his face, and took him to White Memorial Hospital in East L.A. Tatsuo called his mother and his closest sister. He was still in the same state when they arrived.

"Brother! Brother! It's me, David! It's me!"

Ponce's sister broke down crying when he didn't respond or look at her. Their mother was holding black rosary beads with a silver crucifix and a small figure attached to them. She moved the beads to her lips and made the sign of a cross over herself before making one over her son.

"Whatever evil is inside you I rebuke it! I rebuke thee!" she said. "Satan! Begone!"

Ponce immediately tried to sit up but the leather straps around his body held fast.

"Where am I? Mama? What you doing here? What happened?"

His mother and sister sobbed and huddled together, their hands wrapped around the rosary beads.

What Tatsuo was witnessing scared her more than any of the things Ponce had ever said or done to her. She had never seen anything like this before, but she had heard her relatives in Okinawa speak of similar things. They called them *bakemono*, which means "changing thing," or "beast." Tatsuo's mind raced; her thoughts were uncontrolled with one dominating the rest:

What the hell have I gotten myself into?

"Hello?"

It was the night of March 23, 2009. Whenever Tatsuo got a call and Ponce wasn't home, she always had mixed emotions and thoughts: *Is it the coroner's office making notification of his death? Or is it David, telling me to come and bail him out?*

"It's me, David."

"What's up, baby?"

"Guess who I saw right now?"

"Who?"

"You know who."

"Baby, what did you do?"

David Ponce was just leaving Bledsoe. He had finished off the bottle of Cisco and lit another blunt, but he was drunk and high off the blood.

"You know me, baby. I'm a fucking soldier!"

"What did you do, David? You have your bitch with you, don't you?"

"Yeah. I told you me and my bitch was gonna go to work tonight."

"Baby, are you okay?"

"Yeah, I'm cool. I'm on my way home. Don't trip. I'll be there soon."

"Alright," Tatsuo sighed. "Drive carefully."

PONCE PULLED UP TO THEIR APARTMENT COMPLEX AND PARKED.

He put the blunt out in the ashtray. After holding the smoke in for a few seconds, he blew out several smoke rings, savoring them as they hit the windshield and spread like sea fog rolling in on an early Long Beach morning. He pulled down the sun visor, looked at the mirror, and smiled. Then he flipped it back up, got out of the car, and walked into the love nest that he shared with Tatsuo, Room 101 of their very own Ministry of Love.

"Hey, David. What is that on your—?"

Tatsuo gasped as she realized that he had blood spatter and white specks on his face, clothing, and boots. She covered her mouth to keep from screaming when she realized that the specks were most likely brain matter. She loved Ponce, but she had long been frightened of him. The demonic possessions, the thing in Long Beach on Halloween, and now this, blood, and brains on their living room floor. She knew what he did whenever he put on those Timbs. She knew that someone was likely going to die, but she tried not to think about that.

"Plausible deniability," Ponce would tell her, bursting with pride at his retention of jailhouse learnings. "What you don't know, won't hurt you."

But tonight, it was all in her face. She didn't know it yet, but she was witnessing the aftermath of Ponce's rebirth and what he was capable of, the essence of someone's life leaving faint traces on the floor where their son played with his toys. Ponce grinned before walking into the bathroom and taking off his clothes. He put them into a black trash bag and doused them with bleach.

"I need some lighter fluid," he said as he turned on the shower. "And get me some baby oil, some more bleach, and a box of Q-Tips."

She quickly carried out his command, trying her best not to awaken their sleeping son.

"That fucking Cat Eyes was begging for his life, baby. I took him to the desert. He was swearing on his dead mama and grandma that he was gonna pay me back. I told him to start praying 'cause I was fixing to send him to meet them. Then I domed him."

He squirted the lighter fluid into the bag and let everything soak while he took a shower. Tatsuo looked in on their sleeping son. She wanted to go to him, to wake him and tell him that everything was going to be okay, to shield him from the monster with his DNA washing the stench of death from his body. Instead, she softly closed the door and went back into the living room.

She looked at her bonsai tree on a crescent moon table against the living room wall, her only connection to her mother's homeland. A huge, framed print of Scarface was on the wall above it. He was dressed in a disheveled tuxedo, smoke from the cigar in his mouth spiraling out of control, Tatsuo's life along for the ride.

The shower stopped running. Ponce walked into the living room, towel around his waist, water streaming down the faces of tattooed clowns laughing at her. He used the Q-Tips, baby oil, and bleach to clean his gun, polishing it to a shiny gleam before pouring more Ajax and bleach into the bag. He just wiped his Timbs off, though. They were his lucky crime boots.

He went into their bedroom and got dressed. Then he picked up the bag and walked into their son's room. He smiled and kissed him on the forehead as Tatsuo stood at the door, watching. "I'll be back," he said as he walked past her seconds later.

"Where are you going, David?"

Ponce stopped, tilted his head, and looked at her before lowering his eyes toward the bag he was holding. He then kissed her on her forehead in the same manner as he had kissed their son and left.

Tatsuo carried their still sleeping son to the living room and sat on the sofa. As tears streamed down her face, she looked again at the bonsai tree underneath the print of the vicious drug-dealer, safe in his world, having ascended to its heights by blood and murder. Then she looked at her sleeping son, catching an unfocused glimpse of death on the floor brought into their lives by his father. With the bonsai and idolatry of evil, it formed an unholy trinity, bridging a horrible juxtaposition of the beauty and ghastliness of her world and Ponce's.

IT WAS COLD, IN THE LOW FIFTIES.

The wind was biting, but the crisp air was refreshing to Ponce as he stood near Tatsuo's car, holding his bag. While coyotes and wild dogs were creeping toward Bledsoe's remains, he looked up at the sky, the brilliance of constellations on full display. The moon was in a waning crescent phase —just 10 percent of illumination—but with the shimmering night sky filled with stars, he would have more than enough light for what he needed to do.

The rising of the sun would bring the turkey vultures, patiently waiting as the four-legged predators had their fill of Bledsoe. Then, they would cautiously make their way to him and feed, a wake of buzzards feasting on the forlorn before returning to their nesting area where their young awaited the regurgitation of his bone chips. Unaware of the circle of life he had just set in motion, Ponce put the bag in the trunk of Tatsuo's car and set out for the other side of the desert, far away from Bledsoe, where he was going to set it on fire after digging a hole.

It was much easier to bury a bag than it was to bury a body.

CHAPTER TWENTY-FOUR

SEPTEMBER 16, 2009

"I'm getting tired of driving all the way up here, Marty," Gray said as he woke up, rubbing his temples. He had gone out drinking the night before to celebrate one of his friends getting promoted. Whenever someone got promoted, they sponsored something called a "buy-out," where all the drinks were on them. Gray had taken full advantage of the free drinks and was now paying the price.

"Tired? You slept the entire drive, dipshit!"

"Not so loud, Marty. Fuck!" Gray said, still rubbing his temples. "I'm serious, though. This is a long fucking drive. Maybe we should make the Bureau give us per diem, or pay for hotel rooms for us."

"The hell with that, Bobby. They would only pay for one room with double beds, and I ain't sleeping in the same room with your snoring ass. And what are you complaining about anyway? All you ever do is ride. And snore."

"Really? Your old lady never complains about it."

"You couldn't get to first base with my old lady, partner. She's got class."

"That she does. But class obviously wasn't in session the day she met you. Fuck, my head is killing me. Who we talking to today again?"

"Guy by the name of Salamanca. His first name is José. He was the first

172

person to file a missing person's report. The phone number he gave when he filed the report is no longer in service."

"You mean to tell me we drove all the way up here to interview one person? On a wing and a prayer?"

"It's called police work. Now you've been formally introduced."

"Kiss my ass, Marty."

"I called the other person who filed a missing person's report but no one answered. We"ll swing by her address next. Who'd you go out drinking with last night?"

"One of the guys I worked OSS with got promoted."

"Buy-out, huh? Those things can be dangerous. Just don't throw up in my fucking car."

"I ain't gonna throw up. You got any aspirin?"

"Yeah. Look in the glovebox. There should be a bottle of Excedrin in there."

Gray grabbed the bottle and swallowed two pills, washing them down with what was left of the cup of coffee he got before they left the office.

"We're here," Rodriguez said as he parked and pointed at a duplex a couple houses away. "He lives right there. In the front house."

There were several toys in the front yard. Gray rattled the chainlink fence surrounding it and waited. No dogs. The fence was for keeping kids corralled. A husky Mexican man with a shaved head, and numerous tattoos on his arms answered the door when Rodriguez knocked.

"Whassup? What y'all need?" he asked.

"Hello, sir. This is my partner, Sergeant Gray, and I'm Sergeant Rodriguez. We're from Sheriff's Homicide. José Salamanca, right?"

"Yeah. How'd you know?"

Gray was holding the paper-thin poor boy with his right hand. He never held anything in his left hand because it was his gun hand. It was something drilled into police recruits and cadets from the first day of the academy. If they were caught carrying something in their gun hand, they were punished with exercise and/or writing reports, which were called "gig papers." It was a lesson that cops heeded for the rest of their lives, both on and off duty. Gray patted the poor boy containing a photograph of Salamanca and said, "Lucky guess."

Salamanca looked up and down the street before inviting them inside. He closed the door, sat on the living room couch, and told them the tale of his friend Cat Eyes while the two detectives stood in the center of the room.

"We was at a barbecue. Cat Eyes left on his bike to go buy some weed, and he never came back. People say he just left his bike and got in a dark green car with tinted windows. But who the fuck does that? And then I heard talk that Cat Eyes owed money to a weed dealer who was friends with him and a *tinto* we both knew named Snake."

"José, can you describe the dealer?" Gray asked.

"Yeah. He a dark skint Mexican or a Samoan. Or he could be a *tinto* 'cause he sound like one when he talk. He ain't bald, though. He got hair. And he got tattoos on his face and a little size on him like he been to the joint before."

"Do you know him?"

"Not really, but I seen him before, and I heard him talk."

"Go on," Rodriguez said.

"Ain't nobody heard from Cat Eyes since that day. When I heard he left his bike and got in a car, I filed a missing person's report. I told them something bad happened to him way back then."

"Have you heard anything else?"

"Yeah. Word on the yard is that the weed dealer kilt him."

"Alright, José. By the way, did you tell the deputy who took the report all this?"

"Yeah, I told him. He act like I was bothering him."

"How do we get in contact with this Snake, José?" Gray asked.

José pulled out his cell phone and said, "I got a number for him. The cops talked to him already, too."

"You mind giving us *your* number, too?" Rodriguez asked. "The one we had for you is disconnected."

"No problem."

After leaving Salamanca's house, Rodriguez and Gray stopped by the address provided by Rhonda when she filed her missing person's report. When no one answered the door, Rodriguez left a business card while Gray called the number Salamanca had given them for Snake.

"It's out of service, Marty. We're gonna have to track this knucklehead down."

"It won't be hard," Rodriguez said as he headed for the Antelope Valley Freeway. "I'm sure he's been arrested before. We'll find him."

NOVEMBER 6, 2009

Rodriguez and Gray had discovered that Snake had a prior arrest for domestic violence. They went to the address listed for the victim. She was his ex-girlfriend and the mother of his children. Once again, they found themselves in Lancaster.

Rodriguez stopped in front of a house not far from some apartments surrounded by urban strip malls. A young Black woman with a gold tooth answered the door.

"Hello, ma'am. I'm Sergeant Rodriguez, and this is my partner, Sergeant Gray. We're investigating the murder of Tony Bledsoe."

"Who is that? You mean Cat Eyes?"

"Yes, ma'am. We mean Cat Eyes."

"Okay. C'mon in."

They walked in, careful not to step on the toys all over the floor. The smell of fried chicken overwhelmed the small home, the unmistakable sound of grease popping in a frying pan on a stove in the kitchen just a few feet from the front door.

"Something smells good," Rodriguez said.

"Oh, thank you! I just felt like cooking today. Tie'd of fast food, ya' know?"

"I do, ma'am. Nothing like a home-cooked meal."

The woman waved her arm toward a couch and said, "Have a seat, detectives."

"That's okay, ma'am. We'll stand. We've been sitting in the car for almost two hours," Gray said.

"Whatever. Suit yo'self."

"What can you tell us about Snake and Cat Eyes?"

The woman went into the kitchen to tend to her chicken. Gray took his notebook out of his back pocket and started writing just as a small child came running into the room.

"Boy, take yo' ass back in yo' room and play!" the woman said, shooing him away with a spatula. "I'm sorry, detectives. These damn kids gonna make me lose my fucking mind!"

"It's okay, ma'am," Rodriguez said. "I got a couple myself, and they can be a handful."

"You ain't never lied. Anyhow. Snake was friends with Cat Eyes. I ain't trying to be a snitch or nothing, but whatever happened to him was fucked up. Snake was also friends with another guy that er' body call 'the Mexican.' He been to our house a buncha' times. He had a dark car, maybe green. Him and Cat Eyes was in business together. I thank they was selling weed. When Cat Eyes went missing, I heard rumors that the Mexican was the cause. After some deputies came to my house axin' 'bout Cat Eyes, the Mexican stopped coming around. He ain't been back since."

"You talked to the cops already?"

"Yeah, Sahgent Rodriguez. Months ago."

"Humph. Months ago, huh?"

"Yep."

"Don't you think it was strange that the Mexican stopped coming by your house after that?" Gray asked.

"Don't you? You the detective. He at my house all the time, and when the cops come 'round axin' 'bout him and Cat Eyes, all'a sudden he never come back? Yeah. I thank that's very strange."

"Yes. It sure is," Gray said. "By the way, do you have any way to get in contact with Snake?"

The woman blew out a gust of air as she began removing chicken from the frying pan with the spatula.

"Well, he don't care 'bout his kids, so no," she said, putting the chicken on a large plate covered with a paper towel. "And good riddance. I was tied of that muthafucka putting his hands on me anyhow. But I got his sista's number. Will that help?"

"Yes, ma'am," Rodriguez said. "It sure will."

After getting the number, he gave her his business card before he and Gray left. Gray took his gun off his waistband and put it on the seat next to his leg as Rodriguez drove off.

"You ain't got no little kids anymore, *pendejo*. Why did you tell her that?"

"A means to an end, partner. She felt a connection with me after that. It's from the book of conversation. Pay attention. You might learn something."

"Well, if what you just did is in the chapter about lying, then I've already read it," Gray said before suddenly slapping himself in the forehead.

"Shit, Marty! Turn around! We gotta go back!"

"Stop hitting yourself in the head. No wonder you're so fucked up. Why do we need to go back? Don't tell me. You left your recorder."

"No, Marty! My notebook!"

Rodriguez sat in the car while Gray went into the house. A few minutes later, he came out with the notebook, and something wrapped in a paper towel. He opened the car door and got in, pushing his gun aside for more room.

"Shit, Marty. That was a close one," he said as he opened the paper towel and bit into a thigh. The grease was much-needed after the night he had.

"Ain't that a bitch? I compliment her on her food, and you get to eat it. Where's mine?"

"You see she's got kids. *Real ones*. She can't afford to be feeding your greedy ass, too."

"Oh, I see. You'll eat the woman's food, but you won't sit down in her house. You're fucked up, Bobby. By the way, did I ever tell you about that investigator who actually lost his fucking notebook?"

"No, what happened?" Gray asked, licking his fingers.

"Well, this guy, who shall remain nameless, was interviewing the girlfriend of a potential murder suspect at her house, jotting down her statement in his notebook. He and his partner leave after they wrap up the interview. When they get off work later that night, the guy who oversaw the wire room and phone taps calls the dick's partner and tells him that they heard a woman on a wire tell her boyfriend, 'One of the stupid detectives left his notebook at my house'. She then proceeds to read the contents to him.

"The boss of the wire room tells the detective that is how he knew who to call, because they heard her say his name. The detectives go back to her house and ask if she found a notebook. Of course, she says no, and the detectives can't let her know how they knew she had it without compromising the wire operation.

"Fast forward. Now, in addition to trying to catch murderers on the wire, the wire room personnel are tracking down this notebook. Turns out it had made its way into the hands of someone else possibly involved in the murder, a married man with kids. His conversations were also being monitored. One of those conversations consisted of him discussing homosexual exploits with another man. Wire room personnel contacted him and threatened to expose his hidden life unless he returned the notebook, which he did posthaste. Greatest case the wire room ever worked, courtesy of one dumb ass detective."

"Can you tell us what you know about the disappearance of Cat Eyes, ma'am?"

It was November 12, just a few days after the close call between Gray and his notebook. He and Rodriguez were in a small apartment on the outskirts of Lancaster. They were talking to Snake's sister, a petite, attractive young woman with purple and blue shoulder-length braids.

"My son was a good friend of Cat Eyes, Sahgent Rodriguez, just like Snake was. I ain't seen or talked to Snake in weeks. I remember the day Cat Eyes went missing, 'cause it was the day after my son's birthday. All the kids on the street was talking 'bout what happened. A few days later, rumors began spreading that Cat Eyes was dead. No one knew where he was, though. I told a deputy this way back then, but he was rude when I made the report."

"You made a report?" asked Gray.

"Hell yeah! And not only that, I seen Cat Eyes that day. I was on my way to my neighbor's house when I seen him riding his bike near Lingard. It was 'bout three o'clock. A dark green car with tinted windows cut him off. Cat Eyes straddled his bike and was talking with the driver. It didn't look like he was scared or nothing, so I just went in my friend's house. I musta' stayed for twenty minutes or so and when I come out, Cat Eyes's bike was just lying in the street. And that was the last time anybody ever seen or heard from Cat Eyes."

"Did you ever talk to your brother about what may have happened, ma'am?"

"Yeah, Sahgent Rodriguez. When I axed him 'bout what happened to Cat Eyes, he said, 'You know he got shot.' He wouldn't say nothing more that that, though."

"Thank you, ma'am. Here's my card. Have a nice day, okay?"

ON THE DRIVE BACK TO THE OFFICE, RODRIGUEZ NOTICED THAT GRAY seemed agitated.

"What's up, Bobby? No improbable fucking questions on existentialism? No updates on J-Lo's ass? Something else on your mind?"

"Yeah. This kid was John Doe number one-sixty. And that was with three months still left in the year. Who knows what number they're up to now? It's unbelievable how many bodies go unclaimed every year in this fucked up county. It's unreal. You couldn't even write a movie script about this shit. Nobody'd believe it."

Rodriguez sat quietly, searching for something on the radio.

"And you know what else? It's pretty fucking obvious that whoever was in that green car killed that kid. We should've had this information months ago. As a matter of fact, this should've come to the floor when it happened. An abduction that turned into a murder and it just went into a fucking file cabinet. Four middle-school kids, a part-time equestrian, and a goddamned dog did more investigation than our Missing Persons Unit did. What the fuck, huh?"

"Nothing we can do about that now, Bobby. Let's just work the case and try to do something with it, okay?"

Gray put his gun in the glovebox and reclined his seat.

"The Bears are playing the Forty-Niners tonight," he said. "You think we'll get back in time? Why am I even asking you? You probably don't even know. You're probably gonna just watch that stupid movie *Airplane!* again for the millionth time."

"What's it to you, motherfucker? That's the funniest movie ever made. I'll watch it *after* the game. We should be back by half-time."

"Okay, *putz*. Wake me when we get back to civilization."

Rodriguez was as troubled by the casework as Gray was, but he had been around long enough to know not to get upset by things he had no control over. He put a fresh toothpick in his mouth and turned on the CD player. The beautiful vocals of Steve Perry crooning about a small-town girl living in a lonely world filled the car while a city boy born and raised in *Joisy* snored in the passenger seat.

PART FIVE

CHAPTER TWENTY-FIVE

IT WAS THE beginning of February 2010.

The fervor of the Quintuple had long since quieted down. Once the fear that a serial killer wasn't going around killing the homeless, the media had immediately shifted to other, more pressing issues, like celebrity sex scandals, which was just fine with McGuire and Cortes. The less spotlight the better for investigators, but it was almost as if the media was upset that there wasn't a wild man or men running around killing people because they were homeless. Good news doesn't sell, and plain old murders in the wrong zip code is the worst seller of all.

The case had started to fade away as soon as there were no more political platforms to crow from, no more perfidious postulations. Unless a murder victim is rich or famous, zip codes mean everything. If you aren't murdered in the right one, no one gives a fuck. Especially politicians. It hadn't taken long at all for the five people murdered under the dim light of a crescent moon to become as invisible in death as they were in life. Now, there were just two men left to bring the case home. With the spotlight long gone, they could either do that, or let it languish like the thousands of other unsolved murder cases in L.A. County. No one really cared anymore.

McGuire and Cortes were both training other newly assigned investigators by this time. In early March, McGuire and his partner were in the office working on a case they had just picked up. It involved the murder of a three-year-old boy. His mother's boyfriend had beaten him to death with his bare hands because the boy "looked at him with disrespect." Normally, autopsies did not bother McGuire, but the one for the three-year-old did. His grandson had just turned the same age, and it pained him to see such a young child get his ribcage cracked and his cap peeled.

While discussing the case with his partner, McGuire felt a hand on his shoulder. He turned and saw that it was Jim McDonnell, the new chief. McGuire stood up and McDonnell extended his hand.

"Hello. I'm Jim. Can I call you Mark?"

McGuire shook his hand and said, "Nice to meet you, Chief. You can just call me Mac. I appreciate the offer to call you by your first name, but I was raised by a career Navy man. I will always afford your rank the respect that it deserves."

McDonnell smiled and nodded toward the mound of paperwork on McGuire's desk.

"So, this is where the magic happens, huh Mac?"

IN LATE MARCH, Tatsuo Hitomi and David Ponce had a baby girl.

With two children now, Tatsuo felt more trapped than ever. Ponce was getting worse. The frightening parts of him were always present now, unlike before when he could turn his charm on and off. He walked around the house with guns in his waistband all the time. She had to constantly remind him to be careful and not leave them unattended. Their son was getting older and was curious about things.

Ponce would always yell at her for questioning his parenting skills, justifying his need to stay combat-ready the same way every time by saying, "Naw. I'm gonna always have a strap just in case. When you fucking with a soldier like me, you never know who gonna run up in here. I done a lot of shit."

Ponce first began having the seemingly demonic possessions a few months before the five homeless people in Long Beach were murdered. But when the news about the incident came on TV, his reaction scared Tatsuo even more than they did. She remembered it like it was yesterday, because he had jumped off the couch, pointed at the screen, and screamed, "That was me! I killed them all! That LV muthafucka is dead. Fuck him! He's a rat, and he's resting in piss!"

On another occasion, Tatsuo found a newspaper article in the house. It was about a human hand discovered near a school. She asked Ponce why he was keeping it, and his reply chilled her:

"Cause I like seeing it. You know whose fucking hand that is."

Tatsuo was well-read. She knew what Stockholm syndrome was. Sadly, she realized that she was most likely suffering from it. Afraid to stay but too terrified to leave, she was convinced that whatever Ponce did was for the good of their family. Regardless of anything else, she had to remain alive for her kids, even if it meant being a part of horrible things.

In the months following the murders in Long Beach, Ponce would often stare at the walls and mumble about demons. Tatsuo never called for help because it had spun him so out of control the last time. She would just take the kids in her bedroom and lock the door.

She walked on eggshells whenever Ponce was home. He raped her dozens of times, every time she spread her legs for him when she didn't want to but was too afraid not to. She couldn't say no, because she believed her denial would result in a beating, or worse. At times he was gentle; other times he was brutal, leaving her to believe that the gentle version was David, and the brutal version whatever he became during his episodes. As she would lay under him, quietly looking up at the terrible tattoos on his body while waiting for him to finish, she would think, *No. I don't want to do this. But how do I say no to a man who brags about how many people he has killed and walks around our house with a gun in his waistband?*

There are other kinds of rape besides the physical kind. There is the rape of the mind and soul, the crushing of any type of resistance by the thought of the unknown. Every part of Tatsuo's soul was screaming at Ponce to stop each time he entered her as she became an ongoing witness to the murder of her dignity.

CHAPTER TWENTY-SIX

ELDEN MIGNAULT HAD just turned nineteen in the summer of 2010.

Known as "Tripper," he was a member of the Nut Hood Watts 111th Street clique, and the kind of guy who had his own personal storm cloud hanging over his head. His fellow gang members knew there was something wrong with him in addition to his affinity to misfortune, but unschooled in the proper diagnosis of psychiatry, they attributed his behavior to foolhardiness. Whenever he did something stupid, they would laugh and just say, "Tripper a fool, homie! That lil muthafucka crazy!" before lighting another blunt or taking another sip of Olde English 800 or Cisco.

Tripper needed professional help, however. An undiagnosed schizophrenic and manic depressive by any measure, he would alternate between euphoria and despair, and often fantasized about being the fiercest gangster who ever lived. Constantly striving to prove himself, he was always the first to volunteer for any gang missions. He also had a knife fetish, and was always pulling one out and laughing, slicing at unseen adversaries.

His parents gave up on him as a lost cause when he was sixteen, and he was now a part of the ever-growing class of the homeless. He slept over at a different house almost nightly. The gang became his family as he totally immersed himself into the byzantine nature of that lifestyle. His fellow gang members were well aware of his fanatical commitment to the 111th Street Clique:

Anything the hood needed done, Tripper would do. Need a stolen car for a mission? Get Tripper. Need to get rid of a burner with a body on it? Tripper got it. Walls in the neighborhood need to be hit up? Tripper is on the way to steal the spray paint. Need someone to ride on a mission and put in work? Tripper is that guy, fearless and ready to peel a cap at a moment's notice.

David Ponce liked Tripper and had gone on missions with him in the not-so-distant past. He let Tripper live with him and Tatsuo for two or three days, until Tripper started playing with the kitchen knives. His birthday came on the second day he was at their house. Tatsuo wished him a happy one, and he started crying, saying, "No one has ever remembered my birthday before. Thank you so much!"

It was then that Tatsuo realized how bad Tripper's childhood must have been. He would shoot, knife, or fight anyone at the drop of a dime, but a simple birthday wish had brought him to tears. Tatsuo felt terrible for him, but she had kids. She couldn't have someone around them who was so unstable and constantly played with knives. Their father was bad enough with all his guns.

Luckily, Ponce felt the same way as she did about Tripper. He told Tripper that he had to leave and figure it out on his own, so Tripper went back to doing what he did best—couch hopping and standing sentry in the neighborhood, an area so dangerous you had to constantly be aware of your surroundings. If you weren't, it meant that you were "caught slipping."

At half past noon on a blistering day in July, Tripper got caught slipping. He was standing in the 10000 block of Wilmington Avenue when a rival gang member shot him in the head. The police did a cursory investigation, and the coroner's wagon that loaded him up took him to 1104 Mission Road for a date with a cap-peeling and a Y-incision.

Meanwhile, the neighborhood was pissed and began mustering up troops for payback. It didn't have to be the exact gang that murdered Tripper, though. When it was time to go on the mission to avenge him, they would look in that neighborhood first, sure. But if they didn't come across any targets, they would go to other rival neighborhoods until somebody, somewhere, fell.

Before any of that, though, they had to celebrate Tripper's life. They staged a carwash to raise money to pay for his burial and sent out the hood rats, dressed in skimpy clothing, to major intersections in their neighborhood. Holding signs that read, *Carwash, $10*, the women would direct cars to nearby parking lots where other members of the gang drank liquor, smoked marijuana, and washed cars with dirty rags and dirtier water.

They never collected enough money to pay for funeral services, but it didn't matter. The District Attorney's office provided funds to victims of violent crimes to cover things like that. The money generated from the car washes would be used to have a hood party in Tripper's honor, and during the party, the Big Homies would discuss who was going to lead the mission to avenge him. And as always, they would choose David Ponce.

"HEY, LIL HOMIE. WE RIDING FOR TRIPPS TONIGHT. HOLD THIS."

It was August 1, 2010, and Ponce and another Nut Hood member were about to embark on a mission to catch someone slipping. Ponce had picked him because, like Tripper, he was fearless and totally committed to 111 Street. When he had to run a gauntlet of eleven Nut Hood gangsters trying their best to take his head off so he could become a member, the lil homie had held his own.

"You up for this?" Ponce asked as he gave him a loaded Mac-11 9mm semi-automatic pistol.

"Yeah," the lil homie said as he held it, getting accustomed to the the weight. "I got this."

"Good. I'm driving. When we see an enemy, blast they ass. If we get pulled over, I need you to bounce and take the burner with you. I'm on parole. If I get caught with it in the car, I'm going back to prison to finish my sentence. Like I said, just run, and take the burner. The po-po gonna be too busy dealing with me once they see my face."

Then they drank a little Cisco, smoked a little weed, and left the hood looking to inspire another car wash, this time for a rival. Not long into their quest for vengeance, Ponce saw the familiar sight of blue and red lights in his rear-view mirror. His lil homie froze as two sheriff's deputies approached their car. For a second, Ponce no doubt considered shooting it out with them, but accused them of racial profiling instead. The deputies made them get out and found the gun during a search of the car. Now David Ponce was going back to prison for at least thirty-two months.

PART SIX

CHAPTER TWENTY-SEVEN

FEBRUARY 2, 2011

McGuire had been keeping tabs on Ponce with the hope that he got arrested for something, but he had been busy with court trials and several new cases for the past few months. There were no hits on DNA from LV's clothing. The meth pipe, the lighter, and the knife had Kat's DNA on them. There were no prints or DNA other than that of the victims found in the camp. Despite these depressing results, McGuire got pleasant news from elsewhere. He found out that David Ponce was in custody. He had been arrested for having a gun in his car.

Ponce was with a guy by the name of Max Eliseo Rafael, aka Chato. This was the first time his name had ever come up in the investigation. During the booking process, Ponce gave the same address in Lancaster that CCAT had followed him to in 2009. The vehicle he was arrested in was registered to a woman named Tatsuo Hitomi.

Ponce was at the North Kern County Correctional Facility for the next two years, at least. McGuire called the Inmate Security Unit at the prison. He spoke to a liaison officer and asked that Ponce's phone calls and mail be monitored.

"What's his CDC number?" the liaison officer asked.

"Sure. One second."

After McGuire gave the number to the officer, he asked the liaison officer to check for any phone calls that Ponce had made since he'd been at the facility.

"Sure thing, Detective. I'll get back to you as soon as I get the info."

"Thank you, officer."

The liaison officer called back a few hours later with disappointing news. Apparently, Ponce had only made one call.

"Really? That's weird," said McGuire.

"It's probably because he's got a cell phone. If you got enough juice, you could get one anytime you need it. I think he has had one since February 9, 2011, because that's when he made the call."

"What number did he call?"

After giving McGuire the number, the liaison officer told him that Ponce didn't have any mail, either.

"You've been very helpful, officer."

"One other thing," the liaison officer said. "Do you guys have a moniker for him?"

"Yeah. Saint."

"That's the only one you guys have?"

"Yeah. Why? Y'all got another one?"

"Yes. Apparently, someone along the way while he was locked up decided that he should be called Bloodbath."

"Bloodbath? What the fuck?"

"Yeah. What the fuck is right. Mr. Ponce has quite the rep inside."

"That's good to know. Thanks."

"No problem, sir. Call anytime you need help with something."

"Will do. Peace in the hood."

McGuire called Cortes to let him know what was going on. They were no longer partners, having been split up by Nielsen. Now they were both training new guys. McGuire had kept the case file, periodically chasing down leads as they came in. He and Cortes still worked out of the same office, but they were at different desks now and didn't see each other as much.

"That's great, Mac!" Cortes said upon hearing the news. "What did the prison guy say?"

"That he's only made one call since he's been at their facility. They think he has a cell phone. And get this, Hugo. He's known as Bloodbath inside."

"Really?"

"No bullshit."

"What about the guy he got arrested with for the gun?"

"I'm gonna do a work-up on him and see what he's about."

"Okay, then. Well, keep in touch, *amigo*."

"A'ight, den."

Rafael had a minimal sheet but was a confirmed member of the same gang as Ponce. He hadn't been held in custody long for the gun; he was already out. McGuire filed his name away for later. Had he been in custody, he might have taken Cortes to interview him. Not now. Better to wait until he got arrested again.

On March 9, McGuire got the ballistics test results. The Mac-11 was not used in the Quintuple, but the firearms expert did have some promising news.

Microscopic comparisons are often made on fired cartridge casings found at a crime scene to unfired cartridges found in the possession of a suspect. The comparisons can reveal if the cartridge casings and unfired cartridges were ever worked through the action of, or cycled through, the same firearm. The comparisons can also identify "bunter marks," which are marks produced by a head-stamping tool when a bullet is manufactured.

The tool imprints the manufacturer's name and the caliber of the bullet on the cartridge casing. It is then possible to determine which bunter made them based on individual characteristics left behind on the cartridges. It can be used as proof that the cartridges, both fired and unfired, came from the same manufacturing plant.

The cartridge casings from the Quintuple and the cartridges from the Mac-11 had the same bunter marks. Despite his stature as a long-time criminal who considered himself so careful that cops would never get evidence of anything on him, David Ponce had not been careful enough this time. There was a chance that the ammunition he had been using came from the same box.

There are very few coincidences in police work. Usually there is only not enough evidence to prove otherwise. The fact that Ponce was in a car with a weapon containing rounds from the same manufacturing plant was not a smoking gun, but the odor of one was in the air.

McGuire wrote a search warrant for the number he got from the prison liaison officer.

The warrant requested all text message information from February 1 through March 1, 2011. When he got the results a week later, they revealed that the subscriber was Tatsuo Hitomi. The address she used was the same one that Ponce gave when he was arrested. Multiple text message exchanges had taken place between the two while Ponce was in prison. The texts indicated that he was running a yard and the talk was that he might get validated as La Eme.

On March 30, McGuire got a call from a Sheriff's deputy who worked in the L.A. County Jail as a liaison. The deputy had a lot of contact with inmates who wanted to provide information on cases. This was always a sketchy part of police investigations. Jail informants are true rats, and don't do anything for the good of humankind, or because of their conscience. They always want something—usually some consideration on a case they are fighting, money, or a better housing area. It is always a quid pro quo situation. The jail liaison deputy, or JLD, had an inmate who allegedly had information on Leonard Lloyd and his connection to LV.

McGuire called Cortes.

"You awake, bitch?"

"It's noon, *amigo*."

"It's time to get the band back together. We got action on the Quintuple. I'll fill you in on the way."

"On the way where?"

"MCJ. Apparently a JLD over there has someone who claims to know what happened."

"What about Nielsen? He's good with us working together again?"

"Fuck Nielsen. We'll tell him later. This is po-leece work."

"Okay. Fuck him. I'll meet you in front of the station in twenty minutes."

Cortes and McGuire were briefed by the JLD and Mark Lillienfeld.

The JLD had called him before he called McGuire because the Lloyd case was potentially involved.

"Hello, *amigo*," Cortes said to the informant after he and McGuire were introduced to him. "This is my partner McGuire, and I'm Cortes, with an *s*, not a *z*. We're from Long Beach PD Homicide. We understand you might have some information regarding the homeless murders in Long Beach?"

"Yeah, I do. This dude from D-Thirteen did it. They call him Lil Man. He kilt LV 'cause he snitched on Hoodlum. Er' body else was just witnesses."

Here we go with this bullshit again, McGuire thought. "A'ight den, what else have you heard?"

He and Cortes then listened to the man for the next ten minutes, never asking questions or providing any information that he could use to seem more credible. He clearly knew people from the D-13 gang and the area where the murders occurred, but he got most of the details wrong.

"We'll be in touch," McGuire said to the man when he was done. After another deputy escorted him back to his housing unit, McGuire told Lillienfeld and the JLD that they had already vetted Lil Man.

"He's got an airtight alibi for the night of the murders. But this informant did give me an idea."

"What's that, Mac?" Lillienfeld asked.

"Let's order Ponce, Lucky, and Lloyd out of prison and down here to court. We can use your case number on Lloyd, so they don't think the reason they're being ordered out is because of the Quintuple. When they get down here, we'll throw them in cells that are recorded so they can talk to each other."

"I like it," Lillienfeld said. "I'm sure those donkeys will have plenty to talk about."

"IT WAS A BRIGHT COLD DAY IN APRIL, AND THE CLOCKS WERE STRIKING *thirteen*."

To be exact, it was April 13, 2011, and it wasn't cold; it was a pleasant sixty-eight degrees. But as far as David Ponce was concerned, the opening line of Orwell's dystopian novel *1984* could not have rung truer.

He had just arrived at the Los Angeles County Men's Central Jail, the first step to what would eventually turn the world he knew upside down. The second step would occur when he found out that both Lucky and Leonard Lloyd had also been ordered out from their respective prison facilities and were now in the county jail as well.

All phone calls from custody facilities are recorded. There is even a disclaimer given every minute or so advising inmates of this. Some of them simply lack the will or the discipline to be discreet and implicate themselves in crimes regardless.

On May 2, Ponce called Tatsuo Hitomi at the number McGuire had written warrants for, the first of several calls over the next few days.

"You have a collect call from... 'David Ponce' *...an inmate at Men's Central Jail. Do you accept?"*

"Yes. David?"

"I'm here at county jail, baby. They brought me down here for questioning. Some Long Beach cop named Mark McGuire. His name is on the paperwork."

"I had that feeling, baby."

"You don't even know how I feel right now. It's a Long Beach case."

"Do you know for what crime?"

"No, but it's *that* though."

"Is it for *that?*"

"This call may be monitored."

"Hey, hey! Chill out, okay? I need you to call my family and let Motor know what's going on."

"So, it's for sure *that?*"

"Hey, chill the fuck out, okay? Just keep some money on the phone."

"I just can't believe it. I had a feeling it was for that when you told me you were coming down."

"Just stay strong. We'll talk again soon."

MAY 6

"You have a collect call from... 'David Ponce' *...an inmate at Men's Central Jail. Do you accept?"*

"Yes. David?"

"Yes, babe. It's me. Guess what? That fucking Lucky *and* Hoodlum are here. I seen 'em both! And the case number on my paperwork is the same one on Hoodlum case. What the fuck! Why they both here with me at the same time for that fucking case? I need to know if somebody snitched or set me up! Look online and see what Lucky is down here for."

"This call may be monitored."

"Okay, David. I'll see what I can find out. Stay strong, okay?"

"I love you. Kiss the kids for me."

"I will."

MAY 11, 4:40 A.M.

"You have a collect call from… 'David Ponce'…an inmate at Men's Central Jail. Do you accept?"

"Yes. David?"

Ponce is fit to be tied and hadn't slept in almost 24 hours.

"Fuck, Tatsuo! I don't know what's going on, but I been ordered to Long Beach court on the thirteenth and on the sixteenth!"

"I looked online to see who Detective McGuire is. He's working *that* murder case, and his name is all over it! David, I'm scared!"

"Look, Tatsuo. Relax. Stop crying, okay? You remember my work boots? Those brown Timberlands?"

"This call may be monitored."

"Yes… 'sniff'…what about them… 'sniff'…"

"I need you to get rid of them, you hear me? As soon as you can, okay? I'm gonna start cutting my losses so I can get ready to go away forever. I blasted my face again so everybody inside can see how fucking crazy I am or can be! And let Motor know that the police are gonna be looking for him. He'll know what to do."

Unbeknownst to Ponce, Lloyd and Lucky had also been ordered to Long Beach court on Friday, May 13. It would prove to be a most unlucky day for him. Worse than that, McGuire had placed a request to have all three of their phone calls and visits monitored.

Big Brother was watching.

CHAPTER TWENTY-EIGHT

DR. CHRISTINE CHOE was the Long Beach Police Department's psychologist.

Her office was on the fourth floor of Police Headquarters. She had a big window, but the view was not of the beautiful ocean. It was the view of the twelve-story court building next door and people below on the streets going about their day-to-day, including the horde of homeless people who congregated near city hall.

One of Dr. Choe's responsibilities was to interview police officers who had been involved in deadly force. Before they were allowed back to work, they had to demonstrate that they were fit for duty. McGuire decided to pay her a visit on May 12, but not because of any psychological issues. It was the day before he was to confront David Ponce for the first time, and he wanted to be as prepared as possible.

McGuire had a good rapport with Dr. Choe. They first met several years earlier at a class he was teaching about homicide investigations. After the class, she came up to him and asked high quality follow-up questions to his lecture. She didn't look like a cop, though. Thinking she was a student, McGuire asked her what school she attended.

"Oh, I'm sorry, Detective McGuire. I'm not a student. I'm Dr. Christine Choe, the new department psychologist. Nice to meet you."

"It is my pleasure, Dr. Choe."

They shook hands and had been friends ever since.

McGuire peeked in and knocked on the open door to her office.

"Oh! Hi, Detective! Come in, please," she said as she put a beautiful gold-plated Cross pen into a pen and pencil holder on her mahogany desk.

"What's up, doc?" McGuire asked as he closed the door behind him. He glanced around the office. Like her, it was elegant. A beautiful photograph of the Namsan Tower in South Korea hung on the wall, lost amidst framed degrees and certificates from numerous institutions of higher learning, with a degree from USC in the center. Works by Freud, Kant, Nietzsche, B.F. Skinner, and Pavlov held prominent places on the bookshelves along the walls to her left and right.

"What can I do for you, Detective?"

"I need some help on the Quintuple," McGuire said, glancing at the framed picture of her in a Trojan cheerleading outfit on her desk.

"Sure. What do you need?"

"Well, I'm gonna be interrogating one of the suspects soon, and he is a stone-cold killer. This is the most important interview of my career. How should I approach it?"

Dr. Choe picked up her phone.

"Hold my calls, please."

She looked back at McGuire as she cradled the receiver.

"Tell me about him. Give me some background and personal traits."

She then listened intently as McGuire spent the next ten or fifteen minutes telling her everything that he had learned about David Ponce.

"Okay," she said when he was finished. "He will not ask for a lawyer. He is a narcissist. It will not be difficult to initiate conversation with him. Those like him think they are smarter than everyone else. They love to hear themselves talk. They believe that by monopolizing a conversation, they exhibit their 'superior' intellect."

McGuire leaned in and put his hands on his knees as she talked. Had he had teachers like this in school, he may have gone further instead of picking up a pair of drumsticks.

"Once you get him talking, do not interrupt him. Make sure he is aware that you are listening and extremely interested. Lean in toward him. Do not fold your arms across your chest. That demonstrates a lack of interest. And he will try and make you look stupid. Do not take offense. Let him be the smartest person in the room."

"Thanks, Doc."

"Anytime, Detective. Oh! One more thing. Tatsuo? She is his weakness. Use it to your advantage. He loves her very much. He may think *she* needs him, but actually the reverse is true. *He* needs her."

"Good to know."

"Let me know how it turns out."

"I will. We're interviewing him tomorrow."

"Interesting choice of dates. Was it by design?"

"Luck of the draw, but hopefully you'll read about how it turned out on the front page of the Press Telegram soon. I'll talk to you later. Door open or closed?"

"Open. Unless I'm talking to someone, my door is always open," Dr. Choe said as she smiled, took her pen from the holder, and began writing.

CHAPTER TWENTY-NINE

FRIDAY THE 13th

Ponce, Lloyd, and Lucky were transported from L.A. County Jail to Long Beach court on the same jail bus. Before they arrived to lock-up, Cortes, a wizard at gadgetry, one of the many skills he learned from his father, wired three connecting cells with recording devices.

McGuire and Cortes interviewed Lloyd first while Ponce and Lucky sat in their cells. Lloyd yawned when they walked into the interview room where he was seated. A tall, slim man with short, kinky hair, he didn't look mixed at all. He looked 100 percent Black, but when he opened his mouth, it was obvious that he had spent most of his life around Mexican gang members.

"Hello, Mr. Lloyd. Can we call you Leonard?"

"Whatever, *ese*."

"Cool. I'm Detective Mark McGuire and this is my partner, Hugo Cortes."

"What's this about, *ay*?"

"Hold on. Let me read you your rights."

"You don't need to do that. I heard 'em at least twenty times. I don't need no mouthpiece."

"Okay. I'm gonna read them anyway. Next time you get interviewed, you can say you heard them twenty-one times."

When McGuire was finished and Lloyd had waived his rights, he turned to Cortes and said, "Go ahead, Hugo."

"Thanks, partner. Leonard, this is about the guy who testified against you during your trial. Lorenzo Villicana. They called him LV. Do you know who killed him, and did you have anything to do with it?"

"Nope. I'm just doing my time on my case. I don't bang no more, *ese*. I dropped out and PC'ed up. I forgave everybody who lied on me to get me where I am for the rest of my life. The only thang I know 'bout LV is what I seen on the news. I had nothing to do with it. I never had that kind of juice. I'm a nigga, homes. My *barrio* wouldn't do shit for me."

McGuire imagined that if he closed his eyes and listened to Lloyd, a Mexican gangbanger would appear in his head. Instead, he kept them open and listened to a man who looked like he could be his son.

"That's right," McGuire said. "You're in protective custody with all the other dropouts. They keep snitches, and homosexuals in there, too, don't they?"

"*Sí.* And child molesters. *They* still get fucked up, though."

"A'ight den, Leonard. Did you ever hear anything about why LV was killed?"

"Nope. All I heard from Lucky and Saint while I was sitting with them right now is that they thank I put them in this position."

"Did you know Saint from before?"

"His mom live in my hood. I was from D-Thirteen before I dropped out. They called me Hoodlum. Now, I'm just trying to do my time in peace. I ain't got time for that stupid shit, *ay*. Look where it landed me."

"Did you know LV? Personally?"

"*Sí.* Since I was thirteen. He was from D-Thirteen, too. They called him Lyncho."

"Do you still deal with anyone from D-thirteen, *amigo*?"

"Hell, naw, *ese*. I'm dead to them. But LV? That *cabróne* burnt a lotta people in the past. You guys like motive, right? There it is right there. I'm sho' there was a lotta people looking for him for they money."

"Okay, Leonard. I'm done. Mac, you got anything?"

"Nope. Come on, Leonard. Let's get you back to your cell."

McGuire and Cortes interviewed Lucky next. He was hefty, but meek, even though he put on a tough-guy facade.

"Hello, Maleko. This is my partner, Hugo Cortes, and—"

"Is that with a *z*, or an *s*, sir?"

"With an *s*," Cortes said.

"Like I was saying. I'm Detective McGuire. I'm gonna advise you of your rights before we start talking, okay?"

"Okay."

After hearing his rights, Lucky agreed to talk without a lawyer.

"A'ight, den. What do they call you, Maleko?"

"T-Nutt. Or Lucky."

"Mind if we call you Lucky?"

"Nope. Mind if I call you Mark?"

"Not at all. Okay, Lucky. Why are you in prison?"

"Cause of that fucking Lyncho."

"That's terrible," McGuire said as he placed several photographs on the table. "Tell me who you recognize."

"Well, that one right there is me," Lucky said as he pointed out a photograph of himself. "And that's Saint. He from Watts, but we grew up in the same hood. And this is Motor. He grew up in our hood, too."

"How did you feel about LV, Lucky?"

"Man, Detective Cortes, at one time, he was like my big brutha."

"Take a look at this picture. You recognize it?"

"Yeah. That's Motor's black Hyundai."

"Did he own it in 2008?" McGuire asked.

"Yeah."

"Did you go with him in that car to the homeless camp to collect money LV owed to you?"

"Nope."

"Well take a look at these," Cortes said as he disregarded the lie and spread out the crime scene photographs of the victims.

"You know any of these people, *amigo*?"

"Nope."

"Wait a minute," McGuire said. "LV owed you money, right?"

"Nope."

"Didn't you point a gun at some kids and then shoot it in the air? Because you were looking for LV because he owed you money?"

"Nope, and nope."

"But that's the charge you're doing time for. You pled guilty. Why would you admit to doing something and get sent to prison if you didn't do it?" McGuire asked.

"I pled guilty 'cause I was there."

"Uh, huh. Right. You don't remember telling Detective Niloc that LV owed you between eight and nine hundred dollars?"

"Naw. I don't remember saying nothing like that. But I did hear that LV took twenty-five thousand dollars worth of dope from somebody. I don't know who, but that's 'enuff to get yo' cap peelt, for sure. Personally, I never sold drugs."

Lucky leaned back in his chair and adjusted the glasses that made him look smart. McGuire gathered all the photographs and put them in the case file. He didn't want to talk to Lucky anymore. He didn't even want to look at him.

"Thanks, *amigo*. It's been a real pleasure."

Cortes was excited about the prospect of interviewing David Ponce.

McGuire was excited, too, but he was more relaxed, having performed in front of thousands before. It took quite a bit to get him excited. He had a look on his face as if he was on stage at a concert in Madison Square Gardens, waiting for the Maestro of Love to come out.

"Should we slap him with the truth, Mac, or kiss him with a lie?"

"We're just gonna stimulate, my brutha. Put something on his mind."

Ponce was sitting in the interview room, facing the door. He leaned back in his chair and folded his arms. He had been working out and eating well, and his facial tattoo was redone. His arms were completely sleeved with tattoos. The one that stood out the most was the head of a large dragon on his right shoulder.

"Hello, Mr. Ponce. I'm Mark McGuire, and this is my partner, Hugo Cortes."

"With an *s*, not a *z*."

"That's hilarious," Ponce said as he smiled and shook Cortes's hand. "Do people actually give a shit how your name ends?"

"Do you know why you're here, David?" McGuire quickly asked after seeing the vein in Cortes's neck start to bulge.

"Yeah, Detective—? Who are you again?"

"McGuire."

"Yeah. McGuire. That's right."

McGuire noticed that Ponce had shown just a slight bit of recognition when he heard his name. He knew exactly why he was there. After Cortes read Ponce his rights, Ponce looked at McGuire again. It was all a game to him, the smiles, the cordial handshakes, the polite and respectful tone of his voice. But McGuire knew that Ponce wouldn't hesitate to kill him and Cortes if given a chance.

"I understand my rights," Ponce replied. "I don't need no lawyer."

After McGuire read them anyway and Ponce reiterated that he didn't need an attorney, McGuire put his elbows on the table and clasped his hands.

"A'ight, den. Tell us a little about yourself, David. And also, about that day you went with Lucky to LV's camp and LV beat his ass."

And just like Dr. Choe predicted, words started pouring out of Ponce's mouth: He was a proud member of Nut Hood Watts, the 111th Street clique, and they called him Saint. Sure, he was at the fight where Lucky beat up LV, but he didn't have anything to do with the murders. He knew LV from the neighborhood because that's where they both grew up. And he knew Hoodlum, as well. His good friend Motor gave Lucky and him a ride to where LV was hiding. There was another guy with them, but he didn't know him.

"Humph," McGuire grunted. "Well, a'ight den. I have a few follow-up questions."

"Go ahead. The floor is yours, McGuire."

"Okay. When did they start calling you Bloodbath?"

"Bloodbath? What the fuck is that? Nobody calls me that."

"Um, hum. How did you get to the camp where LV was?"

"We walked through those little ass tunnels. It was me, Lucky, and Motor."

"Did you tell Vanessa to shut up?"

"Who is that?"

"LV's girl."

"Oh, yeah. That bitch has...had...a big mouth."

"Do you own a gun, David?"

"Whaaaat? I didn't think you were gonna talk, Cortes. I thought you were just muscle. Naw, no guns. I come from the shoulders, G."

"Who do you live with?"

"I know y'all already know the answer to that dumbass question, Cortes, but I'll play along. I live with my baby mama in East L.A. Long Beach was just my parole address."

"You got any other addresses, David?" McGuire asked.

"Nope."

"Okay. You are obviously aware that me and Detective Cortes are the murder police, the real po-leece. We don't give a shit about a fight or some bullshit robbery. We're about the bodies, in particular, five of them around Halloween in Long Beach in 2008. Do you remember where you were?"

"I was with my baby mama in East L.A. Look, I ain't got nothing to do with whatever y'all talking about. Run my prints on the bullets and shells from the scene. And here, check my DNA. I'll give it to you. I won't even make you get a warrant."

McGuire noticed that whenever Ponce brought up Hitomi Tatsuo, there was a change of intonation in his voice. He decided not to ask Ponce about her. He felt he would get more fruitful information by listening to their phone conversations. Ponce *trusted* her. Implicitly.

"Not necessary, David. But thanks anyway. By the way, how did you know we found shells?"

"Lucky guess."

"Okay. We're done here. Let's go, Hugo."

As they were about to walk out of the room, McGuire turned and smiled at Ponce.

"I'll catch you later."

TWENTY MINUTES LATER, PONCE, LLOYD, AND LUCKY WERE ALL BACK in their recorded cells.

It was obvious that Ponce trusted neither Lucky nor Lloyd. Everything they discussed was in code, but Ponce did leave crumbs. He bragged about running his floor at county jail and mentioned that, "*they missed four witnesses at the scene, but it's okay because they are homeless and have no credibility."*

McGuire and Cortes were confident that Ponce was one of the shooters. The recordings from the jail cell and the interviews were successful because they were able to eliminate Lloyd and Lucky as suspects. Lucky had an alibi, and Lloyd, as he said, didn't have any juice. Not only that, Ponce disliked Lloyd, and their gangs were sworn enemies.

On May 20, McGuire wrote another search warrant for text messages on Tatsuo Hitomi's phone, and for a number that belonged to Kenny Richardson, aka Motor. The text messages were damning. One of them contained information about Ponce's gang affiliation and his elevated prison status, and one was about him being at county jail for five murders even though he had yet to be charged. Another one was Ponce texting Tatsuo that he was not going to accept the death penalty and was going to make correctional officers, commonly referred to as CO's, kill him.

On June 16, Cortes and other members of the Long Beach PD served a search warrant at Tatsuo's residence in Lancaster. McGuire stayed behind in Long Beach to monitor phone calls made by Ponce.

"There's nothing much up here other than prison letters and a laptop that we're taking, Mac," Cortes said when he called McGuire to give him an update. "But I found an Antelope Valley Press newspaper article about some human remains in Lake Los Angeles. It's dated September 10, 2009. That's over a year ago. I think it's a trophy. Ponce may have done another murder out here."

"Beautiful. Save it. We'll look into it when you get back to the office."

Cortes brought everything back to Long Beach PD, following a patrol car containing Tatsuo Hitomi, handcuffed in the back seat, now under arrest for accessory to murder. The letters written by Ponce to her mentioned freeway murders, using a chrome and black "bitch thang," establishing an alibi, and speculating about who one of the witnesses might be.

"Okay, Tatsuo," Cortes said once they got back to the office. "I'm gonna sit you in this interview room for a little while. You hungry?"

"A little."

"I'll be right back."

He grabbed a bag of Lays potato chips, a bag of Doritos, and a can of Pepsi from the vending machines.

"Here you go. Just sit tight. My partner and I will be here to talk to you shortly."

McGuire was reading the letters and newspaper article when Cortes got to his desk.

"What do you think, Mac?"

"I think David Ponce is one of our guys, no question. These letters are strong circumstantial evidence. And would he keep this newspaper article? I think he killed whoever the hand belongs to. What's your take on his girl?"

"She's definitely a homegirl, but she ain't a hood rat. She's smart, and articulate. She even speaks Japanese. How she ended up with Ponce? I haven't got a clue."

"You think she knew about what was going on, though?"

"How could she not, *amigo*?"

"Well, she's either a witness, or a suspect. There's no hiding from this. It's time for her to sink or swim."

CHAPTER THIRTY

"Tatsuo, this is my partner, Detective Mark McGuire."

"Nice to meet you, Tatsuo," McGuire said as he shook her hand.

She smiled at him. It was a charming smile, the kind that well-tipped waitresses flashed as they refilled coffee cups.

"Now I can put faces with names," she said.

"You knew our names?" Cortes asked.

"Yes. I've been following the case," she said as she adjusted the strap on her pink spaghetti-strap lingerie top. She had on a black tank top underneath it, and was wearing a pair of black pants and slippers. She was an attractive, brown-skinned woman with shoulder-length hair dyed slightly auburn. Her eyebrows were sharply lined and arched, her eyes seductive with a hint of green-tinted eye shadow. A piercing on the right side of her lower lip highlighted a deep cleft in her chin. She was naturally beautiful, but there was a hardness emanating from her that told of a life in the streets with bad men doing bad things.

"What are you mixed with, Tatsuo?" McGuire asked. "I must say, you are stunning."

"My mother is Japanese, and my father is Black."

"Military, right? Your father, I mean."

"Yes. They met while he was in Okinawa. That's where my mother and her family are from. My father left us when I was just a baby. I don't remember him."

McGuire looked at her intently. She was still just a kid, in a manner of speaking, a kid who never had a father figure in her life. It was easy to understand why she gravitated to someone like Ponce. He was respected in the neighborhood and could be the strong male figure that she never had.

"Have you ever been arrested before, Tatsuo?"

"Only as a juvenile, Detective McGuire."

"Then you've had your rights read to you before?"

"Yes, sir."

"Well, I'm gonna read them to you again, okay?"

"Okay."

"And the reason you're here is because of five people who were murdered in November of 2008."

"Okay."

Tatsuo agreed to talk without an attorney present. McGuire then laid everything out for her—the letters, the text messages, and the phone call conversations—as her eyes widened with each revelation. When he was done, he leaned forward in his chair and said, "Please, tell us what happened in Long Beach, Tatsuo. It's time to sink or swim."

She put her head on the table. McGuire and Cortes knew that she wanted to tell. There was no need to push her. They had been waiting three years for this. A few more minutes wouldn't matter. And then, quicker than either of them had expected, she sat up and ran her hand through her hair.

"I wasn't there when it happened, but I *was* in Long Beach on Halloween that year. David and I had taken our son to his mother's house because he said there was a neighborhood down there where the people gave out good candy, you know like whole candy bars. Our son was dressed in a costume, and David was wearing a black hoodie and had his face painted all white with black circles around his eyes like Michael Myers from *Halloween*. He just loves those movies.

"But we didn't even get to go trick or treating because he got a phone call and all of a sudden, he says he has 'hood' business to take care of. One of his friends took me and my son home. David didn't come home until the morning of November the second. The first thing he said was, 'Shit went down last night! It was crazy! Make sure you watch the news!' And he just stayed home all that day, telling me to watch the news every time it came on."

"You know anything about Lucky and a fight?" Cortes asked.

"Yes. I can't remember exactly when—I mean it was back in 2008, but David was really mad that night. He told me that he and some guys were supposed to do a robbery, but it didn't go through. I remember when he left his mother's house. He rode a bike to Lucky's house and then they went to where LV was, and LV and Lucky had a fight. Some girl told David to shut up, and it really pissed him off. David told me that he didn't like LV, because he's a rat. He told me that even LV's own homies didn't like him, and if he saw him again, he was going to fuck him up."

"Did he say anything else about that?" McGuire asked.

"Yes. He said that him and the homies were going to have to go back and take care of business."

"Do you know someone they call 'Motor'?"

"His name is Kenny. He is one of David's good friends. They have known each other since they were kids."

"Do you think Motor or Lucky had something to do with the murders?"

"Oh, no, Detective Cortes! Especially not Motor. He isn't that kind of guy. David went to Watts to meet up with his real homeboys. He told me that someone new was getting jumped in that night. He never took Lucky or Motor over there. David is from Southside Nut Hood Watts."

"Do you know who went with him from his neighborhood that night, Tatsuo?" McGuire asked.

"To get jumped in?"

"No. To murder those homeless people."

"No, sir."

McGuire made note of the way she answered. She had looked him in the eyes every time he asked her something. This time, however, she cast her eyes downward.

"Was he wearing some kind of boots that night?"

"Yes, Detective McGuire. He was wearing some brown Timberlands. He called them his crime boots."

"And what happened to them?"

"He called me and told me to throw them away."

"When was this?"

"About a month ago."

"Did you do it?"

"Yes, sir. I did."

"A'ight. Were you guys watching TV together when the news came on about the five murders?"

"Yes."

"What was David's reaction?"

"He got all amped up, you know? He said, "I killed all them bitches!,' and he started talking about how LV is dead, and that he was a rat. And when they showed pictures of the dead people, David pointed at LV and said, 'That's the motherfucker that Lucky fought. He's resting in piss now.'"

"We got a bunch of prison letters from your house this morning, too. In one of them, David is writing about sending people to 'Bobby's World.' What does that mean?"

"I think it means he's killed someone, Detective McGuire. I don't know who Bobby is, or why he uses that name. I could only guess that someone named Bobby is dead, either by him or by someone else."

"Tatsuo, we're gonna take a little break so you can use the restroom. You haven't had a chance to use it since you got here from Lancaster, anyway. A female jailer will be here to get you. As a matter of fact, I gotta use it myself. How about you, Hugo?"

"Yeah. I could use a little break, too."

Ten minutes later, McGuire and Cortes came back into the interview room. The Lay's potato chips and Doritos were still on the table, unopened. She had opened the Pepsi, however, and drank half of it. McGuire had a box of Kleenex with him. He had a feeling she was going to need them for this portion of the interview.

"I thought you were hungry, *amiga*."

"Just thirsty, I guess."

"Tatsuo."

"Yes, Detective McGuire?"

"We know you weren't being one hundred percent honest with us the first time. So, we're gonna give you another chance to tell us the truth. You're either a suspect or a witness. It's completely up to you. Sink or swim, remember?"

Tatsuo put her face in her hands and started crying. "I tried to help him! I tried! I swear! I don't have any other family! He's all I had! I kept telling him that he should've stayed home but he wouldn't listen. I tried helping him to be a better person, but he just won't change!"

Cortes slid the box of tissues closer to her. She grabbed a handful, wiped her face, and blew her nose before continuing.

"David would blame me every time he hurt someone. It happened after every argument we had. He always said that he would not have had to do something if I hadn't made him so mad."

"Did you argue on Halloween night?" Cortes asked.

"Yes. He made me mad when he left instead of taking our son trick-or-treating. After we finished arguing, that's when he told one of his friends —some fat chick—to take me and our son home. He was like, 'Yeah, me and the homie are gonna be on a mission tonight. Fuck this shit.' And then he left, and I didn't see him until November the second.

"He told me that he took one of the lil homies with him. Another person from his gang drove them. They went to where Lucky and LV had the fight, and he grabbed some old man and asked where LV was. Then the man showed David and the lil homie where he was. And him and the lil homie killed LV and four other people who were witnesses. He told me not to worry about it, because LV was a snitch, and the cops would blame Hoodlum's gang."

"Do you know who David took with him?" McGuire asked.

"They call him Chato. He is dark skinned, between twenty and twenty-five years old, and skinny. There should be a picture of him in my computer at a funeral for their homie Tripper, in 2010."

Cortes got the laptop and found a group of color photographs on it. Tatsuo pointed to a man standing on the left side of one of the photographs. He was holding a small semi-automatic pistol. Ponce was standing on the other side, holding a larger one. There were several other gang members standing between them.

"Yes. Him. That's Chato. That's who David took with him that night."

"Excuse me, Tatsuo. I'll be right back, Hugo."

McGuire queried the name Chato on his computer. A male Hispanic by the name of Max Eliseo Rafael came up. He was a member of the same gang as Ponce.

So, it was the muthafucka with him when he got caught with the Mac-11, huh?

215

McGuire thought while pulling up his photo. He compared it to the individual in the photo from Tatsuo's laptop. It was the same person. He printed out the photo and went back to the interview room.

"Tatsuo?"

"Yes, Detective McGuire?"

"Why didn't you tell us who the other shooter was before now?"

"I was scared, sir. And I'm still scared. It doesn't matter if David is in jail. He's still got clout."

"When did you guys move to Lancaster?" McGuire asked, briefly thinking about the future when he and Cortes would have to relocate Tatsuo and her kids for their safety. It was a pain-in-the-ass process, but they had done several relocations before.

"It was in December of 2008. We had gone out there for Thanksgiving, and one of his relatives wanted to move, so we took over the lease on her apartment."

"Look, Tatsuo," McGuire said as he leaned toward her. "You are one of the best baby mamas that I have listened to in a long time. You take care of business. You do what you gotta do to survive and take care of those kids, and you even tried to take care of David, tried to keep him on an even keel. But it's all coming apart right now. And like we talked about being honest and you wanting to keep your kids—I get that. I do. That's what a mother is *supposed* to do. But this is for real. Your baby daddy has at least five bodies on his head right now that we know of—"

"Umm hum..."

"—and we think there's more, a'ight?"

"Tatsuo."

"Yes, Detective Cortes?"

"What's the story with the newspaper article?"

PART SEVEN

CHAPTER THIRTY-ONE

MAX ELISEO RAFAEL, aka Chato, was a dark-skinned man who rarely smiled.

He had not long been jumped in to the 111th Street clique of the Nut Hood Watts gang when the Quintuple occurred. To be jumped in meant to have a prospective member walk through a gauntlet of eleven members assaulting the prospect. But before getting to that point, the prospect had to do things for the gang to merit consideration for membership. Assaulting rivals, up to and including murdering them, was the quickest way into the gauntlet.

Once Rafael had proven himself worthy of membership, he was given the nickname Chato, the name of a famous Apache warrior, which was an honor and a testament to his ferocity. In the gang world, nicknames are not easily obtained. They are earned and bestowed by the most respected members.

When Ponce was given the mission to take care of LV, he chose Chato.

"You got a strap, lil homie?"

"Yeah, Big Saint. A trey-duece."

"Well, we gonna have to get you some better shit than that in the future, but for tonight, it'll do. We on the way to Long Beach to handle some business. Snitch by the name of LV. Fucking rat *puta*. Follow my lead. When I let off, you let off. All dome shots. Nothing to the body, you feel me?"

Then they got in the car, driven by a third homie, and drove to Long Beach where they murdered five people.

Chato performed like a *veterano*—all head shots as instructed. Afterward, they got back in the car where the other homie was waiting, Ponce in the front seat laughing, Chato in the back seat marveling at what he had been a part of, muttering "I killed them" louder than he intended to.

Chato was not a typical Mexican gang member. He was a *paisa,* but he was ashamed of being called that. Everyone in the neighborhood teased him and called him a farmer, but that's not what he wanted to be. He wanted to be a *cholo*, a gangster. Mexican gang members in L.A. are generational, with a long lineage in whatever gang they are members of. They speak Spanish, but prefer to speak English, or *Spanglish,* a mixture of the two languages. Chato strived to be like them, a first-generation gang member from his family, his children destined to follow suit and begin his lineage anew.

He and Ponce became close after the bloodbath in Long Beach even though they were opposites in every way. Ponce was a clown, always laughing and cracking jokes, loving it when someone accidentally hurt themself.

Chato was stoic, even when everyone around him was laughing out loud at one of Ponce's jokes. At the most, he would give a tight-lipped smile. He enjoyed drinking and smoking blunts and did meth from time to time, preferring to sniff it rather than smoke it. But now, he and Ponce were cold-blooded killers linked forever in crime, a Perry Edward Smith, and a Richard Eugene Hickock for the new millennium.

They would drive around together on missions, or even when they were just hanging out, and do ridiculous things, like pulling up to the *paleta* man selling his goods on the side of the street, sticking a gun in his face, and taking what little money he had. They also robbed liquor stores, 7-Elevens, and anywhere else where they felt they could get a quick buck.

When they would return to Ponce and Tatsuo's apartment, Ponce always bragged about their exploits while Chato sat quietly smoking a blunt. Whenever Ponce drifted into fantasy land and became D-Nutt, he loved to rap along to Dr. Dre and Snoop's "Ain't Nothing but a G-Thang," choosing to substitute the words to fit him and Chato:

"One, two, three, and to the foe,
Chato an' Big Saint is at da doe.
Ready to peel caps, so back on up
'Cuz you know we 'bout to blast shit up.
Give me the burna' so I can bust like a bubble,
Chato and Saint togetha', now you know you in trouble.
Ain't nothin' but a Watts thang baby,
Two laced out niggas goin' crazy
Nut Hood is da label dat pays me,
Unfadeable so please don't try to fade dis."

Murder hadn't come easy for Chato, though, and it appeared as if he may have even had a conscience in the beginning. After murdering the five people in the homeless encampment, he was in disbelief that he had been a part of what happened. When he and Ponce got back to the hood afterward, and everyone was celebrating like they had just won game seven of the World Series 5-0, he felt uneasy.

He snorted a line of meth, grabbed a bottle of Hennessy, and lit up the fattest blunt that he could find. Then, he went and put his elbow on the wall in a corner, bowed his head, and thought about what he had done. For the next year, he would often ask Ponce if he had nightmares about what happened that night, because he did, and he thought about it every day.

"When will I stop thinking about it, Saint? When will I get better?"

And Ponce probably told him that one night, he would get in bed to go to sleep, and he would close his eyes and realize that the whole day had gone by and he hadn't thought about the blood and the gore once.

And that was when he would know that he was better.

CHAPTER THIRTY-TWO

"YEAH, TATSUO. WHAT'S with the newspaper article?"

Tatsuo Hitomi cast her eyes downward, as if in shame. She might have grown up in some of the most impoverished areas of L.A. County among gang members, but she still had sparks of Japanese humility and respect.

"People don't keep newspaper articles unless they are about something significant to them. Take me, for example. Do you remember Ron Settles?"

"Detective McGuire, I don't—"

"Of course not. You're too young. Well, he was a good friend of mine. I went to high school with him. He got arrested one night in 1981 by the Signal Hill Police Department. The next morning, he was found hanging dead in a jail cell. I never believed that he killed himself. That affected me. And I still have that newspaper article. There may not be another one in my house, but I have that one. So, let's be real with each other here, okay? This is not a game."

"I know it isn't, Detective McGuire."

"A'ight, then tell us about the newspaper article my partner found at your house this morning. The one about a murder in Lake Los Angeles."

"The one with the found hand?"

"Yes. Was David involved in that as well?"

"Yes. It was a kid called Cat Eyes."

JUNE 17

"You have a collect call from... 'David Ponce'...an inmate at Men's Central Jail. Do you accept?"

"Yes. David?"

"Hey, baby. Why you crying?"

"I got arrested yesterday for accessory to murder! The police said the kids could get taken by DCFS!"

"Calm down, baby. The police are just using scare tactics. Am I gonna be charged for these murders?"

"Yes. And I'm not going down with you! I'll do anything for my kids! You need to re-think this shit! The police have phone records and all kinds of stuff on you! They have a case! They want me to testify against you and tell what I know about the murders! They know who was with you and everything! Our phones have been tapped and the police know everything, even what you asked me to do! The undercover detectives arrested me after I dropped the kids off at daycare!"

"This call may be monitored."

"Fuck, Tatsuo, calm down, will you? What kind of sentence can I get for this bullshit? I love you. I'm not gonna let them take the kids over this bullshit."

"It's not fair for me and the kids or anyone else who has nothing to do with this to go down. You need to go down with whoever else is responsible, David."

"You sure they got my old phone records, too?"

"Yes, they got everything! If you fight this, you're going to lose. I'm going to have to testify against you. I don't want to, and I can't move forward without knowing if you're going to—you know."

"This call may be monitored."

"I understand. I'll always love you. I'm not gonna have you and the kids in that situation. I'm gonna get taken off the main line if I get charged for this case."

"If I have to testify against you, David, and whoever else, I will do it because of the kids. I would hope that you understand."

Ponce started crying as he answered.

"I'm already finished, Tatsuo. If you play the game, you gotta pay the game. I understand what you gotta do. Just stand by my side for eleven years while I'm inside 'cause after that, it's a wrap. I'm gonna attack a CO and make them kill me. Call my homeboys and tell them I said you can testify."

"This call may be monitored."

"I'm not comfortable with that right now, David."

"I'll just write them and tell them what's going on. I'm fucked, Tatsuo. I know what I got coming, and I know where I'm going. It's a wrap. I was just talking about the death penalty last night, but I'm not gonna let them give me that."

"But what about me testifying against the other person?"

"I don't care about that either, Tatsuo. Call my brother and tell him I'm okay with that and that it came straight from my mouth. And you? Move out of the house. I think the police bugged it."

"They took all your letters too, David."

"This call may be monitored."

"Fuck! Now they might validate me as a Big Homie and take me off the line! I'm not gonna fight this shit. I don't care if the police are listening. I understand, baby. Just take care of my kids. And help my mom put money on her phone so I can talk to her. I'm gonna have to tell her, too. I'm gonna have to tell her that I lost everything. I love you."

"I love you, too. Bye David."

DAVID PONCE WAS RETURNED TO A HOLDING CELL WHERE ANOTHER inmate was housed.

The cell was recorded. There is no expectation of privacy in jails or prisons. The inmates all know this, but they get comfortable and often discuss their crimes, the same way they sometimes do while talking on jail phones.

Ponce was well-schooled in the tactics of law enforcement. He was in trouble, and he knew it. Yet, he still had no problem talking about his crimes. The most damning part of what he said would take place over the course of 66 minutes and 60 seconds—666.

CHAPTER THIRTY-THREE

"THAT SHIT WAS all over the news.

"And it was 'cause I domed them, fool, at point blank range, dawg, two bitches and three fools, you know what I mean? I capped all of them, my nigga. No body shots. I hit them all in the face, *bam*, *bam*, *bam*, I knocked their shit, you know what I mean? When I murder people, I've seen them freeze and I've seen them pale as fuck 'cause they can't do nothing 'cause they know it's a wrap.

"When I shot the first bitch, fool I shot that bitch in her face fool, when that bitch was hitting the pookie. I walked right up to that bitch, fool, and my little homie behind me. I walked right up to that bitch like, 'What's up muthafucka? I told you I'd be back with the full fit.' *Bam*. That bitch was like *bam*, *bam*. I hit that bitch right in the face. *Bam*, *bam*. Twice, fool. From here to here. *Boom*. I seen that shit. Knocked her shit smooth out, fool. *Pow*. It just explodes. On the second one, the second one splattered her shit in the back of the tent. *Bam*. The first one just went in. It blew a hole, fool, like this big.

"The second one went in, *pow*, *boom* and busted her shit out. Honestly, they don't have no time to make a face. The second bitch was like, 'Hey, what are you doing?' *Bam*, *bam*, *bam*, *bam*. Hit that bitch like three times, fool. The first one was like right here almost. The other two was in the face and another one in the head. *Boom*, fool. Both of these bitches is slumped on each other like this. And they still moving 'cause of they last nerves, fool. They twitching on each other. Shit leaking out.

"The nigga LV, he was like this, my boy. He was like—he couldn't even move, he was so fucking pale. He knew it was his time to go to Bobby's world. He turned state's evidence against his homie, but he had told on some other shit and then did some other shit. LV was from Dominguez. Right now, he probably would have been like forty-six, forty-seven. He got it good, fool. I gave it to him 'cause that's what I went for like six, my boy. *Bam, bam, bam, bam, bam.* Fuck that *rata.*

"That was my signature work, dawg. That's my signature. I only shoot 'em in the head. Headshots, up close and personal, two to three times. I do it like that 'cause I don't want nobody coming back and saying, 'Yeah, he did it,' you know what I mean? I gotta get that shit right, homie. I wanna see your brains so I know you ain't coming back, you know?

"That shit came to light 'cause of this fool Lucky. When we got to the spot, he bitched up and didn't handle business. I was gonna twist him up, but I gave him a pass and told him to walk home. I was gonna fuck him up, fool. He pumped that whole shit up like he was gonna whup LV's ass, but he didn't handle it right. He's all like, 'LV slanging big dope,' and I wanted to go over there and see Lucky pop his ass. But he didn't handle it correctly. I tells LV, 'You don't know who I am?' He was like, 'Nah, dawg.' And I told him to go ahead and play stupid, but I'll be back. I call my boy, and we ride back a week later, you know what I mean?

"I might get the death penalty 'cause of the way I did it! I creeped up on that ass, my lil homie with me grabbed this muthafucka and asked, 'Hey homie. Where LV at?' And he answers, 'Why? What's up?' And I was like, 'What the fuck you mean what's up? Where LV at?' Then he says, 'Oh, he's over there.' And I tell him to show me, and I snatched him by the shirt. I was holding the fool by the shirt, and I already had my burner out. I told my boy, 'Hey fool, when I pop, you pop, fucker. You make sure it's a dome shot. Not hitting their bodies. Dome shots.'

"So when we get to the spot, there's a bitch, and she was in a circle hitting the pookie. So when I walked up fool, and looked at LV, I was like 'Watts up?' I was like *bam*! 'What's up muthafucka? I told you I'd be back.' He was like, 'Oh, shit.' He turned pale as fuck. But I had the burner out, and this bitch was right next to the entrance, and LV and his bitch were next to her. So I pieced the first bitch, *bam, bam*! I pieced that bitch twice, my boy. I mean I knocked a hole in her shit quick, my boy, hit her again, *bam*! I mean another one, *bam, bam, bam, bam*! I gave it to that bitch four times.

"The first one was right here, second one was in her face, another one right here, and another one like around her mouth or some shit. And *bam*! She slumped over on that other bitch and LV couldn't even move, dawg. He was just froze. *Baca, baca, baca, baca, baca, baca*, I hit his ass like six times, fool. I emptied a whole clip out. They all slumped on each other. Then I just hit 'em again. *Bam, bam, bam, bam*! They was done.

"When I popped, there was another fool that was standing outside of where they was at. So when I popped that first bitch, I hear it behind me. *Bing-bing, bing-bing*, the lil homie let off, you know what I mean? He hit the other fools in the face. I just hear them drop you know what I mean?

"And we got another homie in the car the whole time. We hit the freeway and we driving back to the hood. And I'm happy as fuck, like *bam*, muthafuckas! I told you your boy got out. I told you, that's that old-school gangster shit, player, that's how you do dirt. You fucking do it just like that. And I was excited. I was happy about it, you know what I mean?

"And my other homie, the guy driving the car, come in just looking like, 'Damn big homie, that shit sounded like Vietnam back there! I just heard *bing bing bing bing bing bing bing bing*.' And I told him, 'Damn fool, I gotta get it done, my boy.' And my other homeboy wasn't saying nothing. He was just in the back seat, fool, just like, 'I killed them.' When we got back in the hood, the homie, he grabbed a brew, snorted his line, and smoked a fat ass blunt, like he was trying to get that shit out of his head, dawg, 'cause he was just in the corner like damn, like that shit psycho, my boy. It was prolly his first time.

"Even March, down the line, this fool almost a year later, he was like 'I still be having nightmares 'cause of that shooting that night, dawg,' like he couldn't shake that shit. I was like, 'that shit is real, player,' and he was like, 'I know my boy.' And I'm like, 'I'm fucked, you know what I mean? I know the devil got me now, too.' This shit is old fool. They hitting me with the five from Long Beach in '08, and one in Lancaster in '09.

"I hit this fool in the desert with a fitty-cal, fool. I had him on his knees in the desert in a prayer position. I had gave him a quarter pound of that good shit, that Arizona. But then that bitch disappeared on me. He didn't know who he was fucking with. So I got word to him that he was taking money from the mouths of my kids and food off my table. I told him that if he didn't get my money, I was gonna dust his ass. I told him point blank, period, that I wasn't fucking playing with his ass. 'The next time I see you, I'm gonna fuck you up.'

"I go by different rules. He was a fucking white boy, a wanna-be dealer like one of them *tintos*, them Crips. They called him Cat Eyes. So, I fucking dusted that fool. Right before I caught him, I had got in an argument with my girl. And I was like 'fuck it.' I went to my boy's house to go chill, and I drank a bottle of Hennessy and a big bottle of Cisco. Then I just said, 'Fuck it. Let me hit the corner and go look for that lil muthafucking Cat Eyes.' I don't even think he knew me and my girl had moved up to Lancaster.

"I went driving 'round and I see him riding on a bike. I was like, 'Damn! There go that little bitch!' I'm like, 'Oh hell yes!' So, I roll up on him like, 'Hey, what's up, my nigga?' I acted like I wasn't even tripping and we was friends and shit. I was like, 'Damn, fool, I been looking for your ass. Hop in. We're gonna go smoke some blunts together.' I know Lancaster, dawg. So, I drove this fool to 176 East, way in the desert. I made him get out the car. My intention was just to beat his ass, you know what I mean? After all, a dead man can't pay you what he owe you, right? I was just gonna beat the shit out of him and make him walk home in the desert asshole naked, right?

"He had some cool eyes, though, fool. He did have like cat eyes. His shit was like a greenish-blue. That's why they call him what they do, you know? Anyway. While we was driving, this fool was like, 'I'll pay you back, I swear!' He starts flipping out, you know? He saying he gonna pay me all my money back and he put it on his dead mama and his dead grandparents. Then he starts swearing that he didn't know I was looking for him.

"I said, 'You bitch ass nigga. You fucking knew I was looking for you. Now you wanna just lie to me? Now I'm about to send you to yo' bitch ass mama and she gonna slap the fuck out of you in hell for fucking me out of my money.' So, we finally pull up in the desert... In broad daylight. In broad daylight, fool. I told him to get the fuck out of my car. It's all open. It's all open, my boy. It's nothing but desert. No street. Nothing, fool. I got a cannon. The fitty-cal, fool, the Smith & Wesson. Fitty-cal, fool.

"That muthafucka was heavy, homie, it was meaty. So I told this bitch, I was like, 'Get the fuck out of my car,' fool. So he starts begging, he like,

'Come on, Big Homie.' He got tears in his eyes. I'm like, 'Dawg, get out the car. Man, get the fuck out.' I grab his shirt, fool and kicked him in the ass, *bam*. I'm like, 'Get the fuck out.' I was like, 'Nigga, say yo' prayers, 'cause you gone, homie.' Fuck him. Fuck him on my dead homie's grave, rest in peace, my boy. I'm like, 'Hey, fool, you better say your fucking prayers, homie, 'cause yo' ass is gone, dawg. You gonna meet your maker, muthafucka.'

"'And that mom, yeah, you gonna see that bitch, homie, believe that. She gonna slap the fuck out you, dawg, like I told you. And he was like, 'Hey, come on Big Homie.' He on the ground like, 'Come on.' I'm like, 'What'd I say, nigga?' *Bam*! I cracked him on the back of the head fool, with that big ass barrel. So, I bust his shit open a little bit. And he like, 'Oh come on, man.' And I'm like, 'I ain't playing with you.' I pull the hammer back. I'm like, 'You better start praying. So, he did. He started praying. He got on his knees, fool. I'm like, 'Eleven,' eleven for the block. I'm like, 'Eleven,' for the hood. One hundred eleven block. 'Nine, eight, seven,' and he's praying. I'm like, 'Six, five, four, three, two, one, you up nigga,' *bam, bam, bam, bam*. I gave it to him, fool, all in the back of the head at close range. Shit kicked off.

"*Bam, bam* all on my fucking clothes and boots and shit. *Bam, bam, bam, bam*. As soon as I twisted him, I got back in the car. Fool, I take a big swig of my Cisco. I put my shit in reverse, drive off, call baby, and tell her I'm on the way home. I burnt my shit later. When me and the lil homie got arrested with the Mac-eleven in my baby mama's car, the lil homie starts apologizing. He should have got out and ran with it instead of putting it under the seat.

"But I forgive him, 'cause I love that lil nigga. And the cops ain't gonna never get the guns we used in the thing, because we melted them down. Those are gone. We both went to prison for the Mac, but he only got like seven or eight months because that was the first time he been. He was only like eighteen years old. He had just got put on. He was a late bloomer, you know? Me? I got twelve bodies under my belt, including five at one time. And that ain't even counting all the shit I done in prison or the county jail."

DAVID PONCE WAS IN FACT THE DEMON THAT HIS MOTHER HAD exorcised.

He had just nonchalantly reduced six human beings to mere footnotes in the annals of criminal history. His obscene onomatopoeia would sicken the investigators when they heard the recording later, as they realized that each sound that he made was mimicking a bullet ending a life.

The entirety of the recording was three hours and sixteen minutes, or 3:16, the Bible verse about God so loving the world that He sacrificed His one and only son. With Ponce's history of fighting demons, with his mother seemingly casting the devil out of him, with the most terrifying portions of his confession taking up 66 minutes and 60 seconds, perhaps there is a purpose in so-called angel numbers. Perhaps in them lies an explanation for the unexplained deaths of the innocent while monsters live among us, seemingly unabated.

Coincidences are nebulous things. The more they start to accumulate, however, the less ambiguous they become.

PART EIGHT

CHAPTER THIRTY-FOUR

IT WAS A QUARTER to 3 p.m., just hours after Ponce's chilling account of murder.

"You have a collect call from... 'David Ponce' ...an inmate at Men's Central Jail. Do you accept?"

"Yes. David?"

"It's me, Mom. Have you talked to Tatsuo?"

"Yes, *mijo*. She says the police want you to plead guilty and confess. Please, son, don't confess to something you haven't done."

"Mom, there's a lot more stuff that I've done that they don't even know about. I can't and won't hide it anymore, Mom. I don't want Tatsuo and the kids—"

"This call may be monitored."

"—to go through something that they didn't do. I gotta do what Dad taught me to do and stand up like a man. I done a lot of shit they don't know about. I done a lot. The police want Tatsuo to testify against me, and they got a lot more on me, even the stuff on Linden."

"Please, *mijo*, please."

"Don't cry, Mom, please. I'm gonna tell the police what they want because they got it. Everything they showed and told Tatsuo, they got it. There's no more hiding anything. I'm not going to fight this case because it would jeopardize Tatsuo and the kids. I don't want a lawyer just to lose in the end. It's okay if Tatsuo testifies against me."

"This call may be monitored."

"Ah, David..."

"I wish you would stop crying, Mom. It's not your fault. The police have phone calls, phone records, pictures, and phone taps. I'm gonna go to court and tell them that I'm guilty. If they let me back upstate without filing the murder charges on me, I'm gonna try and escape—"

"Mijo, watch what you're saying. This line is recorded."

"This call may be monitored."

"I don't care anymore, Mom. I know what the outcome is gonna be and I just don't care anymore. I put myself in this position, and no one else did. I wasn't forced to do anything that I did. Bye Mom. I'll talk to you later."

"I'VE KNOWN DAVID SINCE 1994 OR '95."

It was June 20, and Kenny Richardson, aka Motor, was being interviewed by Cortes and McGuire at Long Beach PD. He had been arrested at his house early that morning based on things Ponce said in the jail recordings. He hadn't said enough to file a case against Richardson, but it was enough to get him down to the station.

"We both lived in the Dominguez area," Richardson continued. "David went to prison and when he came home, he was all gangsta'd out. He was on some different shit. He was hard, his face was tattooed, and he said his name was now Bloodbath."

"What gang was he in, *amigo?*"

"I think he joined the Nut Hood gang while he was locked-up. He was never from D-Thirteen."

Cortes and McGuire had dealt with hundreds of hardcore gang members over the thirty-five years on the job they had between them up to that point. Richardson didn't appear to be cut from that mold. They knew that he was no Boy Scout, but they didn't get the impression that he would be involved in something as cold-blooded as the Quintuple. Just as cops need friends who aren't cops, maybe it was just as simple as Ponce needing friends who weren't from his world.

"Did you go with E, Lucky, and David to a homeless camp about a week before the murders?" Cortes asked.

"Yeah. We left from Lucky's house. He was looking for a guy who owed him money. We took my mom's car. That fool E stayed in the car and me, Lucky, and David went to find the guy. Him and Lucky got into a fight. David got into an argument with some big Samoan chick and before we left, I took two dollars from this old man. I didn't rob him, though. I asked, and he gave it to me."

"Why would you ask that old man for money, Kenny? You know those people are barely surviving," McGuire asked.

"I know, sir. And I feel bad about it. I guess I was just trying to be tough, you know? Lucky fighting, David standing tall, and and me doing nothing. I didn't want them calling me a pussy later, so I just did it. I didn't hurt nobody."

"Are you in a gang, Kenny?"

"No. I just used to fuck around with them when they were getting high and rapping. I ain't no gangsta. David was, and he thought he was going to be a big-time rapper one day, too. He called himself 'D-Nutt.' He was decent. At least as good as some of these other phonies lying about being gangstas. David was rapping true shit, know what I mean?"

"Unfortunately, we do," McGuire said. "Were you involved in the homeless people murders, Kenny?"

"No."

"Did you get rid of guns for David? Or take the killers there, that night?"

"No, sir, Detective McGuire. I thought Lucky killed them because he lost the fight with LV. When I heard about the murders, I thought he had just gone back. David's mother called me to let me know that Tatsuo got arrested. I think it was June the seventeenth. She called me later that same day and told me that David wanted me to know that he is not coming home, and he doesn't want anyone else getting caught up in things that he's done, and that he loves me."

"A'ight den, Mr. Richardson. Anything else, Hugo?"

"I think we got all we need, *amigo*."

"Okay, Mr. Richardson. Take it easy."

"Am I going home, sir?"

"Probably. Just sit tight. Someone will be in here shortly."

After McGuire and Cortes got back to their desks, Cortes asked, "What do you think, Mac? You think he's involved in any way?"

"No. He doesn't seem like the kind of guy Ponce would take with him on something like this. And I think that Tatsuo would've told us if she knew he was the driver. Maybe Ponce was concerned that we were gonna charge him with what happened with Sammy. Do I think that he knows about the murders? Hell yeah! But he will never tell on Ponce."

"Agreed. You wanna call Sheriff's Homicide and let them know about the article?"

"How about we grab something to eat first. I don't think there's any rush. They probably haven't looked at the case since it happened. C'mon. I'm buying."

"I WONDER WHAT MADAME LAVIGNE IS DOING RIGHT NOW," CORTES asked as he took a sip of steaming hot black coffee. He and McGuire were sitting in the same booth at the Fish House where she had swindled the city out of at least two hundred dollars.

"Probably at Scotland Yard consulting on the Jack the Ripper investigation," McGuire said just as the waitress walked up with menus. Cortes ordered first before McGuire asked for grilled yellowfin tuna.

"You sure do love seafood, huh Mac?"

"Hell yeah. Is that a problem?"

"Not at all. I just think it's funny that you have no problem eating what comes from the sea, but you won't swim in their home."

Cortes, like McGuire, was an excellent swimmer, but he preferred swimming in the sea whereas McGuire didn't go near it.

"Do you have any idea how many Africans got eaten by sharks when they jumped off those slave ships coming to America?"

"How the fuck would I know that, Mac? How the fuck does *anyone* know that?"

"Exactly. How the fuck does anyone know other than 'a shitload' of them. You think I'm getting my Black behind in the sea? Hell no. And no, I'm not scared of sharks. Call it a healthy appreciation for their dominance of the ocean and a reverence for what my ancestors had to endure. I will eat the shit out of them, especially grilled, but I'll be damned if one is gonna eat me."

Cortes chuckled, called McGuire a little girl, and put a forkful of roasted beet salad in his mouth.

CHAPTER THIRTY-FIVE

"SHERIFF'S HOMICIDE, can I help you?"

"Hello. This is Detective McGuire from Long Beach Homicide. I'm trying to get ahold of whoever is working the case of a found hand in Lancaster in 2009."

"Yes, sir. Let me check for you. One second. Let's see here. Okay. That is assigned to Sergeants Rodriguez and Gray. I'll transfer you to Sergeant Rodriguez. Please hold the line."

"No worries."

While McGuire was waiting, he said, "Hey, Hugo. I know one of the detectives assigned to the case. His name is Marty, if I remember right. I met him at a Homicide Conference. He's a good guy."

"Homicide, Sergeant Rodriguez speaking."

"It's Mark McGuire from Long Beach PD Homicide."

"I remember you. Didn't we meet at a training class or something?"

"Yep. Homicide Conference. In 2004."

"That's right. They call you Mac Daddy, right?"

"Sometimes."

"I ain't even gonna get into why they call you that. What's going on?"

"My partner and I are working that quintuple murder that happened at a homeless encampment in 2008."

"Oh, yeah. I remember that. I had forgot all about it. That story went away quick. I guess there was no political traction left to be gained."

"Exactly. And that's the way we like it. Quiet, so me and my partner can just do our thing."

"I hear you, partner. That scene must have been horrible, huh?"

"Yeah, it was bad, Marty. The guy who reported it got there just before crows were about to start feasting on eyeballs."

"Yikes. Well, what can I help you with today? You guys need some resources for something?"

"No, we're cool on our end, but I think we might be able to help you."

"How so?"

"You handled a found hand case in Lake Los Angeles a few years ago?"

"Yeah. Me and Bobby Gray. The owner of the hand had been dead for a while when we finally found him. Between the four-legged critters and the buzzards, there was nothing much left other than clothes and bones. Please tell me you got some info."

"I got something better than that. I know who your suspect is. I got a witness who can tell you everything you need to know. We found a newspaper clipping when we served a search warrant at a house in Lancaster the other day. The article is about a hand being found 2009. We think your killer and our killer are one and the same. This guy is evil, Marty. If Jack the Ripper had been born a hundred and forty years later and raised on One Hundred and Eleventh Street in Watts, his name would be David Ponce."

"David Ponce, huh? The name doesn't sound familiar. What's his hood name?"

"Saint."

"Nah. Nothing."

"How about Bloodbath?"

"Bloodbath?"

"Yep."

"I don't even wanna know what he did to get that moniker. Still nothing, though. I've never even met a gang member called Bloodbath. Tons of Snipers, Bullets, *Osos*, Jokers, and Clowns, but never anybody called Bloodbath. Hey, I get the Jack the Ripper comparison, but why did you say One Hundred and Eleventh Street in Watts? Is he from Nut Hood, or something?"

"Absolutely. He is one-hundred and eleven percent Nut Hood Watts. Got a big ass tattoo of his hood on his face. He's been a suspect in our case since a month or two after the murders. Our surveillance team followed him to a house in Lancaster during the first part of 2009. It's the same house where we found the newspaper clipping."

"This guy sounds real hardcore."

"He is. He got caught with a burner in his car in 2010. A Mac-eleven for one-eleven. He's still in custody. The witness on your murder is his baby mama, and she's co-op. We're relocating her and their kids. According to her, the owner of that hand was a guy called Cat Eyes."

"Well, Ponce's baby mama is right about the name victim. His real name was Tony Bledsoe. A white kid from the 60s."

"The Rolling 60s? From South Central L.A.?"

"Yep."

"Get the fuck outta here, Marty."

"I shit you not. Anyway, what's Ponce's baby mama's name?"

"Tatsuo Hitomi."

"Get the fuck outta here, Mac."

"I ain't bullshitting. Straight up."

"Well that certainly doesn't sound like a local. Sounds like she's a long way from home," Rodriguez said, trying to picture just how someone with a name like that ended up with a south-central L.A. gang member. The city council people in L.A. may have changed the name, but McGuire and cops who worked in that area when it was the wild, wild west still agreed with Ice Cube.

"Yeah, well, when she opens her mouth, you can tell right away she ain't no geisha girl," McGuire said.

"Well, I for one am looking forward to having a long conversation with Ms. Hitomi."

"I told her that you guys were gonna be talking to her real soon. She will probably request that I be there. I got a rapport with her, you know."

"Oh, okay. Now I know why they call you Mac Daddy. Soft touch with the ladies, huh?"

"I plead the fifth, my brutha."

They both laughed, and Rodriguez said, "Crows, huh?"

"What?"

"Crows. You said your discovering party scared off some when he found the bodies."

"Oh, yeah. They're a big problem in that area where the murders occurred. Pretty much all over the rest of the city, too. Vindictive bastards."

"Well, you know what they say, right? Crows murder and buzzards mourn."

"I know crows are called a murder when a bunch of them are together, but why do they say buzzards mourn?"

"Because a group of them is called a wake. Anyway, let me grab our poor boy. I'll call you back to make arrangements to talk to her. Oh yeah, what kind of car were they in when your surveillance team followed them?"

"A green Nissan. Ponce was arrested with the gun in a different car, though."

"Alright. Thanks. I'll get back to you. I got a new partner, so I gotta get him up to speed."

"A'ight, den. Peace in the hood."

Rodriguez was now partnered with Sergeant Dan McElderry. They had been working together for several months, but they had only picked up a few cases. None of them had been that big of a deal, just people killed in the wrong zip codes one at a time. Rodriguez walked over to the desk of Sergeant Gray, who was with a new partner on another team.

"Bobby, do you have the poor boy on that Lancaster case we handled a few years back? You know, the one that started off as just a hand?"

"Cat Eyes? Yeah, here it is right here."

Gray reached underneath his desk and grabbed one of the six poor boys collecting dust. There were five more on top of the desk, and another three or four next to his chair.

"What's up, Marty? You got something?"

"Maybe."

"Maybe my ass. You gave that dog to me to deal with when all we had was a hand and animal food in the fucking desert. You must have something good to be asking for it back. Here, ya' fucking *maricón*."

Rodriguez smiled, took the paper-thin poor boy, and went back to his desk where he briefed McElderry on the case.

"Sounds like a good one, Marty. And it's connected to a massacre in Long Beach around Halloween of 2008, huh?"

"Yeah, sounds like it."

"Well, those victims in Long Beach certainly got the rag in the barmbrack cake."

"What the hell is that, Dan?"

"You never heard of a barmbrack cake?"

"Fuck no."

"It's a tradition in Ireland. On Halloween, people make cakes, which are actually slabs of fruit bread. They put a rag, a coin, and a ring in each cake. If you get the piece with the ring, you have romance in your future. If you get the piece with the coin, there is a financial windfall in your future. If you get the piece with the rag, then your financial future is doubtful. I said the victims in Long Beach got the rag because you surely can't make any money if you're dead."

"Danny-me-boy," Rodriguez replied in his best Irish accent. "Those victims in Long Beach had been getting rags all their lives. They were all homeless. Even *our* victim was homeless."

McElderry was a clean-shaven white man who kept his hair neatly trimmed. He smiled a lot, had twinkling eyes, and loved to drink scotch, ideally Macallan Rare Cask Single Malt. He had been in the Sheriff's Department for close to thirty years and was well-respected by his peers. He was also a sensitive man. He always tried to see the good in people, no matter what. He felt a huge sense of empathy for the victims. He got to work on the case right away.

"Let me run this David Ponce and Tatsuo Hitomi and see what their sheets look like, Marty."

"Okay. I'm gonna run the car connected to Hitomi. According to McGuire, their surveillance team caught her and Ponce in a dark green Nissan Altima."

"Bledsoe was last seen getting into a dark green car, right?"

"Sure was."

A few minutes later, Rodriguez sat back in his chair and started rubbing his head.

"What you got, Marty?"

"Hitomi was involved in a traffic collision in Long Beach on September 21, 2009, but she was driving a different car than the one Ponce got arrested in. She was in a dark green 1998 Buick. I would be willing to bet that is the car Bledsoe was last seen getting into. She must have fucked it up bad. It's still at an auto wrecking place in Lancaster."

"McGuire wasn't lying about Ponce," McElderry said as he handed a copy of Ponce's booking photo to Rodriguez. "Look at this guy's face. And he's got a lengthy sheet, too. To top it all off, he got arrested in Lancaster by the CHP on September 19, 2009, for DUI. He was driving that green Buick. An empty bottle of Cisco was the front seat passenger."

"That's only nine days after we found Bledsoe. I'm calling the wrecking company to put an evidence hold on it before they make it into a little green square."

The following day, Rodriguez and McElderry went to look at the car. They photographed it and arranged to have it taken to a tow yard where it could be processed for evidence. The next day Crime lab personnel photographed it, dusted it for fingerprints, and futilely examined it for the presence of blood.

Any evidence that was in the car two years ago—and there would have been a significant amount given the carnage generated—was now long gone.

PART NINE

CHAPTER THIRTY-SIX

JUNE 22, 2011

"Hey, Hugo," McGuire said as he turned away from his computer monitor. "We know that Chato is on paper, right? Since he lives in the Sheriff's Department's jurisdiction, how about we get an OSS team to do a parole search at his house. His conditions are the usual, no guns, dope, etcetera, plus no gang activity. And you know he's not complying."

"Smart. We can get him into custody that way, and he won't have any idea that it has anything to do with Long Beach. I'll make the call."

"I'll call the surveillance team and have them tail him to find out who he's hanging out with now that Ponce is locked up," McGuire replied.

Two days later, Max Rafael was in custody. An OSS team found a loaded gun in his bedroom. It was not one of the murder weapons, but he was a convicted felon, so he was going back to prison. Now McGuire and Cortes would be able to put him in a recorded jail cell with his crime partner, David Ponce, to see if they would incriminate each other.

McGuire and Cortes decided to check on Tatsuo Hitomi and see if they could get more information to use when they interviewed Rafael and Ponce again. They met with her at the house where she and her kids had been relocated to.

"Hello, Tatsuo. You doing okay? You haven't had any problems, have you?" McGuire asked.

FREDERICK DOUGLASS REYNOLDS

"No. I'm doing good. No problems."

"And the kids? I know it's been rough uprooting them and all."

"They are doing fine. They ask about their father a lot though. That's something I'm just going to have to deal with, I guess."

"Tatsuo, sometimes you have a habit of remembering shit after we ask a couple of times so we thought we would ask again. Who drove the car the night of the homeless murders? We know David told you."

"It was a new homie from Nut Hood, Detective McGuire. They call him Crook. I don't know what car they were in or what kind of car he usually drives. He's not in jail as far as I know."

"Are you sure that the guns they used are gone, *amiga*? Or do you know where they are?"

"Oh, they're gone, Detective Cortes. When David and Chato got arrested with that gun in my car, I asked David during one of our phone calls if it was one of the guns they used. He told me that they had got rid of those guns. We talked a lot when he had a cell phone in prison."

"Other than the murders you have already told us about, do you know of any others that David may have committed?"

"Yes. He told me that he has really bad dreams about them. He believes they were the souls of all the people he killed or hurt. He said he killed a Black guy in an alley in Long Beach when he was nineteen years old. He chased the guy down and shot him in the head. And he helped beat up a woman and throw her down some stairs when he lived on Linden Street. She died. It was David and another guy. They killed her over drugs. That's all I know, though."

"Okay, Tatsuo. You have our numbers. Call us if you need anything," McGuire said as he and Cortes left.

Tatsuo had been helpful, but they needed a lot more information on Crook and to help make a case against Rafael. They had to interview him. Even if he invoked his Miranda rights, they had to put something on his mind to stimulate conversation with Ponce, whom they weren't worried about at this point. He had given a chillingly candid soliloquy in a recorded cell. He was done. No jury could hear what he said and be able to sleep that night. But Rafael? What Tatsuo told McGuire and Cortes was hearsay, and inadmissible. For him, they needed something more than just her statement. There was no physical evidence putting him at the scene.

They needed a confession, or they needed him admitting his role in the murders on tape.

AUGUST 24

Ponce and Rafael were transported to Long Beach PD jail. They thought it was for appearances in Long Beach court, but the true purpose was to facilitate interviews. The cells they were placed in had recording devices in them. McGuire and Cortes wanted them to talk to each other before they interviewed them. Then, Ponce and Rafael would be put back in a cell together again. Ponce didn't disappoint. He started talking almost immediately:

"Man, Chato, I think we're here for those five murders. This shit crazy and it ain't good. They gonna get at me 'bout that case and they gonna try to bring up some cold shit. I think I'm gonna ask for a lawyer. This shit ain't no joke. And the cops are gonna fuck with my family, too. They showed me a bunch of pictures and talked about Tatsuo the last time I was here."

"The deputies who brought me down here told me that the homicide detectives wanted to talk to me. They just fishing, Saint. Fuck the po-leece. Crooked-ass bastards!"

MCGUIRE AND CORTES DECIDED TO INTERVIEW RAFAEL FIRST.

Cortes called the jailer and requested that he bring Rafael to an interview room where he and McGuire were waiting, and then secure Ponce in another room.

"Hello, Max. I'm Detective McGuire and this is my partner, Detective Cortes. What do you want us to call you?"

"Max is fine."

"Max. A'ight. Let me read you your rights."

Rafael told McGuire he understood and did not need a lawyer. Before asking any questions, McGuire put a booking photo of Tatsuo, the surveillance photos taken during the early stages of the investigation, and photos taken by OSS of Rafael and his house on the table. Rafael looked at them, but said nothing.

"Okay, *amigo*. Do you know why you're here?"

"Yeah. 'Cause I got caught with a burner."

"Your name came up during our investigation into the murders of five people in 2008. We know everything, and you've been identified as one of the shooters," McGuire said.

"Yeah? Well, what y'all witnesses say or see that could tell y'all some bullshit like that?"

"Don't worry about that. You'll find out everything we have sooner rather than later. Is this you?" McGuire asked. "Right here, in this photo line-up?"

"Yeah. That's me."

"A'ight, den. Look at this. You know anybody?"

McGuire put the photograph from Tatsuo's computer with Rafael and Ponce holding handguns on the table. Rafael pointed at it and said, "That's me."

"Who is the other guy holding a gun? Right here?" McGuire asked while pointing to Ponce.

"I don't know."

"This guy. Right here," McGuire said. "You're telling us you don't know him?"

"Nope. Don't know him."

McGuire pointed to the photograph of Tatsuo.

"How about her. Do you know who she is?"

"Nah. Who is it?"

"A'ight. Look at these, then."

McGuire spread the pictures from the crime scene across the table. Rafael turned his head away and folded his arms.

"I don't want to see that shit."

"Okay. It is pretty messed up, ain't it? What kind of sick individual would do something like this, right? Do you remember where you were on November 1st, 2008?"

"Yeah. I was in school."

"Do you go to night school or something?"

"No. During the day."

"I doubt that you were in school when it happened. They were killed on a Saturday night."

"Do you know Saint from the Southside Nut Hood Watts gang, *amigo*?"

"I ain't gonna answer that."

"A'ight den, Max. Are *you* from Nut Hood Watts?"

"I ain't gonna answer that neither. I don't know nothing, and I ain't do nothing."

"What's your gang name?" Cortes asked.

"I ain't gonna answer that."

"Why did you turn away when you looked at the pictures of the dead people?"

"Cause I ain't like looking at them."

"But why, *amigo*? They're only pictures—"

"Cause I just didn't, okay?"

"Are you Chato from Southside Nut Hood Watts?" McGuire asked.

"I don't know who that is."

"Um hum...Who drove you and Saint to the homeless encampment to commit the murders, Max?"

"I don't know what you talking about. Matter of fact, I'm done talking. Period."

"A'ight den. Let's get you back to your cell."

CHAPTER THIRTY-SEVEN

"NOW WE SLAY the dragon, Hugo."

"There you go with that dragon and knight *caca* again."

"*Black* Knight, bitch. I'm the *Black* Knight."

"*Chingalé*. Then what does that make me then? Don Quixote?"

"No. Puss in Boots, you sexy muthafucka," McGuire said as he opened the door to the interview room where Ponce was waiting. He was sitting with one of his wrists handcuffed to the table. He smiled when McGuire and Cortes walked in.

"What's up, fellas? Long time no see."

"What's up, *amigo?*"

"What's up, David?"

McGuire quietly put the surveillance pictures, crime scene photos, and photos from Tatsuo's computer on the table. Ponce was nonplussed, barely glancing at them.

"A'ight, den. David, do you know why you're here?"

"Yeah, I do. Ain't you gonna read me my rights?"

When McGuire was done, Ponce sat back in his chair and said, "Let's rap. I don't need no lawyer."

"David, you've been under surveillance for quite a while now. We've also been listening to your phone calls, and we've looked in your computers, which is where most of those photos come from, except for the bloody ones."

"Damn, McGuire," Ponce said as he laughed. "Y'all been busy with the computers, huh?"

"Oh, this is funny to you, huh?" Cortes said as he pointed to the picture of LV. "Do you know who this is?"

Ponce sucked his teeth and said, "I don't know. Why don't you tell me?"

"We believe this is the guy Lucky threatened to come back and kill if he didn't have his money."

"I don't know who the fuck that is—what's your name again?"

"Cortes—with an s, not a z."

"That's real important to you, huh? Okay, Cortes with an s. I don't know who that is, but the other pictures are of my baby mama, my kids, my brother, and my moms."

"Were you involved in the murders, David?" McGuire asked.

"I got no idea what you talking about. I wasn't there."

"Come on, David. We heard you on the phone talking about how you hit five home runs."

"What does that mean? I'm a Dodger fan. I wasn't talking about this case."

McGuire slid the picture of Ponce and Rafael holding guns at Tripper's funeral across the table.

"Do you know this guy with you in the picture?"

"Of course. I'm in the picture with him, ain't I? That's Chato."

"A'ight, den. Do you remember when this picture was taken?"

"At our homeboy Tripper's funeral."

"That's right. At Tripper's funeral. What happened to the guns?"

Ponce smiled and hunched his shoulders.

"Uh huh. Well, let's talk about the five murdered homeless people."

"Why? I wasn't there and I ain't have shit to do with it."

"Bullshit. We believe the murders are connected to something that happened a week before with Lucky, LV, and Vanessa. Someone threatened them. And we believe that someone was you—"

Ponce giggled and said, "It wasn't me."

"—and a week later you go back to the campsite where the fight happened and make one of the victims show you where the new campsite is. You and Chato walked him across the freeway, and you told Chato to shoot other people while you shoot LV. Is that about right?"

McGuire had no idea whether they made Sammy take them via the tunnels, or across the freeway. When Ponce squinted at the mention of the freeway, McGuire picked up on it. *That's it*, he thought. *That's the way they took. Too bad a CHP unit didn't happen to be driving by.*

With Ponce's bravado faltering, McGuire picked up the goriest scene photographs and started dropping them on the table, Ponce was quiet until the ones depicting Kat fell in front of him.

"I don't want to see that shit."

"Why, David? Do you have nightmares about it?"

"No. Why would I?"

"Tell us about your homeboy Crook, *amigo*."

"What about him?"

"Is he still in federal custody?"

"He not from Nut Hood, and I don't know where he is. We grew up in separate places."

"Well, where *is* he from?" McGuire asked.

"I don't know where he from, but I know he ain't from Nut Hood. And what's up with this anyway? How come I ain't been charged with nothing yet?"

"The investigation is ongoing," Cortes said. "By the way. Did you have any involvement in some murders on Linden when you lived there in 2000? We know you were selling dope out of your apartment."

"Yeah, David. A woman was murdered on either Christmas Day or Christmas Eve. Sad case. A couple of guys beat her to death and dumped her in a trash can. Just because of a little bit of crack. Not even twenty dollars worth. The other case involves a Black guy who got shot in the head. We got one of the shooters. The other one got away. We think it was you."

"I heard about that shit, McGuire. But I ain't have nothing to do with neither one. I heard they were kilt over some crack or some bullshit like that. I lived on the second floor in that apartment complex where those murders happened. I thought somebody got arrested. I don't know who, though."

"A'ight den, David. Just how many people have *you* killed in Long Beach and L.A. County?"

Ponce laughed, slapped his free hand on the table and said, "You guys are good, man! That's crazy!"

"Did you do any other murders while you were living on Linden, David?" Cortes asked.

"Hell, naw. I ain't did no murders on Linden. Period."

"Well, there are witnesses who gave the same physical description that you have, and told the cops that 'D-Nutt' or 'D' from Nut Hood Watts was involved. That sounds an awful lot like you, David."

"You know I'm from Nut Hood, Cortes with a fucking *s*, and my nickname always been D-Nutt, but I ain't kilt nobody. You know what? Here. Take my DNA. Y'all already got my fingerprints on file. If you got witnesses, let them do they job."

"You said that the last time we talked to you. Stop saying it. We already *have* your DNA, *amigo*. It's been in the CODIS system for years. If we ask for it now, it'll be to confirm that you *committed* a crime, not to solve it."

"What the fuck is CODIS?"

"It stands for 'Combined DNA Index System'. And like I said, *your* DNA has been in there for years, so please, stop offering it."

"A'ight," McGuire said. "Let's switch reels a bit. Did you tell Tatsuo to get rid of evidence related to this case? Like some old clothes and shoes?"

"I told her to throw away my Timbs 'cause they was old. Tatsuo ain't got no involvement in none of this."

"No, *mi amigo*. We think she knows a lot more than she told us when we interviewed her in June."

Ponce didn't laugh or giggle this time. His eyes were slits of malevolence as he just shrugged his shoulders again.

"What do you mean in your letters to her when you write about sending people to 'Bobby's world'?"

"Shit, man. Seriously, McGuire? That's just a game. I said that whenever I scored a touchdown. What you thought it meant?"

"Well, we think it means you killed someone."

"No way I meant it that way. I ain't never kilt nobody in my life."

"Tell us about the case you're in for now. Were you and Chato out for revenge for Tripper when y'all got arrested?" Cortes asked.

"Nope. I was just giving somebody a ride home. The police profiled us and stopped us."

"Come on with that bullshit, David. We don't believe that. We know you've been careful because there are no fingerprints or DNA from the homeless murders, but the victims were killed using your signature move of head and face shots. And we know that LV was your main target."

"Okay, McGuire. What kind of motive would I have to peel five caps?"

"Probably because the other four were witnesses. This could also be Southside business, disrespect from Vanessa the week before, or maybe you just didn't like LV. Maybe it's all of the above."

"You wrong on all theories. LV and Lucky had problems, not me. I was there when they argued and fought. His bitch was running off at the mouth. So what?"

"Now we're getting somewhere, *amigo*. Were they killed because LV testified against a homeboy?"

"Fuck do I know? LV and me from different neighborhoods. I knew he testified against Hoodlum, but that shit ain't got shit to do with me."

"How do you and Hoodlum get along?" McGuire asked.

"It's whatever. We're not friends *or* enemies. I wasn't even living in Long Beach when those five people got kilt. The only time I was in Long Beach was whenever I went to see my homeboy Motor or my moms."

"David, I listen to jail phone calls. A lot. I'm a freak like that."

"You peep in windows, too, McGuire?"

"If I need to, yes. God *yes*. Anyway, I heard you admit to the murders while talking on the phone not that long ago."

"I don't know what you think you heard, but I know you ain't heard me admit to no murders."

"Did you get your face tattoo while you were in prison?" Cortes asked.

"Yeah. I got it while I was in Ironwood in 2002 or 3."

"When did you get hooked up with the Mexican Mafia?"

"I'm not. I ain't never put in no work or been validated. I *am* a Southsider, though."

"Come on, David," McGuire said. "Tell us how many people you've killed. And how did you get the nickname of Bloodbath?"

"It was a name I got in prison for the riots I was involved in. I ain't never kilt nobody in my life."

"The first time we talked to you, you said you didn't know who Bloodbath was. Now, you're telling us it's you?"

Ponce leaned back in his chair and yawned.

"We understand that you were getting your tattoos removed from your face. Why did you get them put back on?" Cortes asked.

"I was drunk."

"How about the gun charge?"

"That wasn't my burner. Chato shoulda' took the heat for that. And I'm not active with Nut Hood no more. Even if I did get my face blasted again."

"A'ight den, David. The reason we brought you back for another interview was to give you an opportunity to tell us how many people you have killed, and to give their families some closure."

"Man, whatever. When am I going back to the county?"

"When we're done," McGuire said. "Now why don't you do the right thing and tell us why you killed those poor homeless people? While you are at it, tell us about the rest of the people you've killed in L.A. County."

"Shit, detectives! Does that make me a mass murderer that kills everybody for whatever reason?"

"Oh, no, *amigo*. We believe all your victims were killed for whatever your reasons happened to be at the time."

"Whatever. Look, am I gonna get released on parole next year?"

"No, probably not," McGuire said. "You're a suspect in five to seven murders, David."

"Does that make me a serial killer, then?"

"Why yes, David. Yes, it does."

"Whatever, McGuire. Y'all think I can take a shower now? I'm funky."

"Absolutely. We'll get someone to arrange that for you."

"Man, this whole situation is crazy," Ponce said.

"Yes. Isn't it though?" McGuire asked, gathering the photographs and returning them to the case file. "Someone will be here shortly to take you back to your cell."

As McGuire and Cortes were walking out of the room, McGuire turned and looked at Ponce.

"We caught you, David."

CHAPTER THIRTY-EIGHT

"HEY, WHAT DID they say to you, Chato?"

"They showed me pictures of me, you, and yo' girl, Saint. Me and you was holding burners. And they showed me pictures of the five laid out."

"Me too. And they read all my prison mail. Plus, they know that Crook was the driver."

"Damn, if they mentioned who was driving, this shit gonna get ugly."

"I'm the neighborhood gunner and a Big Homie, Chato. These cops been on me ever since that girl was beat to death, and about that guy who was shot in the head when I lived on Linden, lil homie. They been on me. I don't know how, but they got it in a wrap, my nigga. For them to have me, you, and Crook, they got to have something. I'm worried about my kids. I need to call Tatsuo and have her turn them over to my mom."

"Fuck, Big Homie."

"I think in a couple of days, they gonna put Crook in here with us. I know I'm not getting out, but I'm gonna find a way to get you and him out of this case. Did the detectives show you pictures of everybody at the 'thing'?"

"Yeah, but I just looked away, Saint. Man. I'm still tripping on how Crook's name even came up."

"Me too. Plus, they know I got ties to La Eme."

"Damn, Saint. This shit gonna get hectic."

"Trust me, Chato. That shit in the hood, fool, ain't shit compared to the way I get down inside, dawg. I got long juice. My name carry weight, my boy, Big Saint from the Nut gang."

"Yeah, man. I know."

"This shit go a long way. I didn't put this on my face for nothing. I'm not one of those niggas that, 'Oh, I'm gonna just shoot anyone'. I'm really not. I'm a soldier. I'm a soldier eliminating order, and opposition. I done been to countless riots, I done been through some shit my boy. I'm Big Saint from the Nuez gang, fool, one eleven block.

"My name ring bells, my boy, and the homie that's running the whole county right now, that's my road dawg. Soon as he found out I was here, it was like if I need anything done, if I need anything, tell him. Because we been upstate in riots together blasting fools and shit, that's my boy. I fucked with him on the streets. The hood is the hood, but outside of the hood, I'm a cold muthafucking G to a lot of fools, dawg."

"You a G in the hood, Saint, you know that?"

"Yeah, fool. That's what I'm sayin, dawg, like this shit is no game. Long Beach PD been on me since early 2000, since you was a kid. They been on my bumper, 'cause I been out there doing other shit, know what I mean? I got twelve fools on my belt, like four or five bitches, and like twelve fools, dawg. Your boy is active out there, homie, you know what I mean?"

"I prolly got like four. So, we gonna get out of it, though?"

"I can't say, Chato. It's up in the air, know what I mean, but I'll let you know this much: I'm not gonna fold, fool. And baby's not gonna fold, so—"

"You know I'm not—"

"—you stand your ground, my boy, and like, I was never there, that's what you say, I was never there, 'What the fuck are you talking 'bout, 'cause they don't have no burners—"

"—'cause they ain't got shit, Saint."

"—they don't got no witnesses."

"They ain't got shit, OG."

"The fingerprints, they don't have none of that shit, Chato, because I wiped them shells down on the way over here. That's how I know they don't have nothing. Fuck what they talking 'bout, nigga, if them detectives ever come to question you again. I don't want you to talk unless you got a lawyer present, straight up, like that. And I know they don't really got shit, 'cause I would've already been charged with five counts of capital murder. I know they don't got shit 'cause they don't got no burners. I know they don't got shit 'cause they don't got no witnesses. I know they don't got shit 'cause there's no fingerprints on the burner, there's no fingerprints on those shells."

"No shit, Saint, no shit."

"They have very minimal evidence, but I can't really tell you for sure exactly what they have, but I know they have enough 'cause they pulled your picture. I don't know how the fuck that came about, 'cause I never said nothing, baby never said nothing, and I know them shells was clean, and I know the burners, they don't have them, know what I mean, so I can't tell you, but I do know for sure, the muthafucka that's talking, I know who that is, know what I mean?

"I know exactly who brought that shit up, Chato, and it's the 'thing' though, fool, that happened, some shit that happened a week before the five happened, you know what I mean? And he sayin', 'Oh, yeah, well, I was there,' but he can't say *you* was there, know what I mean? He can't say shit about that, but he can say, 'Oh, yeah, I was there, another nigga was there, and another nigga was there.' They don't have witnesses, unless they call *her*, and that's not good enough, know what I mean?"

"Yeah, I know, Saint, word of mouth, only you got to prove that shit, fuck what you know, it's what you can prove."

"Exactly. Only me and you know."

"Yeah, and I ain't gonna fold, Saint."

"And I'm not gonna fold, either, and I'll put that on my pops rest in peace, and my kids rest in peace. So, you don't got to worry about my end. Baby ain't gonna tell, 'cause she's solid as fuck, trust me when I tell you that dawg, she's not gonna fold. She didn't fold then, and she ain't gonna fold now."

"My bad if I let you down that day we got caught."

"Don't trip, my boy. I'm gonna keep it real, you did, but it's all good, man. I bypassed that shit, dawg, 'cause I used my better judgement, you know what I mean? I know the business, my boy, fuck it. You might have froze up, okay, shit happens, dawg, you know what I mean? Lesson learned. Don't let it happen again, homie, with me or any other homie. If I get outta this shit, I ain't going back to the hood. Even with this shit on my face. I'm cool, dawg. I'm gonna do my family if I step out from this shit."

"You gonna be able to step out, Big Saint. God is good, homes. God is good. God is good."

———————

AUGUST 25

"This is the jailer. Ponce wants to talk to you and Detective Cortes again."

McGuire and Cortes had been sitting at their desks, smiling as they listened to Ponce and Rafael talk themselves into lengthy prison sentences, if not death penalties. McGuire covered the mouthpiece of his desk phone as he turned to Cortes.

"Ponce wants to talk to us again."

"Let's let him stew for a while."

McGuire gave Cortes a thumbs up and told the jailer, "We got other things to do today. Maybe tomorrow."

"What do you want me to tell him then?"

"Exactly what I just told you."

"Okay."

McGuire called the jail the next day when he and Cortes got to the office.

"Ask David Ponce if he still wants to talk to us."

"Oh, he still wants to talk. He bugged me about it all night."

"Beautiful. Now tell him that Cortes and I are on the way to Lancaster so it will have to be later in the day."

McGuire hung up and looked at Cortes.

"We're going to Lancaster, *amigo?*"

"No. We need to go to the DA's office so I can drop off receipts for Tatsuo's rent and food. But first, we gotta swing by my house and make sure Kim fed Cain before she left home. She had a soccer game in Corona today."

———————

"How was the drive back from Lancaster? Did y'all talk to my baby mama?"

"About ninety miles," McGuire answered. "And yes. We talked to her and a lot of other people, too."

It was 5:15 p.m., and he and Cortes were escorting David Ponce to an interview room. McGuire told him this to get him spinning as to what Tatsuo may have told them, and what others might have told them as well. But if it fazed Ponce at all, he didn't show any signs.

"Check it out, Detectives. I got some questions for y'all. I don't like the way I'm being treated while I'm being held here, and I need to know my status."

"You're under investigation for murder. Five of them, as a matter of fact, but if it were up to us it would be seven. Now, is that all you wanted to talk to us about, *amigo*?"

"Yeah. I got nothing else to say unless my attorney is here."

"A'ight den. Let's go."

McGuire and Cortes took Ponce back to his cell. The next time they saw him would be in court in front of a judge.

PART TEN

CHAPTER THIRTY-NINE

SEPTEMBER 11, 2011

Rodriguez and McElderry were sitting in bumper-to-bumper traffic, still at least ten miles from Tatsuo Hitomi's residence. McGuire had been right about her wanting him present when they interviewed her. They were meeting him there, but they were going to be early. They decided to interview Snake first, having recently gotten an address in Lancaster for him.

"What's the purpose of it all, Marty?"

"Purpose of what, Dan?"

"Life and death. What's the purpose? We see innocent babies who catch stray rounds in the head while sleeping in their cribs, doing nothing. Just...living. And then we see the most vicious human beings to ever take a dump between two shoes live through countless shootings. What's with the randomness of it all?"

Rodriguez had noticed that his partner, close to retirement now, was becoming more and more melancholy. It was a valid question, however. They had both seen incredibly evil things over the course of their careers. Rodriguez wasn't at that point of reflection yet. He planned to work for as long as he was healthy and enjoyed the job.

"I don't fucking know, Dan. You been talking to Bobby Gray, or something? Why does there even have to *be* a purpose? Maybe there *is* no

271

purpose. Maybe God just rolls out people like dice. Sometimes babies get snake-eyes. Sometimes pieces of shit get elevens."

"Well, that's simplistic, ain't it, Marty? Surely, you can't mean that."

"I'm dead-ass. And don't call me--"

"Don't you dare, Marty. Don't you dare say that corny shit. I'm being serious here. Maybe there's a certain divinity to randomness. But is death random? Or is it by design?"

"Lookit, Dan," Rodriguez said when he stopped laughing. "This case we're working is a prime example of 'everything happens for a reason.' Bobby Gray and I had a similar discussion a few years ago. I didn't have an answer then, and I don't have one now. I believe in divinity, being a good Catholic boy and all. But I also gotta believe in randomness, because I can't believe God chooses the manner that everyone dies given the horrible ways that some of us go out. What kind of God would let that happen to His children? I think He only chooses the time and place that someone dies. How it happens is where the randomness comes in. The victim on this case was murdered."

"No shit. We *are* the murder police, right?"

"We are, Dan. And sometimes, we are the best there is at what we do. But I'm talking about this specific case. This kid was *murdered*. Complete overkill. And then fucking buzzards and goddamn coyotes and fucking dogs ate him up. Why? Why did he have to go that way? What kind of fucking divinity is that? If his number was up, why couldn't he have walked in front of a speeding truck or choked on a chicken-bone or just died in his sleep? Why this way? And while we're on this subject, why do some of us go out in the most undignified ways possible, with shit and piss in our underwear, an ungodly smell our last contribution to this goddamned planet?"

McElderry sat quietly, pondering for a minute or two, as if he was maybe trying to figure out Fibonacci's sequence before answering. In truth, the answer to Rodriguez's question was even more complex.

"Maybe it's all part of some grand design that we aren't privy to until we become part of the end, Marty. Maybe our whole life is just a journey; a transition to the answers we all seek. Maybe we are just treading water now until the current of death takes us under and it's time for us to know. Maybe randomness is divine in and of itself. We speak for those who can no longer speak for themselves, but what would they say if we could actually hear them? What would they tell us?"

"The only thing I want to hear from them is who killed them. I'll leave the rest up to you and Bobby Gray. Let's go. We're here."

Rodriguez parked a few houses down, like he always did. Old habits are hard to give up; patrol officers never park their cars in front of a house they are going to for fear of an ambush. It was always better to walk up. A car represents a much bigger target.

Rodriguez knocked on the front door. A lean, muscular Black man with shoulder-length braids answered it. He had a long neck with a prominent Adam's apple bulging like a mouse in a black mamba. A strong odor of marijuana rushed past him.

"Y'all here 'bout Cat Eyes?"

"Yes. I'm Sergeant Rodriguez, and this is my partner, Sergeant McElderry. You must be Snake. You want to talk in our car? Would you be more comfortable that way?"

"Nah, y'all come on in so we can get this shit over with."

Rodriguez and McElderry didn't care about recreational drugs like marijuana. They *were* the murder police, after all. As long as Snake didn't fire up a blunt while they were sitting in his house, they didn't have a problem with the smell.

"Y'all wanna sit down?"

"No thank you," Rodriguez said as he watched one of those brown roaches with the eggs on its ass scurry up a wall. "We've been sitting in a car all the way from L.A. We'll stand. This shouldn't take too long."

The house was extremely warm inside. The walls were bare, and there were no plants in the small living room. The room would be comparable to a jail cell had it not been for a large, brand-new flat-screen TV mounted on a wall. It was oddly out of place with the worn-out sofa and loveseat, and a glass-top coffee table with a crack in the middle of it. An ashtray containing the remnants of numerous blunts, and a Bic lighter were the only items on the table.

Guiding Snake to the center of the room away from the walls, Rodriguez explained that he and McElderry were investigating the murder of Tony Bledsoe, whom he may have known as Cat Eyes.

"Tell us what you know, Snake," Rodriguez said.

"Look, man, I ain't no snitch."

"Absolutely not."

"I don't fuck with the po-leece like that."

"God forbid."

"I don't e'en like 'em."

"I hear ya'. Sometimes I don't even like them. We're just trying to make some sense out of what happened to your friend."

"A'ight, Rodriguez. I knew Cat Eyes. And I know he got kilt in 2009. Some deputy interviewed me 'bout him in March of that year."

"You gave a statement to a deputy way back then, huh?"

"Yeah. So did my sister. And we ain't appreciate the way he talked to us and treated us, neither. He was fucking rude, so I blowed him off. If he woulda' come at me like y'all, I woulda' talked to him and told him the truth 'bout what I knew then. Maybe. Like I said, I don't fuck with y'all like that."

Rodriguez took a photograph of Bledsoe out of the poor boy.

"Okay, Snake. Take a look at this."

"Yeah. That's Cat Eyes. That was my nigga."

"How about these?" Rodriguez asked.

"That's David Ponce. He my nigga, too. I met him when we worked at Homeboy Industries. That other picture in yo' hand is the green Buick that him and his girl Tatsuo used to drive."

"You knew her, too?"

"Yeah. She worked at Homeboy with us."

"What happened the day Cat Eyes went missing, Snake?" McElderry asked.

"I seen him and David on Lingard. David was driving that green Buick. I never seen Cat Eyes get in the car, but later on I heard from somebody that he got in at some point. When he went missing, a buncha' people was calling me axin' if I had seen him. I called David and axed if he knew what happened to Cat Eyes, and he told me that he had picked him up, beat him up, and left him in the street."

"That's it?".

"Yeah. But later on, I heard that Cat Eyes got kilt after he talked with David that day."

"Did David tell you that *he* actually killed Cat Eyes?"

"Nah, Rodriguez. And I never axed him 'bout it, neither. I spent a lotta time with David. I knew him real good. When people told me that he kilt Cat Eyes, I didn't believe it. To me, it was outta his character."

"What people, Snake? Who told you that David killed Cat Eyes?"

"Really? You know I cain't do that."

"Hey, can't blame a brother for trying, right? Did you know that Cat Eyes owed David Ponce money for marijuana?"

"Yeah. But I don't know how much."

"Thanks, Snake. You got anything else, Dan?"

"No. I'm good. Take care, Snake."

After Rodriguez and McElderry drove off, Rodriguez said, "That guy said a deputy interviewed him way back when Cat Eyes first went missing."

"So?"

"So, the problem is the deputy that he's talking about gives me and Bobby Gray a supplemental report dated June 29th, 2009, that indicates he spoke with Snake and four other people and none of them had any information. As a matter of fact, his report only lists their names, birth-dates, and addresses."

"Well, that's not good, is it? You think he just forgot?"

"Forgot what, Dan?" Rodriguez asked, furiously chewing on a tooth-pick. "That he fucking talked to five people? Not likely. But what's done is done. Let's just put this case down."

"When did cooperating with the cops get to be so taboo, Marty? I know it has been like this for a while, but my god. The word 'snitch' has become like the bubonic plague. People really believe in 'snitches getting stitches', huh?"

"Yeah. Only most people think the stitches are the ones needed to close a wound after getting beaten up. Those aren't the stitches that gang members are talking about, though. They're talking about more perma-nent ones, the ones coroners use to reseal caps that have been peeled. They'e talking about stitching up Y-shaped incisions after coroners have cracked your ribcage, and removed every organ in your body and examined them before throwing them back inside. Snitching has always been some-thing distasteful. And it doesn't just apply to those in the criminal world. It goes as far back as when we were kids. No one wanted to be known as a 'tattle-tale.'"

"Yeah, but our consequences were a little less severe, Marty. A little teasing or a little ostracism, at the most. But you didn't die for it."

"As you grow older, the stakes get higher, my friend."

McGuire was parked in front of Tatsuo's place when Rodriguez and McElderry arrived.

"What's going on, Mac? This is my new partner, Dan McElderry."

McGuire shook McElderry's hand. The thought went through his mind that although they could not have been more different in appearance and culture, distant relatives of theirs could have been neighbors in the Old Country. The same thought had gone through his mind the first time that he met Chief McDonnell.

"What's up, my brutha?"

"Great meeting you, Mac. I've heard good things about you. Before we go in, did Ponce ever say what kind of gun he used on Bledsoe?"

"He got caught on a recording talking about it. He said it was a fifty-caliber Smith and Wesson revolver. That sound about right based on the victim's wounds?"

"Oh, yeah," Rodriguez answered. "Bledsoe didn't have a head left. They had to put it back together like a jigsaw puzzle."

"I'll bet. Well, let's get you guys acquainted with Ms. Hitomi."

Her place was fresh and clean, the fragrance of Lotus Flower emanating throughout. It wasn't expensive, because the DA's office was paying for it, but it was far different from the place she shared with David Ponce. After the introductions were out of the way, everyone sat down in the living room, none of the cops appearing concerned about bugs.

"Can I call you Tatsuo, ma'am?" Rodriguez asked as he glanced around, smiling when he saw a bonsai tree on a half-moon table against the wall. A framed print of Mount Fuji was on the wall above it.

"Yes, sir," Tatsuo replied.

"Thanks. I love bonsai trees, by the way. So serene and relaxing."

Tatsuo smiled, seemingly a bit more at ease just because of something as simple as one of the detectives commenting favorably on something so near and dear to her.

"Anyway, you can call me Marty—"

"And call me Dan, if you like," McElderry said. "We're here to talk about Cat Eyes. Can you tell us what happened to him?"

"David was proud of that one, Detective McElderry. He even took people to show them the body while it was rotting away. He told me that the guy begged for his life before he killed him, and David made him pray. He owed David money for a drug debt. David was only supposed to beat him up, but he ended up killing him.

"In March of 2009, David had a huge gun. He called it his 'bitch,' or his 'bitch thang.' The barrel must have been ten inches long. David knew Cat Eyes through a guy who lived in Lancaster that worked with us at Homeboy Industries. On the night David killed him, me and David had an argument and he left in my car without telling me where he was going."

"Where did you think he was going?" McElderry asked.

"To look for Cat Eyes. We hadn't been living in Lancaster long. I don't think that Cat Eyes even suspected that we were living there yet. I knew that he owed David a lot of money because David had given him a lot of weed. David had been telling me that whenever he saw Cat Eyes, he was going to beat him up because Cat Eyes was ducking him. When David came back later that night, he had blood all over his clothes and boots."

"Did he tell you anything about how that happened?" Rodriguez asked.

"He told me that he had found Cat Eyes and made him get in the car and they drove out to the desert. He said Cat Eyes was begging for his life, and swore on the lives of his dead mother and grandmother that he was going to pay back the money he owed. He made Cat Eyes pray and told him that he was going to send him to meet his dead mother. David shot him in the head while he was praying."

There was an unintended moment of silence for Tony Bledsoe before McElderry spoke.

"Did you help him clean up, or get rid of his clothes, Tatsuo?"

"Only his boots. But not that night. That happened much later. He soaked his clothes in Ajax and bleach in a bag that night and took it with him when he left. I don't know where he went."

McElderry looked at Rodriguez and said, "Well, that certainly doesn't sound like randomness. Sounds more like divinity, huh, Marty?"

"Excuse me, sir?"

"Don't mind my partner, ma'am," Rodriguez replied. "He's stuck on a conversation we had earlier."

CHAPTER FORTY

OCTOBER 3

"Hello, David. I'm Sergeant Rodriguez and this is my partner, Sergeant McElderry."

Rodriguez and McElderry were at Men's Central Jail to interview David Ponce. McElderry put the poor boy containing little more than a few reports, crime scene photos, and a booking photo from Tony Bledsoe's last arrest on the table in front of Ponce. He wanted Ponce to see all the information written on the poor boy— Cat Eyes listed as the victim, Ponce as the suspect, and the date and location of the murder.

McElderry was very good at his job and knew all the tricks and nuances to get into a suspect's head. His claim to fame was that he had arrested the suspect in the murders of two El Segundo police officers after forty-six years. He was not far from retirement, and this was a heinous case. He would love to help solve it. To put this case down would be cause for a bottle of the good stuff.

Rodriguez read Ponce his rights, and he agreed to talk without a lawyer.

"Look, I ain't gonna bullshit y'all," Ponce said. "I knew Cat Eyes. He owed me $3000 for some Arizona I gave him to sell. I was looking for him, too. When I found him, he was riding a bike. I made him get in the car with me and I drove to Tupac's to get a bottle of Cisco. No one was with us. It was just me and him."

"Did you kill him, David?" Rodriguez asked. "Did you take him into the desert, shoot him, and leave his body?"

"I wouldn't say it was me, but if things are leading up to that..."

"But you were the last person with him, right? And Cat Eyes never came back from the desert, correct? Here. Take a look at these."

Rodriguez slid photographs of Tatsuo's green Buick—the car he kidnapped Bledsoe in—and a picture of the newspaper article documenting the discovery of remains in the desert closer to Ponce. He just shrugged and said, "It is what it is. Y'all already know what happened out there. And like I said, there was no one else involved."

McElderry reached into the poor boy and pulled out a photograph of a Smith & Wesson model 500. He and Rodriguez had researched these handguns based on the descriptions provided by Tatsuo and Ponce while he was in a recorded jail cell. The model 500 is a .50 caliber handgun, purported to be the most powerful one made.

McElderry slid the photo across the table.

"Is this the type of gun you used, David?"

"It look like it. But it ain't an exact match."

"Well? What happened to it?" Rodriguez asked.

"I melted it down with a blow torch."

"How about this, David? What's with the newspaper article?" McElderry asked as he laid a photograph of it on the table.

Ponce swallowed hard as he looked at it, leaning back in his seat and folding his arms across his chest, killer clowns with big guns on his forearms menacing the two detectives.

"It came from your house, David. It was the only newspaper article there," Rodriguez said.

Ponce closed his eyes and leaned his head back as if in resignation.

"Was Tatsuo or anyone else involved, David?"

"She ain't have nothing to do with it."

"Are you sure?" McElderry asked. "She could easily be an accessory."

"Look. I'm basically a good person. I just done some wrong shit in my life. I kilt Cat Eyes. That's on me. Nobody else was involved. And I wasn't under the influence of drugs, neither. It was all me, and I know I ain't never gonna see daylight again."

"THAT'S ONE EVIL SON OF A BITCH, DAN."

Rodriguez and McElderry were driving out of the parking lot, watching all the baby mamas and the real mamas coming and going from the visiting area of the Men's Central Jail facility near downtown L.A. Other than their age, it was always obvious which mama a woman was. The baby mamas wore clothing easily pushed aside as the baby daddies relieved themselves in lotion-soaked socks while looking at an exposed nipple or a glimpse of a shaved vagina. The real mamas were conservatively dressed, some of them looking as if they were on their way to church.

Rodriguez imagined that at one time or another, Tatsuo Hitomi may have been one of those visiting baby mamas, dressed in a collegiate sweater, a plaid micro mini-skirt, and knee-high socks—a chocolate shoji manga figure for discerning adults.

"If that motherfucker thinks he's a good person, then what the fuck does he consider a bad one, Dan?" Rodriguez asked, if for no other reason than to get his mind back on the case, imagining that McElderry may have needed help back from the land of manga as well.

"You know what they say, right? 'No man chooses evil because it is evil; he just mistakes it for happiness, the good he seeks,'" McElderry said, trademark twinkle in his eye.

"Who the hell says that Dan?"

"Boy, you really oughta read more, Marty."

"I read plenty, as long as *Airplane*, the Lakers, Dodgers, or Rams aren't on TV. And how in the hell did that sadistic bastard manage to get with a fine-ass woman like Ms. Tatsuo Hitomi?"

"I guess the heart wants what the heart wants. But something tells me that by the time she realized who he was, she was in too deep to just up and leave. Anyway, how about we go to Corina's? We can continue our conversation about divine randomness and the never-ending sagas of beauty and the beast over a twelve-year-old bottle of Macallan."

"You twisted my arm, Danny-me-boy. Lead the way. And maybe we can get to the bottom of how an eighteen-year-old could write something as complex as Frankenstein."

PONCE CALLED TATSUO IMMEDIATELY AFTER MCELDERRY AND Rodriguez left the jail.

"You have a collect call from... 'David Ponce'...an inmate at Men's Central Jail. Do you accept?"

"Yes. David?"

"The sheriffs just grilled me, Tatsuo. They were asking me all kinds of shit about Cat Eyes. They knew details about what happened, and they showed me pictures of him and the car we had at the time. And they showed me pictures of that fucking newspaper article. I confessed babe."

"This call may be monitored."

"It's a wrap. I'm not coming home. The detectives put this shit together. They tried to say you was an accessory. I told them I acted alone. It was all my doing, on my own. My doings are my doings, and my dealings are my dealings. I don't involve nobody else in my shit."

"Are you gonna plead guilty, David?"

"This call may be monitored."

"I already did. To the detectives. It's a wrap. I'm not gonna involve you and the kids, you feel me? They were talking 'bout adding you as an accessory to murder. I'm not gonna put you through this shit. I love you and the kids, and I don't want the kids dragged through the system. I'm tired of you guys being involved in my shit, Tatsuo."

"Oh, baby. Wow. What are we gonna do?"

"This call may be monitored."

"I'm gonna fight that case out of Long Beach. Fuck that. But this case? This is one murder case I can't fight. I lived a cold-ass life out here. I was doing shit way before you. It's just my time. I know what I said to the detectives. It's a wrap, you know? First court date, I'm taking a plea. Those detectives know too many details. What else could I do? Sit there and play with it—"

"This call may be monitored."

"—let them gaffle you and the kids up? Fuck that. I know I'm fucked. My happy days with you and the kids is out the window. That window closed when I talked to the detectives. I'm not gonna try to make this process long. I'm guilty! I'm guilty! I'm guilty!"

Tatsuo felt a chill go through her bones as she imagined that his eyes were probably looking the way they were when his mother exorcised him in that hospital room.

"This call may be monitored."

"Let's just get this shit done and over with. Give me eight hundred years with out parole. Either way, I'm fucked. I pled guilty today. I confessed."

"Okay, baby."

"I want you to go on with your life. Make sure you keep our kids around my mother. This shit is gonna kill her. I love you, babe."

"I love you, too."

CHAPTER FORTY-ONE

"WOW, MAC. THIS shit is nuts."

McGuire and Cortes were at their desks, gathering all the documents and evidence needed to present a case against Max Rafael and David Ponce to the District Attorney for filing.

"What's nuts?"

"Today is Veteran's Day."

"So?"

"November the eleventh?"

"And?"

"So, there are a lot of elevens involved in this case. Our victims were killed on November the first, by two gangsters from the One-Eleven clique of Nut Hood. Ponce and Rafael got caught with a Mac-eleven. Ponce started a countdown to murder at eleven in the Sheriff's case. Even the moon on the night of our murders was in an eleven percent crescent phase. And now, today, November eleventh, here we are, starting to put the case together for filing."

"Angel numbers," McGuire replied. "It ain't nothing angelic about David Ponce, though. Triple sixes is also an angel number, so there's that."

McGuire noticed Sergeant Nielsen standing in the doorway, a breakfast sandwich in hand and a napkin tucked in his shirt collar like a bib.

"You guys are here awfully early," Nielsen said.

"We got 'em, Sergeant."

"What? You got 'em? For the Lancaster murder, too?"

McGuire and Cortes had kept him in the dark about the meat of the case, so he wouldn't tell the administrators. They would be pushing for a filing and a press conference right away, and McGuire and Cortes wanted the case airtight before then.

"Well, Sheriff's Homicide is gonna be filing the Lancaster murder," McGuire said. "But yes. We got 'em. Max Rafael and David Ponce for our five, and Ponce for another one in Lancaster. As soon as we get everything together, we're gonna put together a PowerPoint presentation for the DA. We should be ready in a few weeks. There's no rush. Neither one of them are going anywhere."

"Good job, guys. I'll let the chief know. And oh yeah... The day after you file the case, I need both of you back with your regular partners."

By the first week of January, McGuire and Cortes had finished wrapping up all their reports, getting all the interviews and recorded statements transcribed, and putting together the PowerPoint. Within thirty minutes of letting Nielsen know, Chief McDonnell and all the command staff were patting them on the back after watching the presentation.

"Well done, Mac, Hugo. You guys already have a DDA to file with?" McDonnell asked.

"Yes, Chief. We think this is a death penalty case, so we're taking it downtown to Major Crimes.

"Well, Mac, I can't think of one more deserving. Keep your sergeant apprised so I can schedule a press conference ASAP. And I need both of you there. That's an order."

After McDonnell walked away, Cortes turned to McGuire.

"Should we bring up Linden Street, Mac?"

"Nah. I told the guys assigned to those cases that Ponce was good for them, but they didn't seem too enthused. I suggested that me and you take over the cases, but they don't want to give them up. I even asked Nielsen."

"And what did he say?"

"That they were their cases. Period."

"Those cases are right there, Mac. Ponce practically admitted to doing them. And it's on tape, too."

"Yeah. I know. Pathetic, ain't it?"

"You hungry?"

"Getting there," McGuire said as he sat down and began dialing. "Let me call Rodriguez to see where they are on filing their case."

"Sheriff's Homicide. Can I help you?"

"Hello. This is Detective McGuire at Long Beach PD Homicide. I was trying to reach Sergeant Rodriguez."

"Oh, I'm sorry. He's the operations sergeant now. Let me transfer you."

"Operations, Rodriguez. Can I help you?"

"Hey, Marty. It's McGuire from Long Beach."

"What's up, Mac?"

"Just letting you know that we're putting our case together against David Ponce right now. We're seeking filings for five counts of murder and one count of kidnapping probably the day after tomorrow. We're filing downtown. Major Crimes."

"Special circs?"

"Yeah. Somebody needs to walk that green mile for this one."

"No shit. Outstanding job, by the way."

"Thanks, brutha. Your case ready yet?"

"Sorry, brother. I'm a house cat now. Not working cases anymore. Bobby Gray is gonna take it across the goal line."

"What happened to McElderry?"

"He's about to retire. All he's doing is cleaning up his other cases. No more working new ones, or old ones either."

"Looks like you aren't gonna be woking murder cases anymore either. Aren't Operations positions grooming spots for the next rank? At least that's what I've always heard, anyway."

"Yeah. Well, we shall see. Let me transfer you to Bobby's line."

"Thanks, Marty. And good luck."

Bobby Gray was sitting at his desk, holding court with several new Homicide investigators, one of them destined to be his kid.

"Sergeant Gray, can I help you?"

"It's McGuire from Long Beach."

"What's up Mac? How about them Giants, huh? They're going all the way!"

"Yeah, Bobby. They look good. Watch out for Brady, though. Hey, what's with Marty being a house cat now?"

"Aw, fuck Tom Brady. And fuck Marty. That fucking *cabróne* thinks he's gonna get promoted. Anyway, what's doing with the David Ponce case?"

"That's what I'm calling for. Hugo and I are taking it downtown to file with Major Crimes the day after tomorrow."

"That's great news! I'm putting the Bledsoe case together right now."

" Cool. I'll let the DA know you're gonna be bringing your case so she can use the same court case number."

"Thanks, Mac. We got bupkis without you guys."

"No worries. It was all good police work. By most of us, anyway."

"Tell me about it."

"Peace in the hood, Bobby."

"*Shalom.*"

McGuire hung up and looked at Cortes. "*Now*, I'm ready to go eat. Someplace healthy, brutha? You pick."

"You know what, *mi amigo*? I'm feeling a lot like a meat eater today. How about In-N-Out? My treat."

They smiled and shook hands. It wasn't the standard handshake of gentlemen who had just closed a business deal, either. It was a slap and grab; a bonding of two men who had battled dragons together many times and come away unscathed physically, if not emotionally.

CHAPTER FORTY-TWO

MCGUIRE AND CORTES got to the office before dawn the next day.

They were dressed in casual clothes, their only mission to put their case together for filing. For one defendant, cases needed four copies. If there were multiple defendants, then two extra copies were required for each defendant. The Quintuple case was at least two hundred pages of investigation.

"We're copying the rest of this shit downtown, Hugo. I'll be damned if we're lugging twelve hundred pages to the DA's office."

"I hear that. Part of me wants to make the city pay for all the paper and ink, though. Cheap bastards."

McGuire laughed as he stood next to the outdated printer, watching it hack and grind as it methodically spit out sheets of paper.

"Hey Hugo, you remember that knucklehead who stabbed all those homeless people to death in Orange County last year? Well, he offed himself in his jail cell last night by drinking Ajax. I guess he had been collecting it in small amounts until he had enough to get the job done."

"The former marine? The one who killed like six people?"

"Yeah. *That* idiot."

"Couldn't have happened to a nicer guy, Mac. Too bad for the families of the victims, though. He robbed them of their justice."

"Well, the cops almost convicted the wrong guy. You know they arrested and filed on one of their victim's sons, right? Poor bastard stayed in custody for three months until they tested blood on the real killer's shoes and found his mother and brother's DNA. Forty years ago, they would've executed the wrong guy."

"This kid's mother and brother get murdered, and he gets blamed for it. How screwed-up is that?"

"Like I always say, you gotta be sure on these murder cases. I would rather let a guilty muthafucka get away than convict the wrong person. I'll take an unsolved any day over trying to humbug somebody into prison so I can look good in front of the bosses or to stroke my own ego."

McGuire suddenly started coughing. It was a nasty, phlegm-filled cough that comes with a bad case of the flu, or worse.

"You okay, Mac?"

"Yeah. I'm a'ight. Just coming down with a little cold, I think."

"Okay, *amigo*. I'll see you tomorrow. Take some cough medicine or something, alright?"

It took two days to present the case to the filing DDA. McGuire was coughing almost the entire time. After updating Sergeant Nielsen in his office when they were done, McGuire went to his desk, turned his computer off, and put on his jacket. It was a little after 1 p.m.

"Where are you going?" Cortes asked.

"I'm gonna get on the bike, Hugo. It's a good day for a ride. I'll see you tomorrow. Go spend time with your wife or go for a run or some shit. I think we've earned it."

After McGuire coughed himself out of the office, Cortes sat down at his desk and began reviewing case files. Twenty minutes later, McGuire walked right past his motorcycle. He went to the medicine chest, swallowed some cough medicine, and got in bed, shivering as Cain lay on the floor next to him.

———

"Good morning."

Chief McDonnell, surrounded by his top administrators, addressed a throng of news reporters on the steps of City Hall. McGuire was still coughing, and feverish.

"Today, five counts of murder and one count of kidnapping have been filed against David Ponce and Max Eliseo Rafael for the murders of five homeless people in November of 2008, with additional charges expected to be filed against Ponce for a Sheriff's Department murder in 2009. I want to make it clear that these victims were not targeted because they were homeless.

"This encounter stemmed from a personal vendetta of one of the suspects as the result of an ongoing dispute with one of the victims over narcotics. The other victims were killed to ensure that there were no witnesses to the crime. I want to commend everyone who took part in this extremely difficult case, particularly Detectives Mark McGuire and Hugo Cortes, the lead investigators."

Rodriguez and Gray, along with several other investigators, including the two investigators from the Missing Persons Unit, watched the press conference on a TV in the lunchroom at Sheriff's Homicide. When it was over the investigators patted them on the back, smiling and shaking their hands. The two MPU investigators forced smiles as they congratulated them, unable to conceal their contriteness.

"Well, what are you gonna do now, Bobby?" Rodriguez asked when he and Gray were alone. "Go play Frisbee with that lil mutt of yours?"

"Mutt? I *know* you're not questioning Bandit's lineage."

"He's a fucking mongrel."

"Whatever, *pendejo*. I think I'm gonna go fishing. I haven't gone in a while. It'll be relaxing."

"Alright, partner. Have a good time. And don't get drunk and fall in like you do at the end of most of your dates."

AFTER THE PRESS CONFERENCE WAS OVER, McGUIRE FELT EVEN WORSE.

He was still coughing and had a fever, but now he was sweating, too. Without saying anything to anyone, he called his primary doctor and told him about his symptoms. The doctor directed him to come in without delay. He had pneumonia. He was given a prescription and told to wait in the lobby before a possible hospital admission.

Rather than heeding his doctor's advice, McGuire walked to the pharmacy and picked up his medication. He then drove back to headquarters to switch cars and pick up some case files from his desk before going home. There were a lot of people waiting to get on the elevator, so he decided to take the stairs. He didn't want to be in a metal box filled with people while he was coughing and hacking.

The first flight was easy, but then he began having a hard time catching his breath and felt a slight tingling on the left side of his body. He had to stop and rest on the handrail every three or four steps. Finally, he took one more step and collapsed.

David Ponce and Max Rafael had been at Men's Central Jail for quite a while now.

Ponce ran the entire floor they were on. Any conflict between Southsiders had to be resolved by him. Some of them may have been mortal enemies on the streets, but in jail and prison, certain rules had to be adhered to. If someone was assaulted or murdered on Ponce's floor and a Southsider was involved, it would have happened only with his permission. And there were jailhouse perks for Ponce, such as unlimited food, watching whatever he wanted to on TV, and access to cell phones.

Southsiders are nothing more than members of Hispanic street gangs that are south of the city of Fresno, the dividing line between north and south. All Hispanic gangs north of Fresno are considered *Norteños*, or Northerners, and those south of Fresno are considered *Sureños*, or Southerners. To run an entire floor in jail is no small thing and must be approved by high-ranking members of La Eme.

Rafael enjoyed the same perks as Ponce, but he didn't get to make floor decisions such as who got certain privileges and who had to be disciplined, which ranged from a simple assault all the way to a shanking in the shower.

Part of overseeing a floor consisted of Ponce leading a daily calisthenics session attended by all Southsiders on his floor. The sessions resembled military boot camp. Southsider rules in prison and jail are stringent; they must maintain cleanliness—both personal hygiene and that of their living areas—and also maintain their physical fitness.

Ponce had been a ruler in hell for several months, but everything changed when he was charged in the homeless case. He and Rafael were now considered high-risk prisoners and moved to "high-power status."

While Gray was getting ready to go fishing and McGuire lay on a stairwell gasping for air, Ponce and Rafael were goldfish in a bowl swimming in the rancid water of solitary confinement. They would remain there until twelve jurors decided their fates.

FOR SEVERAL MINUTES, MCGUIRE WAS AFRAID.

He was afraid that he would die alone, that he would sink instead of swim. He checked his pockets for his Blackberry. *Did I leave it at the doctor's office?* he thought. *Where is it?* He slowed his breathing, realizing that if he didn't get control of it, he could hyperventilate and pass out. *It's okay. Just breathe.*

Visions of the coroner's office went through his head. *If I die here like this, they might peel my cap. I'm healthy. I have a doctor, but I'm not under a doctor's care. Dying like this would make me a prime candidate for an autopsy. Why the fuck did I take the stairs. No one ever takes the stairs. Except for Cortes. That muthafucka does. Sometimes. When he ain't with me. Why am I thinking about him right now? Am I dying? Am I delirious?*

Slowly, McGuire regained his composure and started thinking straight. He was still coughing, but he could breathe easier now. He lay there for five or ten more minutes until he was able to walk. *Fuck those files*, he thought. He got his Blackberry out of the glovebox of the city car and drove home in his personal one. He called off sick the next day and was bedridden for three additional days. He wouldn't return to work until after his lungs cleared up six weeks later.

Responsible for working the deaths of others for so many years, confronting and slaying dragons at risk to self, fresh off solving the most notorious murder case in the history of the city, Detective Mark McGuire had almost died all alone in a stairwell in the Headquarters of the Long Beach Police Department.

IT WAS THE FIRST WEEK OF MARCH 2013.

"Hey, *chupamedias*! Congratulations! Lieutenant? Who the fuck did you pay and how much?"

Sergeant Bobby Gray was at his desk talking to his former partner, Marty Rodriguez, who had just received word of his promotion. It was sweet but poignant; now he was going back to patrol as a watch commander at some patrol station, working the shittiest hours with the shittiest days off because he would be the low lieutenant on the totem pole.

He smiled and flipped Gray off.

"No, for real, Marty. I'm happy for you. Where's the party?"

"At Geezer's in Santa Fe Springs."

"Geezer's, huh? What a perfect choice for your old ass."

"You gonna be there, partner?"

"Wouldn't miss it for the world, my friend."

"By the way, how's the fishing been lately?"

"Fantastic. I caught a big ass yellowfin tuna just a few days ago."

"Did you give it back?"

"Fuck no. I cut it up. It's in my freezer. I'm taking orders, but since you got promoted, I'll bring you a nice cut. On the house."

A week later, Rodriguez was wearing a uniform again for the first time in almost twenty years, going from being a glamorous homicide detective to approving arrest reports by bone-headed deputies. It was a pay increase as far as salary was concerned, but he was taking a pay cut in the grand scheme of things because patrol lieutenants don't get any overtime, whereas homicide detectives feast on it.

Time had carried on for all the detectives who had been involved in the investigations of David Ponce and Max Rafael, cases never ceasing, the Pale Rider galloping without respite through L.A. County. Rodriguez was the watch commander at the Lakewood Patrol Station working Thursday through Monday from 9 p.m. to 5 a.m. Cortes was working with new partners, McGuire was back to work, and Gray was breaking in new homicide detectives, yelling at them for not picking up their telephones faster and for forgetting poor boys.

As a reward for solving the Quintuple, McGuire and Cortes were selected as co-employees of the year for 2012. Cortes was ecstatic, but McGuire didn't show much enthusiasm even though the award was the equivalent of a Grammy award for police officers. Not long after getting the award, Cortes, dealing with marital issues and going through a divorce, retired. It is well known that police work has an adverse effect on some cops, and sometimes they turn to alcohol an/or drugs. It is not so well known that the job sometimes affects spouses, and they seek solace in the bottle, pipe, or needle as well. Cortes's wife lost herself in a bottle like Frederick and Sammy had, and died trying to find her way out. Still in love with a woman he had married when they were only eighteen years old, Cortes took her death hard.

By 2014, McGuire's career was on the downside. He was finally starting to slow down enough to relax. He took his vacation during the winter holidays that year. The day after Christmas, he was relaxing at home with Kim, watching reruns of *The Wire* when he felt a tingling in his left arm. It was similar to what he had felt in the stairwell, but this time it was more intense.

"Baby, I think I need to go to the hospital. I'm losing feeling in my arm."

She took his blood pressure and wasted no time getting him to the nearest hospital when she saw how high it was. He was admitted and stayed for the next three days. An MRI revealed that it was his second stroke. The first one was a lot milder, and probably a contributing factor to his collapsing at work on the stairwell. After he was released from the hospital, the left side of his body stayed numb for the next six months.

The day before he went on vacation would turn out to be his last day as a cop. With the Quintuple still unresolved, he officially retired on July 3, 2015, after twenty-five years of service.

PART ELEVEN

CHAPTER FORTY-THREE

DDA CINDY BARNES was assigned to the Hardcore Unit of the DA's office.

A brunette with a ballet dancer's grace, Barnes had a sparkling personality, a brilliant legal mind, and was deeply regarded among her peers. She had taken over the Quintuple case not long after McGuire retired. Tenacious in the tradition of Homicide bulldogs, she even went to the homeless encampment, crouch walking through Lobster Girl's tunnels. She wanted to walk the path that the killers had taken. She wanted to see how the victims lived—if not how they died—and try to get a sense of what it was like for people who survived on the fringes of society.

A new detective had been assigned to deal with the trial. He was competent, but Barnes had worked with McGuire before. She knew that he was an outstanding detective who always brought well-investigated cases for filing. No one knew this case better than he did, so she picked up her phone and dialed.

"Hello, Mac. How's retirement?"

McGuire had always liked Barnes and was glad to hear from her. He had given her his personal cell phone number years ago when they had a case together. He loved the way she went about the business of prosecuting. Hard-nosed and shrewd, she was perfect for prosecuting David Ponce and Max Rafael.

"Hello, Cindy! Retirement is fantastic. How's the trial coming?"

"That's what I'm calling you about. The other detective is fine, but I would rather have you as the investigating officer. I know you're retired now so you won't get paid, but—"

"Say no more. I got you."

"Really?"

"I don't care about the money. This is just the right thing to do."

"Thanks, Mac. We'll touch base soon, okay?"

"No doubt. Peace in the hood."

Wednesday, September 5, 2017

Because of the notoriety of the case, the trial was held on the ninth floor of the Criminal Courts Building in downtown L.A., next door to the courtroom that OJ Simpson was tried in. McGuire sat in as the investigating officer along with Gray, who was there to handle the Tony Bledsoe portion of the trial.

"Hey, Bobby. Good to see you. By the way, how is *Lieutenant* Martin Rodriguez?"

"Still a fucking *maricón*."

McGuire laughed and then put on his game face as Judge Charlaine Olmedo, a no-nonsense trier of fact whose favorite television show was *American Horror Story*, took the bench.

"Call your first witness, Ms. Barnes."

"Your honor, the people call Detective Mark McGuire."

He walked to the stand and took the oath. Ponce, dressed in black, belt-less slacks and a white long-sleeved shirt with no tie, had followed him with his eyes all the way, smirking the entire time. Rafael was dressed almost the same as Ponce, the two of them looking like malicious Mormons.

Ponce glared at McGuire as he made himself comfortable on the stand and pulled the microphone closer. Rafael didn't glare, but he didn't look away, either.

"Detective McGuire," Barnes said. "How many murders have you investigated or been part of as an investigator?"

"About two hundred."

"Have you ever responded to a crime scene with more than one dead victim?"

"Yes, I've had double murders before."

"How about three?"

"No."

"Four?"

"No."

"Five?"

"Just this one."

And with one of the jurors shaking his head in disbelief at the end of this exchange, so began the trial of the People of the State of California v. David Ponce and Max Rafael.

McGuire was in court every day.

Facing either the death penalty or life without parole, Ponce had nothing to lose. When defendants are on trial and in the presence of jurors, they are in civilian clothes and are not handcuffed. This is done so as not to prejudice the jury, but bailiffs sit behind the defendants to ensure the safety of everyone in the courtroom.

During one of the recesses, Gray pulled McGuire aside.

"Special Enforcement Bureau deputies, huh Mac? Good call. You never know what can happen with these two crazy bastards."

"Yeah, I requested them personally. You know what the usual bailiffs look like. Either they're overweight or doing their nails and reading *Ebony* magazine or *People* or the *National Enquirer*. For this trial, we needed killers with badges in here. Just in case."

Gray shook his head and smiled, tapping the badge attached to his belt next to the gun that was causing him so much pain.

"It's this guy. Nothing fucks with him. He goes anywhere he wants to in California, and shits where he pleases. You ever need something, just call us."

McGuire glanced down at the state seal on Gray's badge, which depicts a grizzly bear that Gray was referring to.

"Impressive," McGuire said. "Just don't forget who fed that mutha-fucka on *this* case."

"What's on your badge, Mac?"

"What? You mean other than *Retired?*"

"Yeah."

Gray watched as McGuire pulled out his wallet and flipped it open.

"What the fuck is that?" Gray asked.

"It's a white woman sitting on a throne on the beach."

"Is that a dog at her feet?"

"No. It's your fucking bear."

CHAPTER FORTY-FOUR

"CALL YOUR NEXT witness, Ms. Barnes."

Just before the jurors had taken their seats, four of the fittest and most well-trained deputies in the Sheriff's Department had brought Ponce and Rafael back into the courtroom. The deputies unhandcuffed them, sat them next to their respective defense attorneys, and took seats behind them before the jurors entered and took their seats.

"Your honor, the People call Tatsuo Hitomi."

She walked past the counsel table, dressed conservatively and with her hair neatly done. Other than lipstick, she wasn't wearing any makeup. She could've been a middle-school teacher to someone who didn't know her, eons from a gun moll who had once attended a hood party. She tried her best not to look at the father of her children. It was a tough pill to swallow; if justice was to truly be served, it would mean them growing up without a father just like her. She could feel him staring at her as she walked to the stand.

She straightened the microphone, adjusted her seat, and after moving a box of Kleenex closer to her, went on to talk about her life with David Ponce. When the jail recordings were played, her testimony was validated as the jurors listened to him boasting about his deeds, discussing perceived weaknesses of the case with Rafael, and their need to be strong and not confess. Ponce's mother cried throughout, clutching her rosary beads tightly with both hands and holding them to her lips.

THE PROSECUTION RESTED ON SEPTEMBER 21.

The next day, Ponce and Rafael were found guilty of five counts of murder, one count of kidnapping, and participating in a criminal street gang. Ponce was also found guilty of murdering Tony Bledsoe. It had been a relatively short trial, given the number of victims, but the evidence had been overwhelming, most of it provided by the defendants themselves.

After the verdict, Gray stepped into the hallway and made a call.

"Hello, Lieutenant. Do I even have to call you that? Or can I still call you *pendejo*??"

"What's the verdict, asshole?"

"You at work?"

"No, I'm on the links tearing up grass. They're gonna make me pay half of the monthly gardening bill if I don't get my shit together."

"Guilty. On everything. That evil fucker is done. And his crime partner, too. But hopefully Ponce will walk that green mile one day. *Kismet*, my friend."

"Great job, Bobby G."

"I didn't do dick. The bulldogs and the bear got help from some white bitch sitting on a throne this time."

"Huh?"

"Never mind. I'll tell you when I see you. Right now, I got a couple of calls to make to two people who filed missing person's reports a long time ago."

McGuire was a few feet away. To him, the verdict was just as bittersweet as the phone calls Gray was about to make. The driver of the get-away car in the Quintuple had never been identified. Now that he and Cortes were both retired, he knew that no one from their former office was ever going to pick up the case and try to identify and arrest him. He didn't kill anyone, but he was just as responsible and just as deserving of a prison sentence. The case was an incomplete puzzle of a masterpiece; it was as if the jagged mountains behind the *Mona Lisa* were missing.

McGuire thought about calling Cortes but felt it would be better to tell him in person over a dinner date; they had a lot of catching up to do. He called Tatsuo instead. She was at her new job, working in an office in the corporate world, looking worlds apart from what she had looked like just five years before. She had gone back to school and gotten her degree while Ponce was in prison fighting the case. Most importantly, their kids had adjusted well to his absence.

When McGuire gave her the verdict, she panicked.

"He's gonna kill me! He's gonna come after me, some way, somehow!"

"No, he's not. They're both done, but David will probably get the death penalty. It's that, or life without parole like Chato. You will never see either one of them again. You're free."

"Are you sure?"

"Absolutely."

"Thank you, Detective McGuire. For everything."

"Enjoy your life, Tatsuo Hitomi. Peace."

She hung up and crossed her legs, her feelings ineffable. She looked down at her shiny black pumps with red soles, tears falling onto her lap. Now, with her *akuma's* imprisonment and her far removed from the grit and dirt of the gang-infested neighborhoods she grew up in, Tatsuo thought about how she was going to live the rest of her life.

JUDGE OLMEDO SENTENCED MAX RAFAEL TO FIVE CONSECUTIVE TERMS of life.

She called the circumstances of his crimes particularly cruel and vicious, saying, in part:

"You will have a long time to think about what transpired that night. The jailhouse statements made by you and Mr. Ponce were very damaging evidence against the two of you. Really, it's your own words that provide the sufficiency of the evidence. Would you like to make a statement to the court, Mr. Rafael?"

Rafael looked at the floor, no doubt thinking about how his life had turned out; how he had eschewed an honorable one and chosen one that he believed to be glamorous and filled with respect. His parents were good and gracious. They were noble in their following of laws and regulations, of earning an honest day's work and ensuring that their children got an education. As the realization of what a truly respectful life entailed dawned on him, he looked at the judge.

"Yes, your Honor," he said. "My only fault was being tied to a lifestyle that never gave me anything."

Rafael was then taken away. He never apologized for the crimes he committed.

"DAVID PONCE, I HEREBY SENTENCE YOU TO DEATH."

It was just over three months after a jury of his peers had decided his fate. Ponce just smirked and giggled as he listened to Judge Olmedo sentence him to death and deliver a scathing assessment:

"Your desire to live a gangster lifestyle led you down a terrible path. The circumstances of each murder were horrific. As such, and at the recommendation of a jury of your peers, you shall suffer the penalty of death...in a manner prescribed by law. All the people you murdered, regardless of their station in life, had hopes, dreams, loves, and family... And in listening to you boast about the murders, your glee in the number and manner of each victim's demise is distorted and shocking."

Ponce declined an opportunity to make a statement to the court. His mother had pleaded for his life during the penalty phase of the trial, taking the stand and begging the jury to spare his life. She was old school with traditional values and a stalwart Catholic. She had done her best to raise him the right way. The jury no doubt commiserated with her, but they saw her son for who he was; they saw him through lenses unmuddied by a mother's unconditional love.

As two SEB deputies guided Ponce toward a meeting with Randy Kraft at San Quentin prison, he looked at his mother without penitence. She was weeping softly, sitting near the front of the courtroom audience, exhausted from her pleas. Ponce smiled at her and mouthed the words, "I love you" before disappearing into the court lockup. Her back heaving as her weeping intensified, she kissed the small figure attached to her rosary beads.

It was Jude the Apostle, the patron saint of lost causes.

ACKNOWLEDGMENTS

First and foremost, I would like to offer my sincerest condolences to the families of Tony Duane Bledsoe, Lorenzo Villicana, Vanessa Malaepule, Frederick Neumeier, Hamid Shraifat, and Katherine Verdun. May the Creator continue to ensure that their souls rest in peace.

I lived not far from where five of these individuals were murdered. I frequented the same places they did, I drove down the same streets they panhandled on, I even gave them money and bought them food on occasion. I also knew most of them on a professional level as well, as I worked at Carson Station and supervised deputies who had cases on some of them. They were people, just like the rest of us, down on their luck for sure, but people who deserved to live.

Acknowledgement pages are tricky things to write. I can sit down at my computer and write a 90,000-word book in three months but struggle to write a two-to-three-paragraph acknowledgment. The biggest problem is making sure no one is forgotten, which, of course, is impossible because as you go through life there are a multitude of people who help you attain any semblance of success. No one does it alone.

From the stranger on a bus who grabs your coattail as you are about to get off to let you know you are leaving behind your briefcase containing your nearly completed manuscript and all accompanying documents and materials, to beta and ARC readers who are brutally honest and pull you back down to earth when you think you are the next Truman Capote, to family and friends, to inspirational authors, to your parents—all the way up to whatever deity you believe in, if in fact you have a belief in something greater than yourself—you should never have a shortage of people to acknowledge. I certainly don't.

When I was in the twilight of my first career, my wife and I adopted a seven-day-old baby boy, Desmond, who was physically at-risk and in danger of being placed in foster care. We have witnessed first-hand how some children fall through the cracks; we have seen how easy it is for some of them to get left behind. I was emotionally invested in this endeavor from the first stroke of my keypad.

Desmond was subsequently diagnosed as autistic. It has been a struggle to raise him. The difficulties of parents dealing with children on the spectrum cannot be overstated. Yet somehow, my wife always knows what to do to make him feel better in any situation; she always knows what to say to soothe him. She is truly the rock in my family, and I will never be able to convey just how much through printed words alone.

It is a no-brainer that I acknowledge the one true God, particularly in these troubled times. He is my strength, and He has guided me through unbelievably tough times. It has never been as dark as I thought it was; there was always a guiding light for me no matter what.

It is also a no-brainer that I thank the brilliant detectives who investigated the cases contained in these pages: Retired Long Beach PD Homicide Detectives Mark McGuire and Hugo Cortes; Retired L.A. County Sheriff's Homicide Detectives Robert Gray, Dan McElderry, and Mark Lillienfeld, and L.A. County Sheriff's Department Captain Martin L. Rodriguez. I am friends with them and speak with most of them often. I know the pain they went through as they investigated these horrible cases.

To my mother Theresa Reynolds, and brothers, David and Derrick Reynolds, who I love dearly and would do anything for; to my dearly departed father, Charles "Delton" Reynolds, the sweetest man I never knew; to my dearly departed mother-in-law, Lynne Baker, who loved me like I was her own; to all my children and grandchildren from the tethered to the estranged; to my Uncle Benjamin "Ted" Kirby and my dearly departed Aunt Sondra Kirby;

To my Uncle Andrew "Buddy" Manley, a man who does not know the meaning of the word quit; to my Uncle James Kirby, a man relegated to the closet for far too many years of his life before being brutally murdered by a homophobic microbe; to Compton PD Officers Kevin Burrell and James McDonald, who gave their lives on the streets of a city that they loved more than it loved them; to Tim "Blondie" Brennan, one of the greatest cops I ever worked with, may he rest in peace;

To LAX Airport Police Chief Cecil Rhambo and Retired L.A. County Sheriff Commander's Joe Gooden and Ralph Ornelas, who all believed in me when few others in the Sheriff's Department did; to Danny R. Smith, a prolific author and writer of the foreword to this book; and to Ralph Pezzullo and Kent Harrington, brilliant authors, and personal mentors.

Most of us don't realize how downtrodden some of our brothers and sisters are, and the brutality that we as humans can inflict on one another. But there will always be those among us who will fight for those who are unable to fight for themselves, who will try and beat back dragons and wolves, who will seek justice for those who can longer speak for themselves.

Although the murders documented in this book certainly occurred, I used my creativity to truly bring the story home, having spoken with several of the people involved. I wanted to bring the victims to life before they met their untimely demises, just as I wanted to highlight the devastation of the foster care system, the epidemic of homelessness, and the evil that walks among us. I strived to shed light on unfavorable, ugly situations, the ones that tend to scatter like those brown roaches carrying eggs when light shines on them.

"It is always darkest before the dawn."
—*Thomas Fuller*

ABOUT THE AUTHOR

Frederick Douglass Reynolds is a retired L.A. County Sheriff's Homicide Sergeant. He was born in Rocky Mount, Virginia and grew up in Detroit, Michigan. He joined the US Marine Corps in 1979 and after a brief stint in Okinawa, Japan, he finished out his military career in Southern California and ultimately became a police officer with the Compton Police Department. He worked there from 1985 until 2000, and then transferred to the Sheriff's Department where he worked an additional seventeen years until he retired in 2017. After retiring, he took up writing as a hobby. *Saint Bloodbath* is his second book. His first, *Black, White, and Gray All Over; a Black Man's Odyssey in Life and Law Enforcement*, has won 22 book awards and was the Grand Prize winner in the 2022 Independent Author Network awards. He lives in Southern California with his wife, Carolyn, and their daughter Lauren and young son, Desmond. They have six other adult children and nine grandchildren.

facebook.com/authorfrederickreynolds
twitter.com/deltonRamsey
instagram.com/fdreynol

ALSO BY FREDERICK DOUGLASS REYNOLDS

A Memoir: Black, White, and Gray All Over: A Black Man's Odyssey in Life and Law Enforcement